INTERNATIONAL BACCALAUREATE

Design & Technology
SECOND EDITION

Peter Metcalfe
Roger Metcalfe
2nd Edition

i

Library Catalogue:

1. Design and Technology 2nd. edition

2. International Baccalaureate. Series Title: International Baccalaureate in Detail

Peter Metcalfe, Roger Metcalfe

ISBN: 978-1-876659-19-6

Cover design by Key-Strokes.

Published by IBID Press, 36 Quail Crescent, Melton, 3337, Australia.

Printed by KHL.

AUTHORS' NOTE

This text has been developed primarily to meet the syllabus requirements of the International Baccalaureate Design and Technology Syllabus. However, it also goes beyond the syllabus to deliver background knowledge and support for the concepts and principles underpinning the program.

In a rapidly changing technological world, texts like this must reinforce the changing nature of design and the role of designers. Designers have both an opportunity and a responsibility to shape our future. Courses such as the International Baccalaureate's Design and Technology program continue to support and encourage the principles of sustainable design, creativity, problem solving and ethical decision-making. It is hoped this text goes some way to supporting these goals.

It is intended that the added depth will provide students of design with a better understanding of the complex relationships between technology, humankind and the environment. On occasions, historical notes have been provided to show the origins of current practice but, in general, the information is as contemporary as possible.

CONTENTS: CORE

CONTENTS: CORE

5 INNOVATION AND DESIGN

6 CLASSIC DESIGN

CONTENTS: ADVANCED HIGHER LEVEL

7 INNOVATION AND DESIGN

8 SUSTAINABILITY

CONTENTS: ADVANCED HIGHER LEVEL

HUMAN FACTORS AND ERGONOMICS

CONTENTS

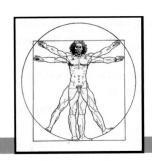

1.1a–ANTHROPOMETRICS

ESSENTIAL IDEA

Designers consider three human factors to ensure products meet ergonomic needs.

© IBO 2012

NATURE OF DESIGN

Design is human centred and therefore designers need to make sure that the products they design are the right size for the user and therefore comfortable to use. Designers have access to data and drawings which state measurements of human beings of all ages and sizes. Designers need to consider how users will interact with the product or service. Use and misuse is an important consideration.

© IBO 2012

AIM

Anthropometric data sets can vary significantly between populations. Particularly in the fashion industry, the variance in these data sets impacts the size range of clothes for particular markets.

© IBO 2012

Anthropometric data: static and dynamic data, structural and functional data

Anthropometry is the study of human body properties such as height, mass and volume and is used extensively in the design of consumer goods. In a report titled 'Physical status: the use and interpretation of anthropometry', (1995). The World Health Organisation (WHO), views anthropometry as, "the singly most universally applicable, inexpensive and non-invasive method available to assess the size, proportions, and composition of the human body."

Structural or static anthropometry includes data from measurements such as those made between joints. Data is recorded using standardised equipment such as calipers. It is easy to collect because the subject is not moving. Height, weight and data related to various body structures are included in this data set.

Figure 1.1a.1 Stadiometer

Functional or dynamic anthropometry includes data obtained while the subject is moving and, while quantitative data is more difficult to obtain, is often of greater use because it demonstrates the range and ease with which movements can be made. Reaction times, reach arcs, grip strength, etc are all examples of dynamic data.

A range of instruments are used to obtain anthropometric data. The main criteria for such instruments is that they are calibrated and are of sturdy design to ensure they provide reliable results.

The stadiometer shown in Figure 1.1a.1 is used to measure vertical distance from the floor to the top of the head of a person standing. A horizontal headboard is attached to a vertical track. The subject to be measured is placed against the vertical scale and the headboard moved down until it touches the head. Height is then read from the scale or recorded from a digital read-out.

The sitting height table is a modification of the stadiometer and is used to measure the vertical distance from the floor or the seat to the top of the head of a person seated in an upright position. The subject is seated such that the shank of the leg is vertical and the head is such that the Frankfort line is horizontal. The Frankfort line is a line connecting the ear hole with the bottom of the eye socket. A horizontal headboard is lowered onto the head and measurements recorded.

Skinfold calipers are used to determine the amount of subcutaneous body fat by gently pinching a fold of skin. Although skin thickness is generally uniform over the body the pattern of fat deposition is not. Two regions have been standardised for testing, the triceps and sub-scapular skinfold (on the back just below the scapula).

The quality of anthropometric data is important when determining the reliability of any inferences or relationships from data sets. Determinations of height and weight can be amongst the most reliable and easily gathered data sets. Body fat data gathered using skin fold calipers, however, can often be unreliable over a population sampling.

Anthropometric data is intended to represent the measurements of the nude body. Cultural restrictions, however, may also prevent the ability to obtain data from unclothed subjects. In order to adjust for this situation investigators make allowances for the type and thickness of the cloths worn.

Perhaps of even more importance is the need for measurements to be undertaken in a methodical,

standardised manner that allows confidence in the data collection.

The World Health organisation (WHO) recommends a strict and standardised quality assurance protocol involving extensive staff training from experienced instructors, constant supervision and monitoring of data collection techniques as well as frequent testing and calibration of equipment.

Primary data versus secondary data

Primary data is collected by the designer, who performs anthropometric measurements on the proposed user group. Because they are performed on a user group it relates directly to the intended population.

Secondary data is collected from a database of anthropometric measurements. Such databases are often national in nature.

Percentiles and percentile ranges

Percentiles refer to 100 equal groups into which a sample population can be divided according to the distribution of values of a particular variable. As an example an individual in the 70th percentile has scored as well, or better than, 70% of those in the total sample population.

Percentile ranges are used to measure dispersion within a sample population. A spread between the 95th and 5th percentiles would be expressed as: P95 — P5. Percentiles shown in anthropometry tables determine whether the measurement given relates to the 'average' person, or someone who is above or below average in a certain criterion. If the heights of a group of adults are sampled, many will have data recorded showing them to be around the same height. Some will be appreciably taller while others may be shorter. The 'same height' group will be near the average or 'mean' and will be displayed in anthropometry tables as the 50th percentile. The 50th percentile in this case identifies the most likely height of an individual within the group. In a design context, determining which percentile value or range may be critical to success depends on what is being designed and for whom the design needs to cater. Age, gender and even cultural background can affect ergonomic design.

Within a gender, the 5th through 95th percentile range will cover 90% of people, only the uppermost and lowest 5% are outside the range. In a mixed population samples where half of the group is male and the other half female, the 5th through 95th percentile range covers 95% of people. This occurs because only the top 5% of men and bottom 5% of women are excluded. If only half of the sample are men and half are women then: 2.5% + 2.5% = 5% of the total sample to be excluded.

Designers cannot accommodate every user. Extremes of any population sample will always require special consideration.

An example of a product using only the 95th percentile would be the standard architectural doorway. The tallest people should then be able to negotiate the opening. The 5th or 50th percentile people being smaller in stature would naturally be catered for in this design as well.

Conversely, 5th percentile data only may be used in such instances as vehicle controls where ease of reach would be the determining constraint. Here data as low as the 5th percentile may be required to gather in a sample population including those with the shortest of reaches.

Even though designing for the mean seems to make sense, the majority of people are actually excluded, i.e. outside the range of this group. Designing for the average user can also be difficult if the range of users cross age and/or gender boundaries.

A design context where 50th percentile data has been used relates to the development of crash test dummies. In 1971 General Motors created Hybrid I, a crash test dummy modelled on the 50th percentile male, i.e. it was developed from data recording average male height, mass, and proportion. Hybrid I was a redesign of 'Sierra Sam', a 95th percentile male dummy (heavier and taller than 95% of human males) used by the aviation industry to test emergency situations involving: ejection seats, aviation helmets and pilot restraints.

Figure 1.1a.2   Early crash test dummy 'Sierra Sam', image by Dwindrim CCA-Share Alike 3.0 Unported

Due to the lack of vehicle data available for occupants other than a male driver, crash test dummies have now been developed for women and children.

The crash test dummy family, Hybrid III, shown in Figure 1.1a.3 now consists of a male, a smaller female and three children based on data replicating a 6-year-old, a 3-year old, and a 12-month-old infant. The use of these models generates very different data from that gathered using the earlier testing of male models. The development of crash test dummies to now incorporate percentile range models across strategically selected age groups is a good example of where particular user groups are identified within a very specific design context.

Many products developed for children will also require careful consideration of anthropometric data and ergonomic design. Specifically, the designing of computer furniture for primary school age students is a complex issue requiring consideration of a large percentile range, 5th–95th, across genders and encompassing significant age variation. Appropriate design would encourage correct posture, reduce fatigue, facilitate ease of use and avert long-term health problems.

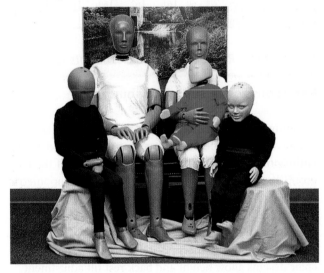

Figure 1.1a.3   Hybrid III crash test dummy family

Percentile ranks are commonly used as a tool for interpreting anthropometric data because of their straightforward ease of use. Care must be taken when using percentiles, however, when considering distributions at the extremes of populations. In these regions, small changes in percentile values can mean large differences in the data which is being reported.

Interpreting percentile tables for user populations

'When a large number of men of a practically homogeneous population are measured, and arranged in groups accordingly, it becomes evident that the individuals are

related to one another by a law of distribution A central type is represented by the most numerous group, the adjoining groups becoming less and less numerous in both directions. Thus, on classifying the measured heights of some 26,000 American soldiers of the Northern army during the late war, the proportionate number of men to each height was ascertained to be as follows'

Here it is seen, (in Figures 1.1a.4 and 1.1a.5), that the mean man is a little under 5 ft. 8 in. in height, the numbers of men shorter and taller diminishing with evident regularity, down to the few representatives of the very short men of 5 ft. and under, and the very tall men of 6 ft. 4 in. and over. The law of relation of height to numerical strength is shown graphically by the binomial curve figured above, where the abscissa (measured from an origin on the left) represent the heights of the men, and the ordinates the relative numbers of men corresponding to each height.

The maximum ordinate, representing the number of mean men, is at m = about 5 ft. 8 in., the ordinates on both sides diminishing almost to nothing as they reach the dwarfish and gigantic limits d and g, and vanishing beyond. The "mean man" thus stands as a representative of the whole population, individuals as they differ from him being considered as forms varying from his specific type.'

Excerpt Tylor E. B., Quetelet on the *Science of Man*, Popular Science Monthly, Volume 1 May 1872 .

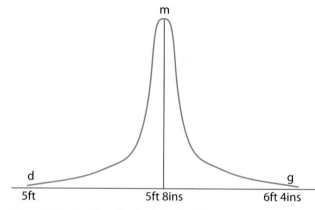

Figure 1.1a.4   Graph of soldier heights

Height in inches	60	61	62	63	64	65	66	67	68	69	70	71	72	73	74	75	76
Number of men	1	1	2	20	48	75	117	134	157	140	121	80	57	26	13	5	2

Figure 1.1a.5   Range of Union Soldier heights 1864

Range of sizes versus adjustability

Designing for adjustability means that provision is made within the design for adjustments to accommodate the anthropometric variability between members of the user group. In other words, adjustability avoids anthropometric mismatch. These adjustments can be performed using mechanical, electrical, pneumatic or hydraulic means. Most cars for example incorporate systems to adjust seat height and steering wheel position. Similarly, many office chair designs allow height and back rest tilt adjustment.

Domestic equipment such as the ironing board are also manufactured with several height adjustment positions to increase the proportion of the population that can use it in an ergonomically appropriate position.

Figure 1.1a.6 represents a population distribution curve in which the broad population range is accommodated due to the inclusion of device adjustability in the design.

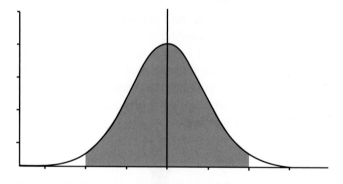

Figure 1.1a.6   Designing for adjustability

The commonly chosen design range of 5th—95th percentile of a population is a trade-off that allows for the inclusion of almost everyone in a design context and only excluding the extremes. The practice of catering for a larger percentile range is often called 'design for more types'. Traditionally, using a range from the 5th to the 95th percentile, is deemed to provide the best coverage without being skewed by extremes, i.e. the greatest 5% and the least 5% in the data range. Consumers outside this range often have to seek customised solutions to meet their needs. Products designed to meet these requirements would include furniture, household appliances, one size fits all free-size clothing, etc.

Clearance, reach and adjustability

When considering adjustability, the percentile range generally considered appropriate is the 5th percentile of females and the 95th percentile of males. Because of the overlap in dimensions of the male and female population this regime would account for 95% of the user population as calculated previously. This would be the case if human dimensions were always in the same proportion. Unfortunately human dimensions are not always in the same proportion, and a tall person can have short arms and a short person may have proportionately longer arms. Multivariate analysis is used to account for all variations and means that more than 5% of the population may be excluded on one or more dimensions if using the 5th to 95th percentile range.

However the cost of accommodating all possible combinations increases dramatically past this range and in most situations is not justified. Figure 1.1a.6 shows an operator sitting on an adjustable chair in front of a computer screen that is also adjustable. While the desk may be of a standard design and height, the other elements in the arrangement together should accommodate most of the user population.

In this situation the most important limiting factors relate to the reach of the individual's arm. The reach envelope for a range of users is defined as a three-dimensional space.

Reliable data is required to develop an appropriate response to reach envelopes when considering a broad population sample. Data may be gathered from anthropometric tables, dynamic measurement or through the use of software simulations. This data can be affected by such restrictions as clothing. Traditionally measurements were taken manually but in recent years video has also proven to be an effective tool for gathering data. Figure 1.1a.7 shows operational areas of an individual from the axis of bilateral symmetry.

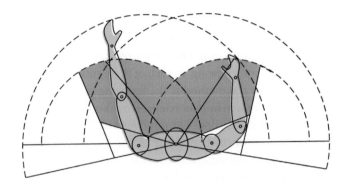

Figure 1.1a.7   Work space envelope, image by Bolumena (own work) GFDL (www.gnu.org/copyleft/fdl.html), via Wikimedia Commons

INTERNATIONAL MINDEDNESS

A wide selection of anthropometric data is published and regionalised, for example, Asian data versus Western European data. The designer must work with data appropriate to the target market.

© IBO 2012

Historically, anthropometric data comes mostly from sample populations generated for use by the military. These selected sample groups bear little resemblance to the general population. What is demonstrated here is the use of appropriate population sample selection. In the same way, data produced for designers to cater for people with a disability must sample specifically targeted groups, designers must take into account sample populations that are appropriate when considering cultural, regional, gender and age variations.

Viewing Distance 450-600mm

Viewing Angle

Straight Wrists

Lumbar Support for Lower Back

Adjustable Seat Height

Feet on Floor

Figure 1.1a.6a   Simulation of an operator sitting at a workstation after adjusting equipment appropriately

THEORY OF KNOWLEDGE

> Do the methods of data collection used in design technology have more in common with disciplines in the human sciences or the natural sciences?
>
> © IBO 2012

Before embarking on this question, a student should examine what methods are being considered. This is ripe with pitfalls as there may be assumptions that need to be identified as to what constitutes methods in each of these disciplines.

Another group of assumptions that need to be identified is the definition of 'knowing' in each of these subjects. It can be argued that the method is the knowing in the natural sciences, whereas in human sciences, method is the means to drawing a conclusion. Do not overlook that there are two main and distinct methods in the human sciences. Given these limitations, how does knowing in Design and Technology compare with knowing in natural sciences and human sciences? How are the methods similar or different?

Consider how the ways of knowing take a role in these methods. Experimentation is not done randomly in the natural sciences. Oftentimes, there is an expected result that is being tested. The expected result is normally arrived at through reason and observation (sense perception) but also may be a product of imagination. Does this happen in Design and Technology? How similar is the projected end result in biology to the end product in design? Human sciences does not work in the same way. We see the end result, and we want to know why.

Exercise

Find a scientific method (you will find more than one) and compare it with the design cycle.

Thoughts and exercises in TOK contributed by Devin Allen

1.1b–PSYCHOLOGICAL FACTORS

NATURE OF DESIGN

> Human beings vary psychologically in complex ways. Any attempt by designers to classify people into groups merely results in a statement of broad principles that may or may not be relevant to the individual. Design permeates every aspect of human experience and data pertaining to what cannot be seen such as touch, taste, smell are often expressions of opinion rather than checkable fact.
>
> © IBO 2012

AIM

> The analysis of the human information-processing system requires a designer to critically analyse a range of causes and effects to identify where a potential breakdown could occur and the effect it may have.
>
> © IBO 2012

Psychological data

Psychological factors are those that impact operations including effects of environmental conditions such as stress, lighting, temperature, humidity, noise, vibration, etc. Psychological human factors data are used in the design and improvement of many products. The effectiveness of a product can be affected by an individual's reaction to a range of external sensory stimuli. Design should take into account these factors to improve the user experience. A range of influencing factors is included in table Figure 1.1b.1.

Stimulus	Factors affecting
Sight	ease of visibility, readability computer screens
Hearing	pitch, frequency, volume mobile phones
Touch	texture, grip, friction, temperature keyboards, dentistry tools
Taste	ingestion of toxins children's toys
Smell	aroma, perfume, odour workspaces

Figure 1.1b.1   Psychological factors affecting design

Methods of collecting psychological human factor data include interviews, questionnaires and observations.

Interviews may be undertaken using individuals or specific focus groups where an experienced interviewer will guide a small group through discussion of product experiences, gathering both negative and positive opinions. Observations may be conducted in-situ or under more controlled laboratory conditions.

As an example of the incorporation of psychological data into design is the development of a mobile phone. Mobile phone design is carefully considered when targeting specific markets. Design variations in colour, shape, materials, use of backlighting and surface finish are all carefully combined to be attractive to different consumer groups. It is not just the functions and services available that sell mobile phones, physical design variations that attempt to meet an individual's psychological needs are also of importance.

Environmental psychology studies the relationship between an environment and how it affects its inhabitants. Typical psychological human factors to be considered when designing an indoor office environment would include:

- lighting

- acoustics

- air quality

- temperature

- worker densities.

Human information-processing systems

Information about our surroundings is continually being supplied by our senses of sight, hearing, touch, smell and taste. This information is sent to the brain for integration and processing. The brain then provides signals to the body's muscles to take the required action. An example of this would be when driving a car; operations such as changing gears, braking or accelerating are a direct response to external stimuli. Given sufficient time an experienced driver often performs these processes without conscious effort. It is this level of familiarity with the vehicle controls that is called upon in times of emergency to maneuver the vehicle to safety.

In the flowchart below, Figure 1.1b.2, the arrows represent the flow of information through the system. The boxes represent functional elements in the processing chain, where information is processed.

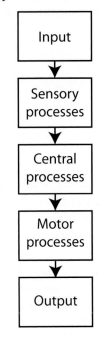

Figure 1.1b.2   Flow chart representation of the human information processing system

When using a mobile phone, the information flow diagram to make a telephone call might be represented as shown.

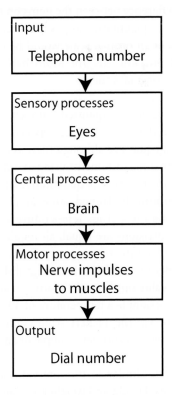

Figure 1.1b.3   Flow chart representation of the human information processing system

American psychologist, Stanley Smith Stevens developed the theory of scales of measurement in 1946. He proposed four types of data measurement scales:

- nominal
- ordinal
- interval
- ratio data.

These four data scales may be further categorized into two groups; categorical and continuous. Nominal and ordinal scales are categorical data, while interval and ratio scales constitute continuous data.

Nominal means 'by name'. As such the nominal scale deals with the classification or division of objects into discrete groups each of which is identified with a name.

The scale does not provide a measure of magnitude within or between categories. An example of a nominal scale would be organisation into: plant, animal or mineral.

The ordinal scale is one that deals with the order or position of items. An ordinal scale can consist of words, letters, symbols or numbers arranged in a hierarchical order. The difference between the items on the scale is not indicated so a quantitative assessment cannot be made. An example of an ordinal scale would be a ranking such as: 1st, 2nd, 3rd, 4th, etc. The Mohs hardness scale also represents an ordinal scale.

An interval scale is organised into even divisions or intervals such that the difference between the divisions or intervals is of equal size although there is no natural zero. This means that measurements using an interval scale can be subjected to numerical or quantitative analysis although the zero is arbitrarily defined. An example of an interval scale would be the Celsius temperature scale where the temperature divisions are equal, although the use of the freezing temperature of water is arbitrarily defined as zero ($0°C$). Because of this, a meaningful statement of the ratio of one value on the scale relative to another cannot be made. For example a temperature of $40°C$ is not twice as hot as $20°C$. The Lickert scale commonly used in consumer surveys is another example of an ordinal scale.

A ratio scale is similar to the interval scale although a true zero exists. Height and weight are examples of a ratio scale since a zero measurement is possible. The Kelvin temperature scale is also a ratio scale because a natural zero exists. The Richter scale of earthquake intensity is also an example of a ratio scale, in which zero represents

no earth movement. In this case each unit on the scale represents a order of magnitude on a base 10 logarithmic scale.

Human interaction with the environment occurs on a spectrum from the precise and quantitative at one end to the more qualitative experiential at the other. It is often necessary within this spectrum to assess and rank experiences and to measure outcomes using different scales.

In the design of a car for instance, an ordinal scale might be used to assess preferences on stylistic or aesthetic grounds among a number of alternative designs, while a ratio scale would be used to assess differences in fuel economy. A nominal scale would place the car designs into categories such as small, medium, large or SUV.

Evaluating effects and reasons for a breakdown in the human information processing system

Information about our surroundings is continually being supplied by our senses of sight, hearing, touch, smell and taste. This information is sent to the brain for integration and processing. The brain then provides signals to the body's muscles to take the required action. An example of this would be when driving a car; operations such as such as changing gears, braking or accelerating are a direct response to external stimuli. As we have observed, given sufficient time an experienced driver often performs these processes without conscious effort. Response times are shortened and safety improved.

An individual's ability to draw information from their surroundings and successfully process this is limited. This limitation in humans is due to 'cognitive bottlenecks' occurring because of the finite number of resources available to be allocated to the process. When information processing capacity is exceeded, overload may occur leading to decreased response rates. One of an individual's coping mechanisms when dealing with an over abundance of information is the 'filtering' process. Filtering reduces inputs to a manageable capacity. The filtering process varies with individuals but is primarily derived from past experience, past practice and cultural background (including customs).

Pilots in training are taught to "Aviate, Navigate, Communicate". This helps prioritise tasks during crises and prevent a cascade of problems. First see that the aeroplane is flying safely. Next, make sure you are not lost. Finally, pay attention to the radio and other people.

A breakdown in the information processing chain, however, could occur at any stage. The information input could be incompatible with the sensory receptors. In the processes given in Figure 1.1b.3, for example, the input may be too high in frequency to be detected.

In a varied population some sensory acuity improving or degrading with age. Examples include general eyesight, depth perception, hearing, sense of taste etc.

At the central processing stage, the incoming information may be incorrect, no suitable responses to it may be available or damage to the central processor may prevent processing as may arise through damage associated with a stroke. Other factors could also involve information overload where there is too much, conflicting or confusing information for an individual to make a reliable judgment.

At the output stage the body may be unable to perform the actions specified by the central processing unit through a range of factors such as lack of dexterity, flexibility strength etc. If the motor outputs required from a process are incompatible with the capacities and capabilities of an individual due to age, skill level, disability, infirmity or frailty they will be severely impeded.

Young children may not have the size, strength, fine motor control, or skill to perform some tasks, while those at the other end of the spectrum in old age may have similar problems. People with disabilities such as arthritis and Parkinson's disease may also not have the fine motor control required.

Stress is a major contributor to impeding information processing and physical performance. When dealing with stress on a daily basis the body uses endorphins to create a feeling of well being. If continued, or spikes in the amount of stress occur, a chemical imbalance may be generated between the range of neurotransmitters the body employs.

In handling daily stress the brain uses feel good transmitters called endorphins (opioids). When large amounts are needed to handle stress, the ratio of many of the other transmitters, one to another, becomes upset creating a chemical imbalance. At this point the individual feels acutely stressed and physiological affects include increased heart rates, higher blood pressure and muscle tension. Psychologically a feeling of insecurity, impaired decision making and even depression may occur.

User responses to environmental factors

Research shows employees who are dissatisfied with their work environment are less productive. Negative affects on their physical health and mental disposition lead to higher absenteeism, lower quality worker production outcomes and unsatisfactory customer service.

How environmental factors induce different levels of alertness

Loud noises, above 85 decibels, task complexity and task duration may all affect the onset of decreased alertness. Quieter environments i.e. those of less than 50 dB allowed for easier concentration, however, at noise levels between 50 and 70 dB, ambient noise has been found to improve a subject's performance on creativity tasks. It is believed the background noise enhanced a subject's performance by creating such a minor distraction as to allow the subject to concentrate more fully.

Lighting can affect visual acuity or the accuracy with which an object may be seen. Contrast in an object is the best indicator of improved visual acuity and appropriate levels of light can assist in clarifying this contrast. At night or in darkened rooms, red and blue light can increase alertness but has no affect on performance or sleepiness of the individual. The intensity of lighting has its most profound effect during the nighttime hours. Alertness and performance have been shown to be better under bright lighting as opposed to dim lighting in the nighttime hours, however, there was little performance or alertness difference found between bright and dim lighting during the daylight hours.

Research shows that all levels of additional noise in an environment can reduce alertness. Higher levels of noise are a greater contributor to fatigue. While complex tasks require concentration and focus, overly complex situations can lead to information overload and stress. It is also noted, low level tasks requiring little attention may also lead to reduced alertness.

An environment of cool dry air, particularly if directed over the face is the most conducive to alertness while a hotter more humid environment will tend to encourage drowsiness.

The importance of controlling environmental factors to maximise workplace performance

Thermal comfort, particularly in office spaces can be a critical factor in determining staff morale and productivity. Air temperature such as radiant temperature has the strongest influence on humans due to the absorptive nature of the human body. Higher temperatures can lead to worker heat stress and eventually heat exhaustion. Thermal comfort for office spaces can be difficult to achieve however, considering there would be a range of psychological responses to the environment.

It is generally considered that when 80% of a given population feels comfortable then a situation of 'reasonable 'comfort' is achieved. Air temperature alone, however, is not a valid indicator of reasonable comfort. Many other factors influence workspace comfort for employees and are essentially grouped into the following factors.

- Air quality is often dealt with in the form of air conditioning to assist with controlling ventilation, movement of air and humidity. It may also filter pollutants from the environment. Unfortunately air conditioning may also generate problems such as air movement, less than optimal temperatures, noise etc.

- Building acoustics in the form of quiet spaces encourage concentration by minimising noise that may cause distractions and disruptions.

- Lighting including opportunities for the provision of natural lighting and views to the outside. Adjustable task lighting also allows individuals the ability to control lighting conditions to their liking and relative to the task being undertaken.

- Worker densities and the creation of adjustable and adaptable spaces supplying space that is flexible enough to be personalised to fit an individual's work style.

Open-plan offices are often developed to allow for greater worker density. They also allow for larger amounts of unrestricted space. This may be in the form of reducing the number of interior walls and replacing them with partitions or in some cases reducing the size of partitions themselves.

The purpose of removing or lowering walls is to remove barriers to communication and provide people with the feeling or perception of space. Partitions of reduced size also allow freer movement of air and distribution of light from windows. The disadvantages associated with this, however, include the reduction of barriers to general noise transfer, reduced personal privacy and the opportunity for greater visual distraction. Standard space allocations in offices are often based around the requirements of job specific tasks, seniority or status within an organization.

While open-plan offices free up communication and provide more public space there also exists a need for individuals to have their own personal space. The amount of personal space an individual requires varies and may be influenced by culture or upbringing. This comfort zone or personal space is also known as, 'defensible space', a termed coined by John Calhoun in the 1940s.

Defensible space is incorporated into office design to overcome the sense of overcrowding and the negative behaviours or feelings this may create. Through the judicious use of barriers or partitions, personal spaces may be created while still maintaining an open plan. The creation of areas such as these allows employees to customize their space within an office and improve the individual's feeling of comfort, safety and control.

Office space designers may use the; "*Physical Work Environment Satisfaction Questionnaire*," (PWESQ), to measure worker satisfaction and better inform their designs. This tool takes into account aforementioned environmental factors relative to a worker's occupational health and safety, but also includes physical demands and work systems.

Assessing the impact of perception in relation to the accuracy and reliability of psychological factor data

Because individuals perceive the world in different ways, the gathering of psychological factor data is not a precise science. This may be a factor of an individuals upbringing, experience, culture etc. Qualitative data is gathered in this context to better elicit meaningful responses from individuals and groups. Examples of the type of information required and why the responses are so varied include:

Individuals experience temperature in different ways. A range of comfort zones will exist based on body mass, manner of dress or even physiological changes that can be developed from exposure to a particular temperature or environment over time. Space is another part of the environment perceived differently by individuals. Comfort zones or personal space vary from culture to culture. Responses to taste are also a factor of culture and experience. Value may be perceived as a function of cost, features, prestige, rarity etc., or a combination of these factors.

> The origin of psychology as a mainly Western academic subject needs to be taken into account in applying any psychological factors to global design problems.
>
> © IBO 2012

INTERNATIONAL MINDEDNESS

Psychology is defined as the study of the development of the human mind and in particular how it affects behaviour. While Western cultures may claim the early bulk of academic writings in the field, a range of cultures in the ancient world including Egyptian, Chinese, Greek and Indian speculated on human behaviour and the state of an individual's mind. It wasn't until the late 1800s that psychology was recognised as an independent discipline in Germany and the United States and broke away from the field of philosophy. The psychologies of East and West vary considerably with equally valid application within their own culture. Generalising, the West tends to identify with the individual and focus on rationalising existence, while the East tends to have a more communal approach with a focus on the mystical.

The most recent affects of globalisation see companies branding their products with symbols from a diverse range of cultures. Some companies are experimenting with the application of a duality of symbols mixing foreign and local cultural identities particularly when importing products into 'foreign' markets.

> How might the collection and interpretation of data be affected by the limitations of our sense perception?
>
> © IBO 2012

THEORY OF KNOWLEDGE

Sense perception is one of the eight ways of knowing and an integral part of the acquisition of knowledge. Scientific knowledge that is taken in primarily through our senses is called empirical knowledge. The TOK student should have an awareness of the tenets of the argument between empiricism and rationalism.

To address this question we must first ask ourselves how do we define senses. The traditional definitions of the senses include; touch, taste, visual, auditory and smell were identified by Aristotle. However, there are other categories that arguably should be included. equilibrioception (sense of balance) and kinesthetic (the sense of movement) are just two examples among many. In TOK terms, of primary importance is the ability to effectively defend one's definition of senses with examples, real examples. Once this defence is secured, then examination of how the sense(s) lead to knowing should proceed.

In a most basic sense, we can witness an event happen. Knowing in the arts, history, and human sciences, all have sense perception as the channel through which the stimulus enters into the human mind. From the perspective of the natural sciences, human beings both witness an event and ask why, then look for observable results to confirm what the rational mind believes is true. Here is where the beginning of limitations to the senses can start. Our eyes can only see so far, our ears hear a limited range of frequencies, and therefore what can be achieved

through the senses is finite. However, students should not end their examinations here. Consider the extent to which technology has assisted our sense in seeing, hearing, and touch. With these extensions, we can access observable phenomena that would have been missed earlier.

Another limitation that should be examined is how observation affects what is being observed. In the human sciences, when collecting qualitative data, a real person is being asked to respond and real people respond subconsciously when being observed. If a person is presented with a glass of water when they visit me at my home, why do they drink? Is it out of thirst, politeness, habit, or all three? The researcher as a human being also has an emotional state and that state will affect how the researcher processes qualitative data. To make this more complicated, one of the tenets of string theory tells us that a particle appears as it does simply because of the perspective of the observer.

Finally, the student should question themselves as to whether taking information in through a sense is really knowing. When we see something happen it still needs to be processed. The mind has to compare it with similar events to categorise it and give it meaning. This is much more a function of reason than of sense perception.

Exercise

Select a common household product. Ask a series of blindfolded participants to name and describe the item based on touching and holding the object only.

Have the candidates record their 'observations' on paper.

Ask each of the participants to review their notes and determine what allowed them to make the range of decisions recorded. Which decisions were based on tactile information only. Which decisions were deduced or determined based on prior knowledge?

Thoughts and exercises in TOK contributed by Devin Allen

1.1c–PHYSIOLOGICAL FACTORS

NATURE OF DESIGN

Designers study physical characteristics to optimise the user's safety, health, comfort and performance.

© IBO 2012

AIM

Understanding complex biomechanics and designing products to enable full functionality of body parts can return independence and personal and social well-being to an individual.

© IBO 2012

Physiological factor data

Physiological data refers to information gathered focusing on the functioning of an individual's major organ systems. The systems they refer to, and some of the data gathering that takes place are shown in the table below.

System	Data gathering
Heart	Measuring heart activity, blood pressure, heart rates etc
Brain	Measuring responses with respect to central and peripheral nervous systems
Sight	Eye movement, tracking etc.
Respiration	Lung capacity and oxygen exchange
Hearing	Audiology and balance information

Figure 1.1c.1   Physiological data collection

An example of the use of biomechanics appears in the area of sporting equipment design. The study and use of biomechanics can lead directly to better designed sporting equipment manufactured to enhance an individual's performance or prevent injury. These products are manufactured and customised for the needs of elite athletes but may be mass-produced for use by recreational sportsmen and women. Equipment examples include choice of more responsive materials for tennis racquets and golf clubs, swimsuits creating less drag and damping technologies built into javelins to reduce vibrations induced by forces applied transversely during its initial acceleration.

Comfort and fatigue

Design for discomfort is a recent approach in design to improve productivity or efficiency. The basic premise is to create a situation or environment that feels either uncomfortable or provides comfort for a limited period of time.

Airports and fast food chains are quoted regularly as providing limited comfort. This is designed to facilitate movement of customers and discourage long-term use of facilities. While designers have carefully constructed seating to provide comfort for limited periods of time, this approach is not always appropriate. In airports, early check-ins, extended stopovers, flight delays and even cancellations can cause passengers to need seating to provide comfort for extended periods of time.

Shopping malls, supermarkets and bus stations have experimented, (with some success), playing classical music to create an environment aimed at discouraging anti-social behaviour and loitering of young people around their premises. The purpose is to create a soundscape that is unpleasant or unwelcoming to targeted groups while at the same time creating a pleasant experience for others.

Maturing fast food chains have also retargeted their marketing towards families and the provision of sit-down meals aiming to attract restaurant clientele. This naturally extends purchases and improves the company's bottom line but without appropriate seating, return customers may be difficult to attract.

Biomechanics

Biomechanics is the study of the mechanical laws relating to the movement of living organisms particularly in relation to animals and the human body.

Within the design of any device or product are a number of assumptions made by the designer regarding the biomechanical capacities of the user population. That is to say, that successful operation assumes that sufficient pressure will be able to be brought to bear to push and activate a button, or toggle a switch on a control panel, or that sufficient force can be applied to turn the handle of a can opener or corkscrew.

While assumptions are made in designs, these assumptions are based on anthropometric measurements establishing the population distributions for capabilities such as strength, dexterity and fine motor control.

Age related muscle weakness and a number of medical conditions such as arthritis, Parkinson's disease, Multiple Sclerosis, etc. can significantly impact on assumed capabilities. In order to accommodate these groups of users, special adaptations or modifications may be required either to the original design or through the development of adaptive technologies that amplify biomechanical capabilities such as those shown in Figure 1.1c.2

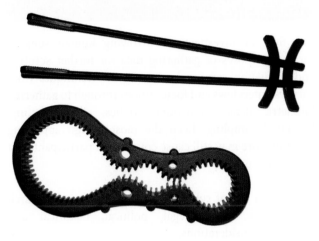

Figure 1.1c.2   Biomechanical aids

Biomechanical engineers examine the application of engineering principles and practices to everyday situations.

Through the careful study of how people physically interact with products biomechanical engineers design or re-engineer products to feel comfortable, prevent or mitigate injury and enhance human performance.

Applied to entire population ranges, young, elderly and those with a disability, biomedical design involves a process called 'design for inclusion'.

Backpacks, child safety harnesses, and tennis racquets are just some of the products that biomechanical engineers use their knowledge and creativity to design and test. Biomechanical analysis may be employed to examine the data field of events surrounding the use, misuse or difficulties associated with a product design. It may also produce results surrounding age appropriateness of equipment.

In many occupations and leisure activities, some form of protective helmet must be worn which will add to the load that must be resisted by the muscles of the neck. This is of particular concern to sections of the armed services, and search and rescue, where extra equipment such as night vision goggles or heads up display, (HUD), units may be attached to the front of the helmet.

As an example of testing personal protective equipment, bicycle helmet design may be reviewed for injury prevention or mitigation. Various loads and impacts may be examined and how the helmet and various configurations translate forces to the wearer's skull and skeletal system as shown in Figure 1.1c.3.

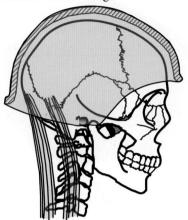

Figure 1.1c.3   Spinal loading of protective helmets

Product designers should also carefully consider biomechanical data when developing packaging. As a demographic, older consumers have difficulty opening packages. These include lids on jars, soft drink bottle tops, ring pull openers and child-resistant screw caps. Reduced muscle strength, dexterity and complications associated with such diseases as arthritis make it difficult for older individuals to open packages. Better designed packages or assistive devices that provide grip and a mechanical advantage would make a task such as opening a container much easier.

Figure 1.1c.4 shows a plastic covered metal device designed to open a range of jar lids. The force required to open a jar has been lessened through the mechanical advantaged produced by the length of the utensil lever arm. The frictional grip force required by the hand has also been enhanced through the introduction of a serrated metal contact strip.

Figure 1.1c.4   Metal jar opener

The cone-shaped flexible rubber moulding shown in Figure 1.1c.5 fits a range of lid sizes and relies on the frictional resistance generated between the lid and the rubber utensil. The soft grip material improves the user's 'feel' of the lid.

Figure 1.1c.5   Rubber moulding

This four in one jar opener pictured in Figure 1.1c.6 uses a 2nd order lever to supply a mechanical advantage. The rubber lined metal construction provides a strong body with a high coefficient of friction.

Figure1.1c.6   Lever based opener

INTERNATIONAL MINDEDNESS

It is important that the physiological factor data are either regional/national data or great care is taken when applying data from one source to a potentially inappropriate target market.

© IBO 2012

National and regional environments are affected by a range of factors over time including nutrition, lifestyle, socio-economic makeup, immigration and ethnic composition. These factors all lead to changes in physiological factor data. Regular and targeted updating of anthropometric databases is crucial to successful product design. Understanding market directions and trends in human factors relate specifically to appropriate product innovation, ergonomics and product development.

THEORY OF KNOWLEDGE

This topic is about human factors. How do ethical limitations affect the sort of investigations which can take place where human subjects are involved?

© IBO 2012

The field of investigations involving human subjects for the purposes of gathering data for further scrutiny and evaluation can involve a range of techniques from surveys, interviews and focus groups through to gathering biometric data, behavioural studies, allergy testing, biological sampling. Even the most benign appearing questionnaire may still cause concern for participants if it breaches issues of privacy.

The ethical use of subjects for the purposes of research incorporates moral, legal, political, historical and economic considerations.

Care must be taken as to how data is gathered, who has access to the data and for what purposes the data will be used. In an attempt to avoid exploitation of subjects the protocol of informed consent is at the heart of ethical guidelines. A better knowledge of the field may be obtained by examining the various codes and guidelines established around the world over an extended time.

In the United States the Department of Health and Human Services (DHHS) defines a human research subject as, "a living individual about whom a research investigator (whether a professional or a student) obtains data."

Methods of gathering this data are characterised as following:

- intervention, including physical sampling and manipulation of the environment and/or the subject

- interaction, incorporating all forms of personal communication between the subject and the researcher

- capture of private information under conditions where information is freely given and also when behavioural observation does not take place without the subject's knowledge. This information is understood to remain private within the realms of the investigation.

- private information is data that may be used to identify an individual.

A number of ethical guidelines and protocols exist to protect the rights of individuals and guide researchers in the development and execution of testing. Over time, a number of codes of practice for dealing with human subject research have been developed. The reasons for their development is just as important as is their content. Social conditions, technology and political intent have all influenced the need for and final establishment of these ethical guidelines. Important examples are highlighted below.

- Nuremberg code (1949). Developed in response to Nazi experiments on human subjects during World War II subsequently deemed as crimes against humanity for unethical research practices, the Nuremberg code requires trial participants to provide voluntary consent and not be exposed to injury or harm. Under this code studies must also provide proof of the studies benefit to society.

- Declaration of Helsinki (1964). Published by the World Medical Association the Declaration of Helsinki documents a code of research ethics based on the Nuremberg Code concentrating on medical research.

- The Common Rule (1991). This ethical standard incorporates both biomedical and behavioral research in the United States. All government sponsored research is required to adhere to this code and most research institutions also comply.

- APA Ethics Code. The American Psychological Association (APA) regulates psychology and associated research. The guidelines particularly focus on the use of deception in research.

Exercise

What responsibilities do data managers have to respect the privacy of individuals when personal information is freely volunteered?

SAMPLE QUESTIONS

1. Human factors design is also known as:

    A   ergonomic design
    B.   ergonome design
    C   workplace design
    D   anthropometric design.

2. Ergonomics involves

    A   designing new products
    B   designing for aesthetic appeal
    C   testing products in extreme environments
    D   designing for people and their interaction with products.

3. Four types of data measurement scales are

    A   nominal, ordinal, interval and ratio
    B   normal, ordinary, scattered and ratio
    C   natural, ordinal, relative and comparative
    D   categorical, continuous, nominal and ordinal.

4. Designing for adjustability provides

    A   for arthroscopic investigations
    B   caters for ergonomic adjustability
    C   designs that consider anthropomorphic variations
    D   means for adjustments to accommodate anthropometric variability .

5. Design for comfort is aimed primarily at

    A   older population groups
    B   individuals with a disability
    C   products that are difficult to use
    D   improving productivity or efficiency.

6. Compare and contrast static and dynamic data gathering techniques.

7. Discuss approaches to data gathering such as using a Likert scale.

8. Explain how culture may influence psychological responses to product design?

9. Explain how perception can affect the reliability of psychological human factors data.

10. Under what circumstances may a breakdown in the human information processing system occur?

RESOURCE MANAGEMENT & SUSTAINABLE PRODUCTION

CONTENTS

2

2.1–RESOURCES & RESERVES

ESSENTIAL IDEA

Resource management and sustainable production carefully consider three key issues – consumption of raw materials, consumption of energy, and production of waste - in relation to managing resources and reserves effectively and making production more sustainable.

© IBO 2014

NATURE OF DESIGN

As non-renewable resources run out, designers need to develop innovative solutions to meet basic human needs for energy, food and raw materials. The development of renewable and sustainable resources is one of the major challenges of the 21st century for designers.

© IBO 2014

AIM

Much of the development of new resources is the product of creating sustainable solutions to existing problems.

The legacy of the industrial revolution is now being felt as we face resource depletion. The challenge for designers is to continue to develop products that meet the needs of humans, while conserving the environment for future generations.

© IBO 2014

Renewable and non-renewable resources

Renewable resources are those that are consumed at a lesser rate than they are replaced by natural processes. Renewable resources may take the form of energy or commodities. Some resources require careful management such as geothermal power, plantation timber, and water. While others such as wind, solar and tidal energies are perpetual in that they are deemed inexhaustible.

Non-renewable resources include materials that, due to their rate of depletion and extreme time scales involved in their formation, are finite and therefore exhaustible. Fossil fuels such as coal, oil and natural gas are all non-renewable. Mineral and ore reserves such as iron, diamond and bauxite are also considered non-renewable.

Reserves

Reserves are that portion of an identified resource that can be economically and legally recovered. Reserves can be divided into two groups consisting of proven reserves and probable reserves.

Proven reserves represent those resources that are considered economically recoverable using current technologies.

Probable reserves represent those resources that may reasonably be considered economically recoverable using current or future technology.

Figure 2.1.1 shows the Chuquicamata Copper Mine in Chile representing the largest open cut copper mine in the world and second deepest at 850 metres. Although the area had been mined for centuries, when modern mining began in 1915 reserves of over 690 million tons of copper were estimated.

Figure 2.1.1   Chuquicamata copper mine in Chile, image by Reinhard Jahn, Mannheim Creative Commons Attribution-Share Alike 2.0 Germany via wikicommons

Today, plans are in progress for underground mining to begin to access ore bodies below the open cut pit, with copper reserves estimated at 1.54 billion metric tonnes.

Renewability

As previously discussed regarding renewable resources, the quality of renewability relates to the ability of something to be renewed and is generally only associated with natural or living resources. It is a concept related to the concept of sustainability.

The recycling of materials represents a way in which the materials contained within products that have reached the end of their useful life can be employed in new products. The recycling of PET bottles and paperboard are just two examples where recycled materials are transformed into new versions of their previous incarnations. By returning materials to the product stream through recycling rather than discarding them as waste, we reduce the amount of new raw material that is needed and give natural resources time to replenish.

INTERNATIONAL MINDEDNESS

The impact of multi-national companies when obtaining resources in different countries/ regions can be a significant issue for the local population and have major social, ethical and environmental implications.

© IBO 2014

Multi-national companies have a wide range of political, financial, technical, legal and human resources at their disposal when pursuing natural resources.

The impact and influence such companies can have on local communities can be profound. Infrastructure development and investment in a previously isolated region can attract complimentary industries and services along with increased training and employment opportunities. Population increases can lead to the establishment of new schools, medical facilities, shopping and entertainment centres.

Because of these benefits many governments offer inducements such as tax subsidies, and additional infrastructure to attract such developments. Where health and safety, and environmental protection legislation is not strong, however, the drive to reduce operating costs can also lead to governments being asked to reduce environmental restrictions and safety protocols that would be required in the company's homeland. In this regard, multi-national companies have the ability to play off one region against another in order to obtain the most advantageous conditions for their operations.

The advantages of new resource development by multi-nationals do not always benefit local communities, however, particularly in locations that are isolated. In these situations many resource companies have adopted a fly-in/fly-out (FIFO) system. Rather than establishing permanent residences that would bring work to the local building industry, temporary housing is established in company maintained camps. Within these camps all of the accommodation and meal requirements are catered for while the worker is rostered to be on site (typically two to three weeks). At the end of their rostered period, workers fly back to their families living in major population centres. Such systems over time have been found to place strains on family relationships and lead to increased stress for the workers, while at the same time offering little material benefit to the local community.

THEORY OF KNOWLEDGE

> To what extent should potential damage to the environment limit our pursuit of knowledge?
>
> © IBO 2014

At one level the student is here being asked to examine what value do we place on knowledge compared to the environment. Can we create a rating scale similar to the matrices used for the precautionary principle to determine the level of potential damage acceptable before we limit our pursuit of knowledge? If the damage to the environment were to be permanent would that affect the decision? What about not just degradation of a region but loss of biodiversity, or potential for species extinction? Could such destruction ever be justified? Notice also that the question deals with the pursuit of knowledge, that is, our techniques and methodologies. Many rules exist today regarding experimentation on animals in laboratories. Any experiment must pass an ethics review panel that evaluates the potential gains in knowledge against the potential for pain and suffering of the animal.

Environmental impact evaluations are routinely performed these days when commercial developments are proposed for greenfield sites but such developments would not normally be considered to be in the pursuit of knowledge.

What sort of knowledge would we be pursuing that might lead to environmental damage, 'scientific' whaling, genetically modified crops, release of biocontrols to reduce pests? Biocontrol has a long history in which a species is introduced to the environment to control another species. Biocontrols have had a checkered history, including the successful release of the Rabbit *Calisivirus* to control the population of the European rabbit in Australia and the disastrous release of the Cane toad (*Bufo marinus*) in Australia to control the cane beetle?

2.2–WASTE MITIGATION STRATEGIES

ESSENTIAL IDEA

> Waste mitigation strategies can reduce or eliminate the volume of material disposed to landfill.
>
> © IBO 2014

NATURE OF DESIGN

> The abundance of resources and raw materials in the industrial age led to the development of a throwaway society, and as resources run out, the many facets of sustainability become a more important focus for designers. The result of the throwaway society is large amounts of materials found in landfill, which can be considered as a new source to mine resources from.
>
> © IBO 2014

AIM

> The exploration of possible solutions to eliminate waste in our society has given rise to ideas developed as part of the Circular Economy. By redesigning products and processes, the waste from one product can become the raw material of another.
>
> © IBO 2014

Re-use

Re-use involves the repeated use of components or products employing the same or an alternative purpose than that originally specified. Examples include: glass containers, plastic drink bottles, fabric bags etc.

Repair

Repair relates to restoring a product or component to a good or sound working condition after deterioration or damage. Repairs may be functional or cosmetic. Examples include: mending clothes, repairing damage to vehicle bodywork, replacing faulty computer components.

Increasingly the cost of repair of consumer products has become such that replacement is often cheaper. In this respect many items today are manufactured on the basis of planned obsolescence in which it is expected they will have a limited useful life, at the end of which they will be replaced rather than repaired

Recycling

Recycling is often defined as the series of activities, including collection, separation and processing, by which products or other materials are recovered from the waste stream for use in the form of raw materials in the manufacture of new products. Recycled products may be reprocessed back into their original form eg. used glass jars recycled back into new bottles, or, it may involve materials being reprocessed into a new product eg. waste paper being recycled into cardboard (Figure 2.2.1). This reprocessing excludes the recovery of materials for energy. Thus it does not include reclaiming materials for use as fuel for producing heat or power by combustion.

Figure 2.2.1   Baled paper ready for recycling

Recondition

Reconditioning or remanufacturing is the process by which used products may be returned to their original manufactured specification or a close approximation to it. Reconditioning is aimed at extending product life until it is no longer commercially viable to continue. It may also refer to upgrading of components as new technologies become available. Reconditioned products generally come with a renewed warranty guaranteeing their quality. Examples include: reconditioned car engines, re-treaded tyres, upgrading computers with replacement modules.

Re-engineer

Re-engineer involves the revision of an established design to achieve an improvement of some sort such as cost, performance, safety, manufacturability, quality, waste reduction, usability, etc.

Pollution/waste

Most production processes result in the creation of pollution and/or waste during the various stages of manufacture from raw material extraction to transport, processing, manufacture and packaging.

Pollution/waste comes in many forms such as excess heat, exhaust gases, chemical discharges, product rejects and left over packaging.

Methodologies for waste reduction and designing out waste

In order to move toward sustainable manufacturing designers are increasingly focusing on reducing waste that will otherwise find its way into landfills or as environmental pollution. Figure 2.2.2 provides a schematic representation of the waste management hierarchy, moving from the least favoured option of waste disposal through to the prevention of waste generation.

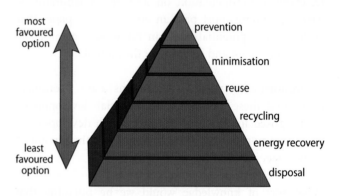

Figure 2.2.2   Waste management hierarchy, image by Drstuey, Stannered, Creative Commons Attribution-Share Alike 3.0 Unported via wikicommons

Methods of waste reduction include:

- Product recovery and reuse.

- Avoid use of unnecessary packaging.

- Produce to order, eliminate over supply.

- Production optimisation to reduce waste.

- Material substitution that favours recycling.

- Use energy efficient equipment and lighting.

- Storage designed to reduce product deterioration.

- Quality assurance practices to reduce rejects based on poor quality.

The most efficient means of reducing waste is to address the problem at the design stage following design for manufacture (DfM) guidelines. These guidelines include provisions for adoption of designs that favour the efficient selection of materials, ease of assembly/disassembly along with repair, recovery and recycling.

The DfM process may be deconstructed into three complimentary components incorporating design for: materials, processes and assembly.

Design for materials is a mechanism by which designers select appropriate materials with the aim of reducing toxic substances, hazardous waste, polluting emissions and the quantity of materials required. Wherever possible single component materials are specified for moulding and recyclable materials are specified and marked for later identification. These measures assist in the later disassembly and recycling processes. Similar specifications are also applied to packaging.

Design for process involves reductions in: the amount of energy consumed, number of production processes employed, waste generated and emissions produced. The number of parts that require additional operations include: plating, painting, printing, labelling, insertion of screws, caulking, riveting and welding are decreased.

Design for assembly is an approach used by designers to analyse components and sub-assemblies with the goal of reducing costs through the reduction in the number of parts and maximizing the efficiency of assembly processes. Consideration of tools to be used during assembly may also be important. Reduction in the number and variety of fasteners and tool types used during assembly is preferable.

Further Reading

"*A description of the design for end-of-life process*". Centre for remanufacturing & reuse. [Available online]

Dematerialisation

Dematerialization can be defined as the progressive reduction in the amount of energy and/or material used in the production of a product, and corresponds with the goal of waste minimisation. Some of the interrelated factors associated with dematerialization are indicated in Figure 2.2.3.

Dematerialisation does not mean a decline in the use of materials will occur, as increased production may result in a growth of material use overall, although the individual use of material per unit decreases with design changes and miniaturisation.

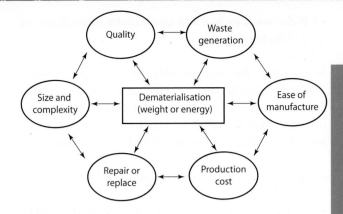

Figure 2.2.3   Factors affecting, and affected by, the dematerialization process. Herman, R. et al. (1990). Dematerialization [Available online]

This phenomenon is sometimes referred to as Jevons' Paradox or the rebound effect. In 1865, the English economist William Stanley Jevons found that the increased efficiency of newer steam engines resulted in an increased use of coal rather than a reduction. This was because the increased efficiency led to the increased expansion of steam power. Economic and population growth, of course, also strongly interact with many of the factors.

Modern electronics provides many examples of dematerialisation. Email for example, has largely replaced the Fax and greatly reduced the flow of surface mail, to the extent that many countries are reviewing the need for traditional postal services.

Product recovery strategies at end-of-life/disposal

Historically, disposal of products such as refrigerators, cars and electronic products has been the responsibility of governments. Traditionally these unwanted items have been buried in landfill or incinerated with little consideration given to reuse or recycling. Not only is this process wasteful of many materials that may be recycled but also has serious impacts on the environment. Suitable landfill sites close to the source of waste materials are increasingly difficult to find and consume land that would otherwise be public space. Even when appropriate sites are found, the burying of community and/or industrial waste generates its own set of problems including:

- Risk of subsidence.

- Generation of odours, flammable and toxic gases.

- Attraction of scavenging bird and vermin populations.

- Release of pollutants into the atmosphere in the event of a fire.

CORE

- Pollution of surface and groundwater through run-off and leaching.

Increasingly, the responsibility for recycling is being directed towards the manufacturers of the goods. New regulations are being introduced that require manufacturers to collect or 'take-back' their products at End-of-Life (EOL). The aims of this legislation are:

- Reduce amount of hazardous wastes sent to landfills.

- Increase availability of scrap, reducing the demand for virgin new material.

- Encourage design changes that reduce waste and improve recyclability.

Collection methods vary depending on the products under consideration and include.

- drop-off

- point-of-purchase

- curb-side collection

- combined/coordinated

- permanent collection depot.

In 2000 the European Union (EU) introduced the End-of-Life Vehicle (ELV) directive (2000/53/EC). This directive required automobile manufacturers to re-use or recover, at their cost, over 85% by weight of their vehicles by 2006, rising to 95% by 2015. At first covering only those vehicles registered after 2002. In 2007 the legislation was changed to cover all vehicles produced by a given manufacturer. Progress toward these goals within the European Union are summarised in Figure 2.2.4. While the decision as to when EOL has been reached is the prerogative of the consumer, and the manufacturer must take back the vehicle, the manufacturer is not required to physically retrieve the vehicle but rather must provide a network of collection centres.

A similar take-back directive was issued by the European Union (EU) in 2002, concerning waste electrical and electronic equipment (WEEE). The directive (2002/96/EC) required that from 2005 the producers of electrical and electronic equipment had to establish collection systems for the following product categories

Medical devices.

Lighting equipment.

Household appliances.

Automatic dispensers.

Consumer equipment.

Electrical & electronic tools.

Monitoring and control equipment.

Toys, leisure and sports equipment.

IT and telecommunications equipment.

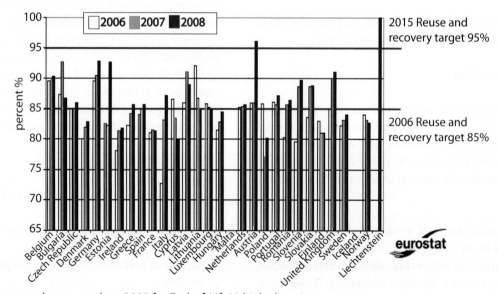

Figure 2.2.4   Reuse and recovery data 2008 for End-of-Life Vehicle directive

Collection is typically accomplished through:

- municipal sites

- point of purchase

- producer take back.

Figure 2.2.5 shown a typical collection point at an electronics store for the receipt of used mobile phones and printer cartridges.

Figure 2.2.5   Used phone/cartridge collection point

Further Reading

Toffel, M.W. (2003). *The growing strategic importance of end-of-life management*. Californian Management Review, Vl.45 (3), pp 102-129. [Available online]

Jofre, S. & Morioka, T. (2005). *Waste management of electric and electronic equipment: comparative analysis of end-of-life strategies*. J Mater Cycles Waste Manag., Vol 7, pp 24-32. [Available online].

Circular economy – the use of waste as a resource within a closed loop system

The circular economy refers to an economy based on the use of renewable sources of energy and the recycling of materials to create a sustainable economy, as illustrated in Figure 2.2.6. In this way the circular economy is intended to mimic the processes of a biological ecosystem as opposed to the currently prevailing relatively linear economic model in which non-renewable energy sources are used to create products which at the end of their life are buried in landfills or incinerated, characterized as the 'take-make-consume-dispose' economy.

Examples of the operation of such a circular economy can be seen in the use and reuse through recycling of polyethylene terephthalate (PET) in the beverage industry and the recycling of paper and cardboard.

Figure 2.2.6   Circular economy

In 2014, the European Commission released the Communication *Toward a circular economy: a zero waste programme for Europe*, in which they suggest that a circular economy is required to achieve future economic sustainability. China and a number of other counties are also examining the means of developing circular economies.

INTERNATIONAL MINDEDNESS

The export of highly toxic waste from one country to another is an issue for all stakeholders.

© IBO 2014

A consequence of many manufacturing processes is the production of waste some of which can be hazardous to the environment and human health. The method by which this waste is managed is therefore an important issue for industry and the community in general. Common attitudes to waste management up until the later stages of the twentieth century were, however, largely concerned with where the unwanted material could most economically be dumped. Several public health tragedies highlighted the dangers of this philosophy. Perhaps the first of these was the mercury poisoning of thousands in the city of Minamata Japan discovered in 1956, resulting from the eating of seafood contaminated by methyl mercury waste being discharged into Minamata Bay. The neurological condition caused became known as Minamata disease with a total of 2 265 victims identified and thousands more awaiting recognition. The second high profile instance of poor waste management is the 1978 "Love Canal" tragedy in the city of Niagara Falls, New York, where housing had been built over a former dumping site for toxic chemical waste.

These tragedies and others, added weight to the concerns of the environmental movement and warnings of environmental harm sounded by scientists such as Rachel Carson in *Silent Spring* (1961) and Barry Commoner in *The Closing Circle* (1971).

Restrictions and regulations regarding the disposal of waste products began to grow along with associated costs, particularly for those classes of waste considered to be harmful to human health and the environment.

One way around such restrictions was to transport the waste to a jurisdiction where such regulations are more lenient. A trade therefore developed in which waste produced in factories in developed nations and which was difficult to disposed of, was transported to developing countries were environmental restrictions were few. Two events led to an international effort to ban such exploitation.

In 1986, the cargo ship *Khian Sea* was carrying incinerator ash from Philadelphia for disposal in Bermuda. On arrival, however, permission to off-load was denied due to the revelation that the ash could contain toxic heavy metals. After 14 months sailing without finding a port in which to discharge their cargo, Haiti offered to take the waste as fertilizer and 4000 tonnes was discharged on a beach before permission was rescinded. The *Khian Sea* spent the next two years at sea changing its name several times in an attempt to find a country that would accept the waste, before dumping it at sea.

In 1988, 8 000 barrels of industrial waste described as relating to the building trade was sent from Italy to the town of Koko in Nigeria where it was stored on a farm for $100/month. Several months later the barrels began to leak. The waste was later found to contain dioxin, asbestos and over 150 tonnes of PCBs. Italy was eventually required to repatriate the waste.

In order to prevent the exploitation of less developed countries by developed countries through the shifting of responsibility for waste management, the United Nations, meeting in Basel, Switzerland in 1989 prepared the Basel Convention on the Transboundary Movement of Hazardous Waste and their Disposal. The Basel Convention as it has come to be known entered international law in 1992 following ratification by 118 Parties (countries). The convention states that parties will:

- minimise generation of hazardous waste

- ensure adequate disposal facilities are available

- control and reduce international movements of hazardous waste

- ensure environmentally sound management of wastes

- prevent and punish illegal traffic in hazardous wastes or other wastes

- create a regulatory system applying to cases where transboundary movements are permissible

- prohibit the export of hazardous wastes and other wastes if the State of import does not consent in writing to the specific import

- prevent the import of hazardous wastes and other wastes if it has reason to believe that the wastes in question will not be managed in an environmentally sound manner

- prevent hazardous wastes or other wastes being exported to or imported from a non-party

- agree not to allow the export of hazardous wastes or other wastes for disposal within the area south of 60° South latitude.

Concern was raised; however, that hazardous waste could still occur if it was classified as material for recycling. An amendment to the Convention known as the Basel Ban was subsequently introduced in 1995 banning the export of any hazardous waste from a developed country to a less developed country for any reason, including recycling. This amendment has been accepted by 79 countries but is yet to be accepted by the required number to come into force. The ban is opposed by a number of countries including Australia, Canada, Germany, Japan UK and USA.

Further reading

Brown, M. (1979). *Love Canal.* Sociology 101.net [Available Online]

Odubela, M.T., Soyombo,O., Adegbite, F., and Ogungbuyi, K. (1996). *Transboundary illegal shipments of hazardous waste, toxic chemicals (pesticides) contraband chlorofluorohydrocarbons: The Nigerian experience.* 4th International Conference on Environmental Compliance and Enforcement. April 22-26, Chiang Mai, Thailand. [Available Online]

Eze, Chukwuka N. (2008). *The Probo Koala incident in Abijan Cote D'Ivoire: A critique of the Basel convention compliance mechanism.* 8th International Conference on Environmental Compliance and Enforcement. April 5-11, Cape Town, South Africa. [Available Online]

Clapp, J. (2002). *Seeping through the regulatory cracks.* SAIS Review, vol. 22 (1), pp 141-155. [Available Online]

THEORY OF KNOWLEDGE

The Circular Economy can be seen as an example of a paradigm shift in design. Does knowledge develop through paradigm shifts in all areas of knowledge?

© IBO 2014

In this question, students need to demonstrate that they understand what is meant by a paradigm shift. Thomas Kuhn introduced the concept as a means of differentiating between how normal science progresses and the disruption that occurs when a new theory introduces a radical change in the way the world is seen to operate.

The concept of a paradigm shift does not suggest that knowledge does not develop at other times. Kuhn pointed out that the usual process of knowledge accumulation occurred during the periods of normal science, during which the consequences and insights of the new paradigm are tested and expanded upon.

Many examples of paradigm shifts are available from science, any one of which could be used as an example of the understanding prior to the introduction of the new theory and the growing contradictory evidence that led to the paradigm shift, followed by developments of that theory in subsequent years.

A short list of theories leading to paradigm shifts are provided below.

Darwin's theory of evolution
Wegener's theory of continental drift
Newton's theory of optics
Einstein's theory of relativity.

Can a similar fluctuation in the development of knowledge be recognised in all areas of knowledge?

2.3–ENERGY UTILISATION, STORAGE AND DISTRIBUTION

ESSENTIAL IDEA

There are several factors to be considered with respect to energy and design.

© IBO 2014

NATURE OF DESIGN

Efficient energy use is an important consideration for designers in today's society. Energy conservation and efficient energy use are pivotal in our impact on the environment. A designer's goal is to reduce the amount of energy required to provide products or services using newer technologies or creative implementation of systems to reduce usage. For example, driving less is an example of energy conservation, whilst driving the same amount but with a higher mileage car is energy efficient.

© IBO 2014

AIM

As we develop new electronic products, electrical energy power sources remain an ever important issue. The ability to concentrate electrical energy into ever decreasing volume and weight is the challenge for designers of electronic products.

© IBO 2014

Embodied energy

Embodied energy represents an assessment of all of the energy associated with a product throughout its life cycle, including the energy required to obtain, process and transport the raw materials used in its manufacture. The embodied energy throughout the product life cycle 'cradle to grave' is therefore an energy balance involving the embodied energy of manufacture plus the embodied energy of operations/ maintenance/repair plus the embodied energy of dismantling/retrieval/disposal.

Using the concept of embodied energy the environmentally friendly credentials of a wide variety of disparate products can be tested.

Measurements of embodied energy can be expressed in a number of ways such as the megajoules of energy expended per kilogram of product (Energy MJ/kg), or as embodied carbon expressed as kg (or tonnes) of CO_2 released per kilogram of product ($kgCO_2$/kg). Estimates of embodied energy for various materials can differ significantly, indicating the difficulty in making such assessments. The embodied energy for a small list of materials is provided in Figure 2.3.1 taken from the *Inventory of Carbon and Energy* ('ICE') V2.0, prepared by the University of Bath in 2011.

Material	Energy MJ/kg	kg/CO₂/kg
Aluminium (33% recycled)	155	8.24
Cotton fabric	143	6.78
Wool carpet	106	5.53
Nylon 6.6	138.6	6.54
Polycarbonate	112.90	6.00
PVC (general)	77.20	2.61
Copper (average 37% recycled)	42.0	2.6
Steel - virgin	29.20	2.59
Steel - recycled	8.80	0.42
Glass (general)	15.0	0.86
Plywood	15.0	1.07
Timber (general)	10.0	0.71
Ceramic tiles	9.0	0.59
Bricks (common)	3.00	0.24
Gypsum plaster	1.80	0.12

Figure 2.3.1   Embodied energy

Taking values such those in Figure 2.3.1 as a starting point, the estimate of embodied energy involved in the life cycle of a product such as a refrigerator, automobile or even a building can be assessed with relative ease and the embodied energy offset somewhat by the introduction of recycling programs.

The alternative or complementary approach is to examine the possibility of replacing a high embodied energy material with one of lower embodied energy. While the concept of material substitution is simple and generally followed where practical, the engineering reality is often more complex since the differences in material properties would often involve a complete redesign. Aircraft fuselages for example, if manufactured from steel rather than the higher embodied energy aluminium or composite materials would incur a much higher energy penalty due to the increased weight.

Figure 2.3.2 shows the embodied energy in the production of various materials compared with the embodied energy in a building in which these materials are used. From this figure it can be seen that while the embodied energy in a kilogram of aluminium is high the amount used in most buildings means that its contribution to the embodied energy of the building, taken as a whole, is low. By contrast, although the embodied energy in the production of a kilogram of concrete is low, the amount of concrete used in many modern buildings can mean that concrete makes up the highest proportion of embodied energy in the building.

While a large proportion of concrete from demolition sites is still sent to landfills, recycling is increasing, with the concrete being crushed and recycled as gravel in new constructions and as aggregate base material for roadways.

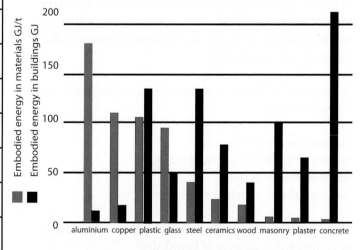

Figure 2.3.2   Comparison of embodied energy in a variety of materials and embodied energy in buildings.
http://michaeljamescasey.com/research_buttons/emergy.pdf

The calculations are however more complex when estimates of the embodied energy in modern electronic devices are required. It has been estimated, for example, that the production of a single semiconductor microchip far exceeds the energy associated with the use of a computer over its typical lifetime of three years, which contains many semiconductors.

Figure 2.3.3 shows a 300 mm diameter silicon wafer with numerous microchips formed on the surface and awaiting separation.

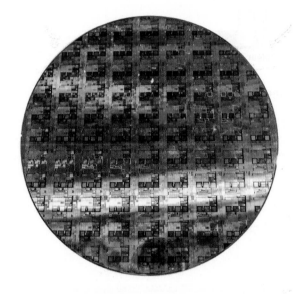

Figure 2.3.3   300 mm silicon wafer prior to the separation of the individual semiconductor microchips. [Creative Commons]

The semiconductor would therefore seem to be an obvious candidate for recycling, in order to reduce the embodied energy in such products. However, although the manufacture of the raw material for semiconductors manufacture, pure silicon metal, is relatively high in terms of embodied energy, the majority of the embodied energy in semiconductor manufacture is concentrated in the fabrication of the semiconductor itself, using such processes as chemical vapour deposition (CVD). Because of this, and in contrast to many conventionally manufactured products, the recycling of semiconductors is relatively ineffective.

Further Reading

Williams, E.D, Ayres, R.U. & Heller, M. (2002). *The 1.7 kilogram microchip: energy and material use in the production of semiconductor devices.* Environ. Sci. Technology, Vol.37, pp5504-5510. [Available online]

Jackson, M. (2005). *Embodied energy and historic preservation: a needed reassessment.* APT Bulletin, Vol. 36(4), pp 47-52. [Available online].

Distributing energy - National and international grid systems

Thomas Edison created the world's first large-scale electricity distribution network when he supplied 110 volts of DC to a small number of customers in Lower Manhattan. For years, a significant and acrimonious battle raged between Edison and Tesla over the most suitable style of current to be adopted in a widespread fashion. While AC cannot be stored in a battery for later use, it can be readily transformed to higher or lower voltages. Because of this, very high voltages can be transmitted from power stations and later stepped down by local transformers for domestic use. Similarly, small individual transformers can be used to operate portable low voltage appliances. Unfortunately DC voltage cannot easily be changed to allow us to reduce transmission losses through a conductor. The result of this is that DC cannot usually be sent efficiently over long distances. This was a major factor in the widespread adoption of AC for electrical power distribution.

In 1888, Alternating Current won the day with Nicola Tesla being generally credited with its establishment as an efficient and safe means of electrical transmission over long distances. However, even at the beginning of the 20th Century, electricity was still a relatively expensive commodity by comparison with other sources of energy such as gas, which was still well entrenched in the supply of energy for lighting, not to mention heating and cooking. Electricity availability, such as it was, was confined to the provision of lighting and was therefore generated only during the evening.

Once AC power was adopted, economies of scale developed as interconnected generating plants sprung up across the countryside. Demand increased, reliability improved, capital investment requirements reduced and lower costs were offered to consumers. The supply of electricity supported the rapid growth of infrastructure and economic development of industrialized nations. In many situations the expansion of government built generation plants was boosted by the needs of WWI. These plants were later connected to domestic networks sometimes requiring long distance transmission.

Today, most modern communities receive their electricity supplies through connection to a regional or national grid. These grids comprise a number of electricity production centres strategically positioned around the country such as those shown in Figure 2.3.3. From these centres, power is distributed through a network of wires to the rest of the country. The generation of power at the various centres is scheduled based on forecasts of expected requirements. Computer coordination between the electricity generators allows the unforeseen demand from one region to be accommodated by drawing on excess supplies elsewhere in the grid. Unfortunately these units generally require continuous operation and while power output can be ramped up or down within limits they cannot be quickly brought online from rest. In order to accommodate peak loads standby gas turbines are often used as back-ups, as they can be quickly started and stopped as required.

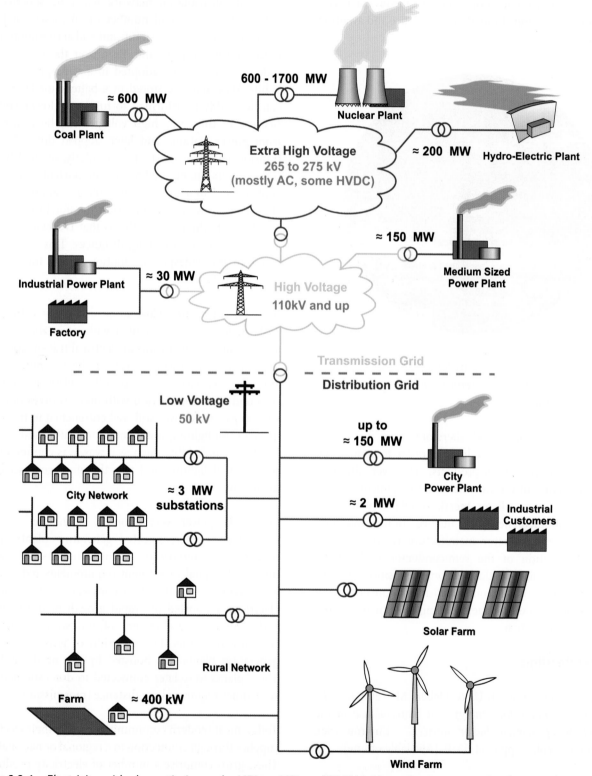

Figure 2.3.4 *Electricity grid schematic, image by MBizon MBizon [CC-BY-3.0(creative commons. Org/licenses/by/3.0)], via Wikimedia Commons*

With the exception of hydro-electricity, the production of base-load electrical power is achieved using steam driven turbines. Heat used to turn water into steam is supplied by nuclear energy or the combustion of fossil fuels such as coal or gas.

Local combined heat and power (CHP)

As can be seen from Figure 2.3.5, the generation of electrical energy using conventional means results in a large amount of excess heat that is typically lost to the atmosphere during production. Because of this, the efficiency of electricity production seldom exceeds 37%.

The associated benefits of CHP are reduced:

- fuel costs

- CO_2 emissions

- energy costs to consumer.

CHP is particularly applicable to large buildings and industrial sites which operate their own electrical generators. In these situations the waste heat can be used to provide hot water or air conditioning. The installation of CHP systems in large buildings also offers the saving of energy losses through transmission lines.

Data reported in TWh

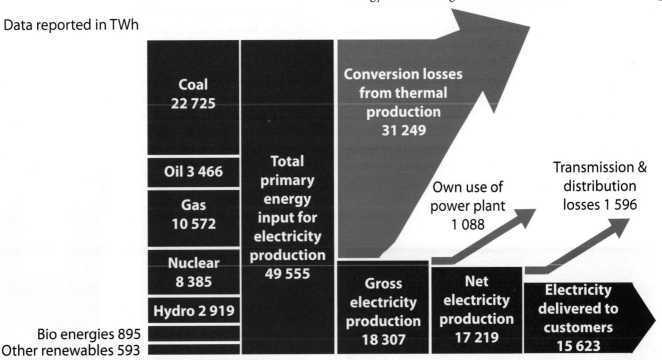

Figure 2.3.5   Energy flows in the global electricity system
Source: Combined Heat and Power© OECD/IEA, 2008

In addition to these heat losses, further losses are also sustained during the transmission and distribution of electrical energy to customers.

In an attempt to recoup some of the energy lost in waste heat, local combined heat and power (CHP) systems also known as cogeneration is becoming increasingly popular. Such systems aim to collect the waste heat from electricity production and pass it through a heat exchanger where it can be used to heat air or a fluid such as water as illustrated in Figure 2.3.6.

The term cogeneration is therefore used to indicate that from one fuel source two forms of useful energy are generated, electricity and heat. Using CHP technology efficiencies of around 75% have been claimed.

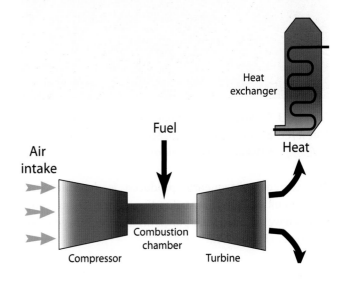

Figure 2.3.6   Cogeneration system producing both electricity and useful heat

Systems for individual energy generation

Solar energy may be harnessed in one of two ways for domestic use. Solar energy may be collected as thermal energy where it can be used to heat water or gathered and converted into electricity via a photovoltaic cell.

Photovoltaic panels use sunlight to produce electricity by means of the photoelectric effect. Albert Einstein explained this effect in 1905 for which he was later awarded the 1921 Nobel Prize in theoretical physics. The photoelectric effect involves the release of free electrons from a material when the surface is exposed to photons of light.

When materials such as the semi-conductors, selenium, germanium and silicon are exposed to light the photons of light are absorbed and electrons are released from the surface leading to a positive and negative terminal forming. If conductors are connected to these terminals a photovoltaic cell (solar cell) is created in which an electric circuit is formed and an electric current created.

Individual solar cells are typically arranged in a frame to form a module or panel that can provide a standard voltage. By connecting panels an array is created (Figure 2.3.7).

Figure 2.3.7   Solar panel, image by Wayne National Forest [CC-BY-2.0 (http://creativecommons.org/licenses/by/2.0)], via Wikimedia Commons

The current subsequently produced is dependent on the amount of light that strikes the surface. Today many homes have installed solar panels on their roofs to generate electricity (Figure 2.3.8).

Figure 2.3.8   Array of solar panels

The solar panels generate direct current electricity during daylight hours which is passed to an inverter unit for conversion to AC electric power (Figure 2.3.9) and used within the home, reducing the need to draw power from the grid. When power is generated in excess of that needed by the home the excess is pushed onto the grid and acts to supplement the grid supply generated by power plants.

Figure 2.3.9   Inverter installation for household solar power

Off-grid solar arrays require battery back-up to store energy for use when panels are unable to generate a current.

Quantification and mitigation of carbon emissions

Thermal radiation originating from the Sun maintains the temperature of the Earth and makes life possible. In a natural cycle, solar radiation heats the Earth and is re-radiated back into space. Over a number of years, concerns have been raised by the scientific community that human activity has been increasing the proportion of gases in the atmosphere that absorb and emit thermal radiation rather than allowing it to be re-radiated to space. These gases are known as Greenhouse gases (GHGs). By trapping thermal radiation the GHGs act to increase atmospheric temperatures in a manner similar to the glass of a glasshouse or greenhouse. While a number of GHGs occur naturally such as water vapour, carbon dioxide, ozone and nitrous oxide these and other synthetic GHGs also enter the atmosphere as a result of human (also called anthropomorphic) activity. The gases identified as being greenhouse gases are shown in Figure 2.3.10 along with their relative contribution.

Gas	Formula	Contribution %
Water vapour and clouds	H_2O	36 - 72
Carbon dioxide	CO_2	9 - 26
Methane	CH_4	4 - 9
Nitrous oxide	N_2O	6
Ozone	O_3	3 - 7
Hydrochlorflurocarbons	HCFCs	< 0.1
Hydroflurocarbons	HFCs	< 0.1
Perflurocarbons	PFCs	< 0.1
Sulphur hexafluoride	SF_6	< 0.1
Nitrogen trifluoride	NF_3	< 0.1

Figure 2.3.10   Greenhouse gases

Although concerns were raised in the 19th century regarding the potential for climate change as a result of industrial activity creating increased greenhouse gas (GHG) emissions, such warnings were not taken seriously until the 1960s. An early focus of these concerns was the atmospheric increase in carbon dioxide (CO_2) largely created by the burning of fossil fuels such as coal, oil and gas. It is perhaps a result of this early identification that attempts to measure and reduce GHG emissions are generally framed in terms of carbon dioxide (or, short hand, as 'carbon emissions'). In fact there are a number of greenhouse gases among which, paradoxically, CO_2 is comparatively weak.

In order to obtain an overall measure of the creation of GHG emissions and the effectiveness of mitigation measures, each of the greenhouse gases are assigned an equivalent CO_2 value usually written CO_2e. This value takes into account the fact that different gases absorb different amounts of heat and remain in the atmosphere for different amounts of time. This difference is represented by a 'Global Warming Potential' (GWP). The GWP for each of the Kyoto Protocol GHGs is shown in Figure 2.3.11. Using this index, their effect as a GHG is equated with the amount of CO_2 required to obtain the same effect. In this way different GHGs, even those with no carbon, such as nitrous oxide, can be compared in their effect.

Gas	Avg. life in atmosphere (years)	100 year GWP
Carbon dioxide	poorly defined	1
Methane	12	25-28
Nitrous oxide	114	265-289
Hydrochlorflurocarbons	1-270	140-11 700
Hydroflurocarbons	1-270	124-14 800
Perflurocarbons	800-50 000	7 390-12 200
Sulphur hexafluoride	3 200	23 900
Nitrous trifluoride	550-740	16 800-17 200

Figure 2.3.11   Greenhouse gases (GHG) controlled under Kyoto Protocol (2013)

Using this concept 1 kg of any GHG can be expressed in terms of its CO_2 equivalence by multiplying by its Global Warming Potential (GWP) as below.

$$1 \text{ kg } CH_4 \times 25 = 25 \text{ kg } CO_2\text{e}$$

$$1.5 \text{ kg } N_2O \times 265 = 398 \text{ kg } CO_2\text{e}$$

By establishing equivalence between the GHGs a summation of the effect of all of the gasses can be obtained and the benefits of mitigation efforts quantified.

From Figure 2.3.10 it can be readily noted that water vapour is not listed among the Kyoto greenhouse gases even though it is recognised as the most significant greenhouse gas. This omission is made because the amount of water vapour in the atmosphere is not directly under human control. As temperatures increase, the amount of water vapour in the atmosphere also increases. If therefore, human activity acts to increase the amount of greenhouse gases in the atmosphere the increased warming leads to an increase in water vapour. In this way water vapour acts as a positive feedback loop, magnifying the contributions of human activity. Since only human activity is under our control monitoring is focused on the gases in Table 2.3.11.

Figure 2.3.12 shows the GHG emissions by sector for the European Union in 2008. While individual details will vary by country throughout the world and year to year, the general breakdown will be similar. From this figure it can be seen that the top six sectors, energy industries, road transport, household and services, manufacturing and construction, agriculture and industrial processes accounted for almost 90% of GHG emissions. It is these top six sectors therefore that the greatest gains in GHG emissions are likely to be made.

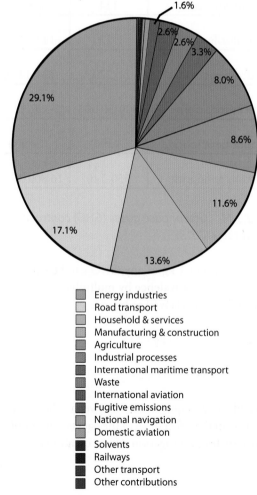

1.6%
2.6%
2.6%
3.3%
8.0%
8.6%
11.6%
13.6%
17.1%
29.1%

- Energy industries
- Road transport
- Household & services
- Manufacturing & construction
- Agriculture
- Industrial processes
- International maritime transport
- Waste
- International aviation
- Fugitive emissions
- National navigation
- Domestic aviation
- Solvents
- Railways
- Other transport
- Other contributions

Figure 2.3.12   Greenhouse Gas emissions by sector EU 2008

Batteries, capacitors and capacities considering relative cost, efficiency, environmental impact and reliability

A battery consists of an electrochemical cell converting stored chemical energy into on-demand electrical energy. Alessandro Volta is credited with the development of the first battery or 'voltaic pile', shown in Figure 2.3.13. It was built of many individual cells, each consisting of disks of copper and zinc or silver separated by cloth soaked in acid or brine.

Figure 2.3.13   Alessandro Volta's voltaic pile, invented in 1800, the first electric battery, image by Luigi Chiesa (own work) CC-BY-3.0 (www.creativecommons. org/licenses/ by/3.0), via Wikimedia Commons

A feature of battery storage then as now is the presence of two terminals of differing materials (usually metals) known as the anode (–ve) and the cathode (+ve). The terminals are separated by an electrolyte which stores the energy of the battery as chemical energy. As part of this chemical reaction electrons build up on the surface of the anode, creating a potential difference between the anode and cathode. When the battery terminals are connected by a wire, a circuit is formed allowing electrons to flow from the anode to the cathode. Over a period of time the reactants are depleted and the battery will no longer provide a current unless the battery is capable of recharging. During recharging the electrochemical process within the electrolyte is reversed with the aid of an external power supply. Common battery combinations are summarised in Figure 2.3.14.

Battery	Anode	Cathode	Electrolyte
Zinc-carbon	Zinc	Manganese dioxide	Ammonium chloride
Alkaline	Zinc powder	Manganese dioxide	Potassium hydroxide
Lithium-ion	Carbon	Lithium cobalt oxide	Ether
Lead-acid	Lead	Lead dioxide	sulfuric acid
Nickel-iron	Iron	Nickel oxyhydroxide	Potassium hydroxide
Nickel-cadmium	Cadmium	Nickel oxyhydroxide	Potassium hydroxide
Nickel-metal hydride	Metal Hydride	Nickel oxyhydroxide	Potassium hydroxide

Figure 2.3.14   Common battery combinations

Today, batteries come in many sizes, from miniature cells used to power small portable devices to back-up battery systems providing emergency power for industry. They have now become a commonplace technology powering everything from essential everyday items to industrial machinery.

The mobile phone industry owes its current success to the development of smaller and less bulky phones. This was brought about by simultaneous innovations in battery technology and more energy-efficient electronic components. Battery technologies have continued to develop alongside the miniaturization of electronic devices and their subsequent computerisation. A selection of batteries for consumer items is shown in Figure 2.3.15.

Innovation in this field continues as technology strives to improve battery life and increase power delivery in smaller, lighter and cheaper packages. The range of battery sizes and energy capacities include:

- micro batteries for: watches, calculators, mobile phones, hearing aids etc.

- small batteries for portable equipment including: torches, toys, remote controls, radios, laptops, UPSs etc.

- medium sized batteries for powering automobiles, motorbikes, lawn mowers, forklifts etc.

- large batteries find application in; industrial situations as reserve power supplies powering conventional submarines, storing power from solar cells.

While battery storage technology has enabled a vast array of consumer electronic devices, the limited availability of large scale battery technology for the storage of electricity produced by renewable energy sources such as solar and wind, has delayed the introduction of green energy. The primary obstacles to the widespread use of solar and wind has been their intermittent nature and the problem of how to store excess energy for later use. Nevertheless, battery storage has been used in a number of places where conventional grid electricity is unreliable. Because of its isolation, the city of Fairbanks Alaska is not part of a regional electricity grid. As a back-up power source the metropolitan area, with a population of over 100 000 people, uses a giant 1 300 tonne nickel-cadmium battery, see Figure 2.3.16. The battery can provide 12 000 homes with back-up power for 7 minutes and was installed to reduce the impact of frequent power outages that were being experience.

Figure 2.3.15   Selection of common batteries

Figure 2.3.16   Ni-Cd battery system for electrical power back-up in Fairbanks, Alaska

33

An alternate approach to large scale battery storage has been the development of 'flow battery' technology. In this technology, rather than storing the electrolyte in the battery it is stored in large tanks. Two different electrolyte materials are stored and are pumped into either side of a vessel with a central membrane, separating the electrolytes. Increasing the capacity of a flow battery system is as simple as adding additional storage tanks. Vanadium redox and zinc-bromine are two of the more familiar types of flow batteries. Spent electrolyte can be later recharged.

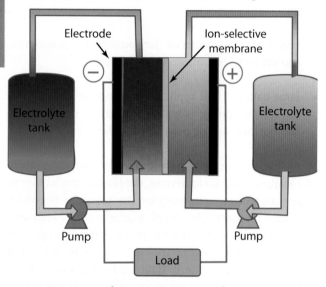

Figure 2.3.17   Principle of a 'flow battery"

A flow battery is used on King Island, Australia to store energy generated by the wind farm (Figure 2.3.18).

Figure 2.3.18   'Flow battery' chemical storage tanks

Capacitors store energy temporarily as an electrostatic charge between two plates that are separated by a non-conductive material such as glass, rather than electrochemically as for batteries. These devices offer the advantages of rapid charging and discharging but generally provide only relatively low energy densities and are typically used to smooth voltage supplies.

Newer capacitors, known as super capacitors (also known as ultra capacitors), offer the potential of storing much higher levels of energy, while maintaining high charge/discharge rates. The earliest of these differ from conventional capacitors in that they employ an electrical double layer as indicated in Figure 2.3.19 and are known as electrolytic double layer capacitors (EDLC).

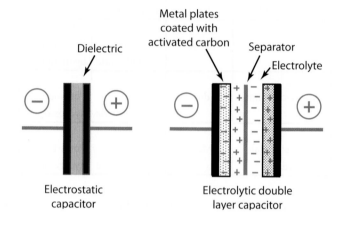

Figure 2.3.19   Comparison of an electrostatic capacitor with a EDLC super capacitor

The EDLC capacitors use metal plates coated with a porous layer of activated carbon. This creates a high surface area for a charge to develop. Between the plates is an electrolyte with a very thin barrier known as the separator. When the plates are charged, an opposite charge develops in the electrolyte on either side of the separator, creating an electric double layer. This double layer effectively performs the function of a dielectric material in a conventional capacitor. As a consequence, the distance between the static charges is effectively very small.

Because capacitance increases with the surface area of the plates and as the distance between them decreases, the EDLC capacitors are capable of developing very high capacitance of the order of 70 farads compared to 10^{-6} to 10^{-2} farads for conventional capacitors.

As may be seen from Figure 2.3.20, the electric double layer capacitors (EDLC) exhibit good power density compared with batteries, but poor energy density. Newer super capacitors, however, such as Lithium-ion capacitors (LIC), offer energy densities approaching that of rechargeable batteries but with much faster charge/recharge rates.

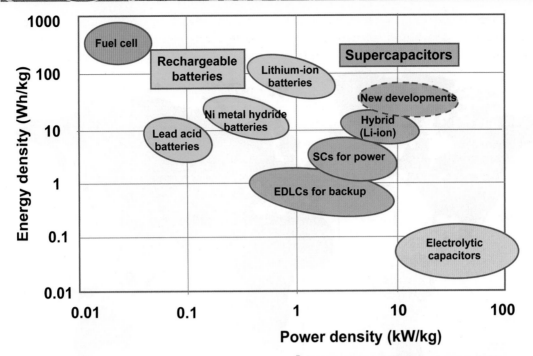

Figure 2.3.20   Comparison of conventional and super capacitor storage

Supercapacitors find applications today in hybrid vehicles, regenerative braking systems, as protection for CMOS logic chips, in UPS systems and solar power arrays and to smooth power generated by wind turbines.

Following an investigation into the effects of increased energy efficiency, Sorrel (2007) found that, as efficiencies in operation were achieved and waste reduced, the environmental gains associated with these developments were largely lost by the increase in consumption. This situation arises because, as the energy efficiency of devices such as super capacitor grows, their use increases.

Further Reading

Sorrell, S. (2007). *The Rebound Effect: An assessment of the evidence for economy-wide energy savings from improved energy efficiency.* Sussex Energy Group for the Technology and Policy Assessment function of the UK Energy Research Centre, Sussex. [Available online]

INTERNATIONAL MINDEDNESS

There are instances of energy sources (e.g. oil and electricity) crossing national boundaries through cross-border networks leading to issues of energy security.

© IBO 2014

Trans-national networks both large and small are commonplace today in the delivery of energy. These networks can involve overland or subsea pipelines or maritime transport in the case of oil and gas. Two thirds of the world's natural gas is estimated to be located in Russia, the Middle East and the USA. Transport from these locations is either directly via pipelines or in the form of Liquefied Natural Gas (LNG), which involves cooling below −163°C in order for it to be condensed to a liquid for transportation by special ocean going tankers of the sort shown in Figure 2.3.20a.

Figure 2.3.20a   LNG Carrier, image source: Wikimedia Commons

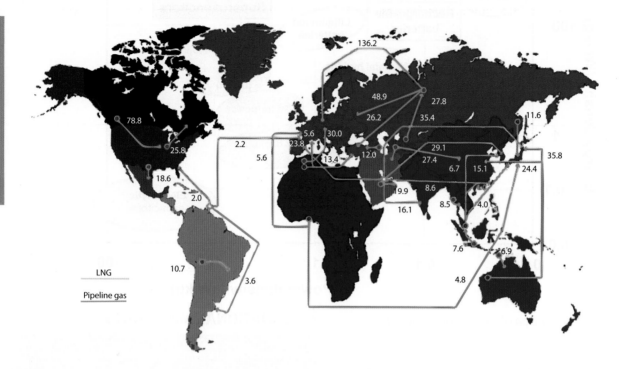

LNG

Pipeline gas

Figure 2.3.21   Gas trade movements, image source: Wikimedia Commons

Tankers of this sort transport LNG from source countries in Russia, Middle East, North Africa, Australia and Malaysia around the world. Figure 2.3.18 illustrates the major LNG routes.

On delivery, regasification is undertaken for transmission via pipelines to the final destination.

Europe obtains its gas from four networks:

- indigenous supplies

- imports from Russia via pipelines

- imports from North Africa via pipelines

- LNG imported largely from the USA via tanker.

These networks have been established over time in order to provide security of energy supply to the recipient nations and foreign exchange for the source nations. Such exchanges at their simplest are the basis of international trade. Energy, however, is unique among the products of international trade in that it is essential to the economy of every nation. Because of this, supply disruption or threat of disruption can be used as a strategic weapon in geopolitical disputes and war.

The network of gas pipelines supplying much of Europe is dependent on Russian supply, which provides approximately one third of Europe's annual gas requirements.

The supply of gas from external sources has also allowed a number of European countries such as Bulgaria and France to ban, on environmental grounds, the local extraction of gas from shale oil deposits using controversial hydraulic fracking technology.

Trans-national energy networks also exist for electricity production, particularly in Europe, and while gas is part of the mix in its production, coal, nuclear power and, increasingly, renewable sources of energy are being used. By forming a network of generators throughout Europe a number of benefits are obtained, these include:

- creation of economies of scale

- promotion of energy efficiency

- addressing variability of supply

- improving load factor and load diversity

- coordination of maintenance schedules

- ensuring sufficient capacity for peak demand

- providing a diversified portfolio of generating capacity.

All of these factors provide a higher level of energy security than operating in isolation, although from time to time the high level of interconnectedness has resulted in system wide failure.

Further reading

Stevens, P. (2003). *Cross-border oil and gas pipelines: problems and prospects.* Joint UNDP/World Bank Energy Sector Management Assistance Programme (ESMAP). [Available Online]

Pritchard, R. (2006). *What governments need to know about cross-border gas projects.* Resources Law International, Sydney, NSW. [Available Online]

Bahar, H., and Sauvage, J. (2013). *Cross-border trade in electricity and the development of renewables-based electric power: lessons from Europe.* OECD Trade and Environment Paper No. 22013/2. [Available Online]

UCPTE/UCTE. (2003). *The 50 year success story- evolution of a European interconnected grid.* Secretariat of UCTE, Brussels. [Available Online]

THEORY OF KNOWLEDGE

> The Sun is the source of all energy and essential for human existence. Is there some knowledge common to all areas of knowledge and ways of knowing?
>
> © IBO 2014

In answering this question students will need to reflect on what we mean by knowledge and the ways in which we acquire knowledge, or what the TOK calls the ways of knowing, and which are often divided into four basic categories.

- Sense perception

- Language/authority

- Emotion/intuition

- Logic/reason.

It might be argued that one commonality between the various ways of knowing and the knowledge gained is that they are all seeking meaning regarding the World around us and our place in it.

Students might usefully reflect on how the various ways of knowing approach issues of meaning and attempt an explanation. Do the various ways of knowing lead to different answers?

The search for meaning flows from the trait we share as humans of self-awareness that, as far as we know, no other animal species possesses.

Further reading

Neperud, R.W. *Transitions in Art Education: A search for meaning. UIC Spiral Art Education.* https://www.uic.edu/classes/ad/ad382/sites/AEA/AEA_05/AEA_05a.html

Schneider, A. (2007). *Ways of knowing: Implications for public policy.* Presented at annual meeting of American Political Science Association, Chicago. August 29nd - September 2. [Available Online]

2.4–CLEAN TECHNOLOGY

ESSENTIAL IDEA

Clean technology seeks to reduce waste/pollution from production processes through radical or incremental development of a production system.

© IBO 2014

NATURE OF DESIGN

Clean technology is found in a broad range of industries, including water, energy, manufacturing, advanced materials and transportation. As our Earth's resources are slowly depleted, demand for energy worldwide should be on every designer's mind when generating products, systems and services. The convergence of environmental, technological, economic and social factors will produce more energy efficient technologies that will be less reliant on obsolete, polluting technologies.

© IBO 2014

AIM

The legislation for reducing pollution often focuses on the output and therefore, end of pipe technologies. By implementing ideas from the Circular Economy, pollution is negated and waste eliminated.

© IBO 2014

Drivers for cleaning up manufacturing: promoting positive impacts; ensuring neutral impact or minimizing negative impacts through conserving natural resources; reducing pollution and use of energy; reducing wastage of energy and resources

The drivers for cleaning up manufacturing can be divided into three basic groups: social, political and economic.

Communities today hold expectations that manufacturing plants will not harm the environment or adversely affect the health and safety of employees. Community pressure through protest and negative publicity can influence decisions regarding the introduction of clean technologies.

Similarly, political decisions regarding the legislation of clean air and water targets set conditions on acceptable pollution levels and timetables for compliance.

In the end, most decisions are made based largely on economic considerations regarding profitability. Such decisions will take into account whether the clean technology is being incorporated into a new manufacturing plant or is being retrofitted, the offer of government incentives such as tax relief or subsides, the effects on production costs and material output and competitiveness in the market place.

The role of legislation to provide impetus for manufacturers to clean up manufacturing processes

Well into the twentieth century, little or no consideration was given to the effects of manufacturing on the environment in terms of air and water pollution. If manufacturing plants were required to comply with pollution limits as part of their operations these requirements were often set at generous levels, largely matching normal operating conditions and requiring only limited anti-pollution technology.

In recent years many governments have introduced stricter clean air and water legislation along with independent monitoring to confirm compliance.

With the introduction of environmental legislation that often includes targets of continued improvement, manufacturers are increasingly being led to the exploration of new clean technologies. It has been observed that, in some cases, this has not only resulted in the introduction of both more efficient processes with reduced pollution but also cost advantages and increased competitiveness.

The extent to which legislation leads to these benefits can depend on the strength of the legislation as illustrated in Figure 2.4.1.

Legislation that imposes relatively weak requirements can lead to manufacturers introducing incremental improvements in their process and pollution control technology. By contrast, it has been suggested that when strong legislation is introduced, some industries are provoked into radical changes introducing new processes and products.

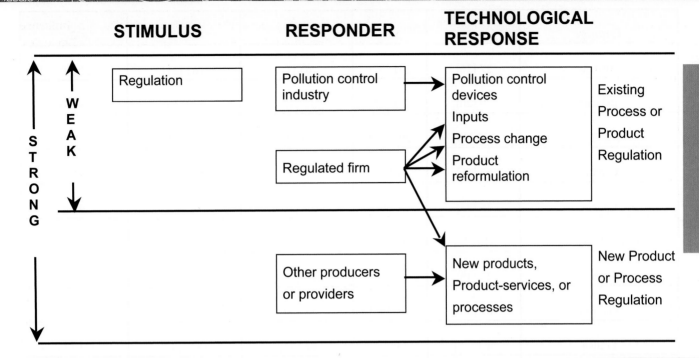

Figure 2.4.1   Model for legislation-induced technological change, chart from Ashford and Hall (2011), The importance of regulation-induced innovation for sustainable development. [Available Online]

International targets for reducing pollution and waste

In 2005, the Kyoto Protocol based on a principle of "Common but Different Responsibilities" asked countries to agree to a reduction in their greenhouse gas (GHG) emissions, in order to combat Global Warming. The "Common but Different Responsibilities" principle was adopted as recognition that the developed nations had a responsibility for much of the GHGs in the atmosphere and that imposing emission restrictions on the developing nations would place development restrictions on them that the developed nations had not been subjected to. Targets were agreed based on a reduction from 1990 levels and were aimed at accomplishing an average reduction of 5%. This protocol established two periods 2008 to 2012 and 2012 to 2020. Of the 156 countries that had signed by 2005, only 37 industrialised countries plus the 15 countries making up the European Union were required to meet GHG emission targets. Notable exceptions at the time were Australia, Canada, and the USA who were concerned about the impact such reductions would have on their economies especially since the developing nations were not required to agree to reductions, including major polluters China and India.

By 2013, 192 countries had signed the Kyoto Protocol including Australia and the USA, although the USA was yet to ratify the Protocol. Canada which had signed the Protocol in 2002 pulled out in 2011. Figure 2.4.2 shows the 2005 emissions of a number of European nations in thousands of tonnes and, in brackets, the percentage reduction targets for 2020. In particular, emissions of SO_2, NO_X and NH_3 contribute to the acidification of lakes, rivers, forests and other ecosystems.

The agriculture sector is responsible for over 90% of NH_3 emissions across the European Union. NH_3 also contributes to eutrophication whereby a body of water increases the concentration of nutrients (particularly phosphates and nitrates) to a point where unhealthy rates of algae bloom. Impacts then may occur in ecosystems surrounding streams, swamps, lakes and rivers. NH_3 is also a significant air pollutant that can be responsible for a number of respiratory problems in humans. Reduction in emissions in the European agricultural sector comes about through a reduction in livestock numbers (particularly cattle since 1990). Changes in the handling and management of organic manures and the decreased use of nitrogen-based fertilisers has also aided in emission reductions.

Plans to reduce SO_2 emissions include the use of low-sulphur heavy fuel oils, industrial flue gas desulphurisation and reducing the sulphur content in fuels.

NO_X improvements are expected as a result of selective catalytic reduction to domestic and industrial combustion facilities and bans on open burning of waste.

In October 2014 the EU announced that it would aim to reduce greenhouse gas emissions by 40% on 1990 levels and increase renewable energy and energy efficiency to 27% by 2030.

Country	SO$_2$	NO$_2$	NH$_3$	VOCs	PM$_{2.5}$
Austria	27 [26]	231 [37]	63 [1]	162 [21]	22 [20]
Belarus	79 [20]	171 [25]	136 [7]	349 [15]	46 [10]
Belgium	145 [43]	291 [41]	71 [2]	143 [21]	24 [20]
Croatia	63 [55]	81 [31]	41 [1]	101 [34]	13 [18]
Cyprus	38 [83]	21 [44]	5.8 [10]	14 [45]	2.9 [46]
Czech Republic	219 [45]	286 [35]	82 [7]	182 [18]	22 [17]
Denmark	23 [45]	181 [56]	83 [24]	110 [35]	25 [33]
Finland	69 [30]	177 [35]	39 [20]	131 [35]	36 [30]
France	467 [55]	1430 [50]	661 [4]	1232 [43]	121 [26]
Germany	517 [21]	1464 [39]	573 [5]	1143 [13]	121 [26]
Greece	542 [74]	419 [31]	68 [7]	222 [54]	56 [35]
Hungary	129 [46]	203 [34]	80 [10]	177 [30]	31 [13]
Ireland	71 [65]	127 [49]	109 [1]	57 [25]	11 [18]
Italy	403 [35]	1212 [40]	416 [5]	1286 [35]	166 [10]
Netherlands	65 [28]	370 {45]	141 [13]	182 [8]	21 [37]
Norway	24 [10]	200 [23]	23 [8]	218 [40]	52 [30]
Poland	1224 [59]	866 [30]	270 [1]	593 [25]	133 [16]
Spain	1282 [67]	192 [41]	365 [3]	809 [22]	93 [15]
Sweden	36 [22]	174 [36]	55 [15]	197 [25]	29 [19]
United Kingdom	706 [59]	1580 [55]	307 [8]	1088 [32]	81 [30]

Figure 2.4.2   European emission reduction targets 2020

End-of-pipe technologies

End-of-pipe technologies: represent the conventional approach to pollution reduction and involve the addition of technology at the end of the process to remove pollutants from the waste stream. While there are multiple mechanical, biological and chemical approaches that may be adopted, a more realistic and effective response is to minimise the waste stream and pollutants before they are generated. End-of-pipe technologies include settling ponds, spray scrubbers, electrostatic precipitators and cyclones. Materials removed from the waste stream are typically sent to land fill although some, such as flyash, have been recycled as additions to products such as concrete.

Reduced emissions and waste can also save resources in terms of raw materials and energy requirements. Cleaner manufacturing or production technologies also reduce the need for managing pollutants.

In economic terms, it is cheaper to prevent any potential environmental damage and deal with these issues at the source rather than try to mitigate their effects after the offending emissions, wastes or inefficiencies have already occurred. These pollutant reducing measures are often less dramatic and smaller in scale than their end-of-pipe counterparts.

Advantages and disadvantages of incremental solutions

Advantages include the exploitation of existing technologies, improvements to competitiveness, predictable development and low levels of uncertainty.

Disadvantages include a crowded mature marketplace with many competitors and potential for market growth small.

Advantages and disadvantages of radical solutions

Advantages include the exploration of new technologies, high potential for market growth, creation of new industries and fewer competitors.

Disadvantages include high uncertainty of success, possibility of high market resistance (idea before its time) and development unpredictable incorporating specific starts and stops.

System level solutions

System level solutions involve the integration of governmental industrial, environmental and trade policies. Through integration, innovation in waste reduction processes can be fostered. An important role of governments in this respect is to set targets and reduce inter-agency conflicts. Favourable tax concessions may be offered to those industries that integrate pollution controls into the process, reducing waste as opposed to end-of-pipe technologies that only deal with pollutants at the end of a process.

International agreements and trade policies also need to take into account the globalised nature of production and trade to avoid the transfer of polluting industries to regions with lower environmental standards.

INTERNATIONAL MINDEDNESS

The development of clean technology strategies for reducing pollution and waste can positively impact local, national and global environments.

© IBO 2014

The term 'clean tech' was first coined by Ron Pernick and Clint Wilder, authors of "*The Clean Revolution: The Next Big Growth and Investment Opportunity*." They identified a number of features motivating clean technology including:

- globalisation of markets

- changes in consumer attitudes

- costs of conventional technologies

- the growing and vocal Chinese middle-class

- research and development costs of large companies.

The 2011 Canadian Clean Technology Industry Report stated that "the global clean technology industry was estimated to be $1 trillion in 2010 [and was] forecast to grow to $3 trillion by 2020". Adopters of clean technology aim to minimise environmental impacts while at the same time improving a company's financial performance and attracting social benefits. Examples of clean technology include any systems, processes and equipment that reduce waste/energy consumption, use less non-renewable resources and minimise environmental impacts locally, nationally and globally. The use of clean technologies locally can affect global conditions in the following positive ways:

- Slowing the depletion of atmospheric ozone - ozone depletion increases exposure levels of solar UV radiation, thus increasing the incidence of skin cancer and cataracts.

- Reducing greenhouse gas production - greenhouse gases have been linked to global warming, rising sea levels and climate change.

- Minimising the direct and indirect pollution of oceans - polluted local waterways find their way across international boundaries and into shared water supplies and eventually oceans.

- Stopping rainforest denudation to improve carbon dioxide uptake and increase oxygen production.

THEORY OF KNOWLEDGE

International targets may be seen to impose the view of a certain culture onto another. Can one group of people know what is best for others?

© IBO 2014

This question deals with the notion of independence and the right to self determination. Students could usefully examine this issue from the point of a group of individuals with beliefs/practices different from the surrounding society and extend such considerations to nation states and issues of sovereignty.

Where and under what circumstances would the legitimacy of a belief in the right to impose the views of one culture on another come from?

When would the imposition of the views of society (majority group) on a minority group be justified/unjustified. Many would maintain that, as long as no harm/offence is being caused, we should 'live and let live'. Society certainly has laws that impose restrictions on the actions of its members. Most of these laws relate to restrictions on actions that might lead to harm to others in the community and that promote civil order.

- What about laws banning certain forms of religious dress?

- Cultural practices such as female circumcision?

- Water fluoridation?

- Coal seam gas exploration and fracking?

Students might reflect on the Kyoto Protocol "common but differentiated responsibility" with regard to different greenhouse gas targets for developed versus developing nations. Reductions in GHGs will require significant changes to many industries, some will rise to the challenge and flourish while others will fail. Are the warnings by scientists of the dangers for others (World population) if greenhouse gas emissions are not reduced sufficient to impose industry restrictions that may affect the livelihood of many?

2.5–GREEN DESIGN

ESSENTIAL IDEA

Green design integrates environmental considerations into the design of a product without compromising its integrity.

© IBO 2014

NATURE OF DESIGN

The starting point for many green products is to improve an existing product by redesigning aspects of it to address environmental objectives. The iterative development of these products can be incremental or radical depending on how effectively new technologies can address the environmental objectives. When newer technologies are developed, the product can re-enter the development phase for further improvement.

© IBO 2014

AIM

The purpose of green design is to ensure a sustainable future for all.

© IBO 2014

Strategies for green design (incremental and radical)

Designers and manufacturers are increasingly considering the relationship between their products and the environment. Products on shelves everywhere proclaim their environmental credentials using terms such as 'environmentally friendly', 'sustainable', 'eco friendly' and 'green'. Quotes of international standards and certification abound.

Green design refers to products that have a benign or reduced effect on the environment for their entire life cycle. More specifically, it refers to the minimising of environmental impacts associated with product design, materials extraction, manufacturing, use, maintenance and end-of-life disposal. Other terms associated or interchangeable with green design include; sustainable, environmentally friendly and eco-design.

In pursuit of green design there are two basic strategies that are followed, known as incremental and radical (or disruptive) improvement.

Incremental design as the name implies aims for progressive small improvements in the design. Operations undertaken to obtain incremental improvements that strengthen market position typically involve:

- process streamlining

- product optimisation

- parts standardisation

- improvements in reliability

- benchmarking against competitors.

The incremental design strategy would sit naturally within most quality assurance continuous improvement programmes.

By contrast, radical improvement aims to make bold changes in the product design that leap well ahead of competitors with a new product or service. Because of the degree of change involved, it is also described as disruptive innovation, because it disrupts the status quo. Radical innovation involves greater risk as success is not guaranteed and substantial funding may be required to progress.

The introduction by Dyson of cyclone technology to the vacuum cleaner could be viewed as radical improvement as it introduced a dramatic change to the established technology.

Green legislation

Eco–labelling is a legislated requirement within the EU. In 1992 this program was introduced to certify products that met stringent criteria relating to the production and disposal of manufactured goods. Originally, the eco-label program was designed to assist with sustainable development but inclusion of an environmental rating on products is now perceived as a competitive, marketing advantage.

The International Standards Organization (ISO) is a network of national standards institutes spanning the globe. It is the largest producer and publisher of standards in the world. ISO 14000 is a group of management standards developed to deal with a range of environment related procedures including: environmental management systems, labelling, life cycle analysis, auditing etc. Adherence to these environmental management standards may make companies eligible for certification. This may then in turn be a requirement of their suppliers and thus certification could become a prerequisite for doing business in some fields.

Timescale to implement green design

In order for the implementation of green design to be credible, a clear vision of the design objectives needs to be established at the outset and targets for its implementation established. These targets need to be reasonable in terms of timeframe and have agreed methods of monitoring to establish progress towards the goal.

Without the establishment of intermediate goals problems encountered along the way can be ignored and program drift occur, leading to cost and completion over-runs.

Drivers for green design (consumer pressure and legislation)

There are many forces acting on consumers and manufacturers alike to encourage the development of environmentally sustainable products. In many countries government policy now mandates manufacturing and production requirements based on legislation. European and national legislation is shifting responsibility for discarded products more and more to the producer. The need is thus generated for more efficient processes and procedures to design, develop and assess products with regard to their environmental impact. Examples of existing government policies include the EU 'take back' program and the US Clean Air Act.

Consumers are now also better informed about the environmental impact some products and their manufacturing practices have on the environment.

This increased environmental awareness translates into consumers making purchases based on this additional criterion. Many companies now promote their 'green' credentials through advertising campaigns, product information sheets and web links explaining their policies. Companies must respond to legislation and market demands but an increasing number also have a social conscience and may even see financial benefit when developing product lines.

Design objectives for green products

There are many interpretations of what constitutes green design, however, the World Business Council for Sustainable Development has developed a list of criteria intended to reflect the principles or objectives associated with the development of green products and includes the following:

- Reducing toxic dispersion.

- Extending product durability.

- Enhancing material durability.

- Maximizing sustainable use of renewable resources.

- Increasing the serviceability of goods and services.

- Reducing the material and energy intensity of goods and services.

- Potentially requiring certification to become a prerequisite for doing business in some fields.

Strategies for designing green products

Strategies for green designs are aimed at reducing the impact of the product on the environment. Many of the considerations dealt with earlier in the present chapter form the basis of these strategies and include design for:

- longevity

- disassembly

- reduced waste

- energy efficiency

- dematerialisation

- systems integration

- recyclability and repair

- reduced embodied energy.

The prevention principle

In 1972, a review of occupational health and safety undertaken by the National Coal Board in the United Kingdom and chaired by Lord Robens found higher levels of inspection and regulation were required to ensure workplace safety and that proscriptive legislation was not the answer but rather that:

"The primary responsibility for doing something about the present levels of occupational accidents and disease lies with those who create the risks and those who work with them". This approach emphasizes the responsibility of companies to thoroughly assess their operations for risk and introduce management systems to protect the health and safety of their employees.

'Robens Style Legislation' has subsequently been introduced in many parts of the World placing a greater responsibility on companies to be 'proactive' in identifying health and safety concerns and to introduce appropriate preventative measures. This principle also requires the integration of health and safety concerns into the product design process. Sometimes referred to as Prevention through Design (PtD), it aims to address occupational health and safety concerns through each stage of the product life cycle.

In performing these assessments, the concept of acceptable level of risk is used and a number of risk assessment processes are available to assist in the identification of risk and to evaluate severity of outcome should they occur and likelihood of occurrence. These include the following:

- Fault Tree Analysis.

- What if/checklist analysis.

- Risk Assessment Matrices.

- Failure Modes & Effect Analysis (FMEA).

- Hazard and operability analysis (HAZOP).

In dealing with identified risks and their prevention a system known as the 'hierarchy of controls' is used, which orders the risk control measures from most desirable to least desirable.

- Eliminate.

- Reduce.

- Incorporate safety devices.

- Warning systems.

- Administrative controls.

- Personal protective equipment (PPE).

In environmental law, the prevention principle maintains that all efforts should be taken to avoid or prevent damage to the environment passing across international borders. This principle has been expounded a number of times.

Principle 21 of the United Nations declaration on the Environment in 1972 states that:

"States have, in accordance with the Charter of the United Nations and the principles of international law, the sovereign right to exploit their own resources pursuant to their own environmental and developmental policies, and the responsibility to ensure that activities within their jurisdiction or control do not cause damage to the environment of other States or of areas beyond the limits of national jurisdiction".

This statement became Principle 2 at the Rio Declaration on Environment and Development in 1992.

A number of countries have introduced legislation to enact the prevention principle, notably Germany and France and most countries have some form of legislative requirements for the control and monitoring of polluting materials, their safe disposal and handling and protection of personnel.

The movement of pollution and the subsequent effects on those distant from the source has been a problem for centuries, but became of particular concern with the changes in production introduced with the industrial revolution.

As cities grew in size the disposal of sewage in particular became an increasing problem as raw sewage was typically emptied into the street or, via canals, to the nearest river. Under favourable conditions sewage would be safely diluted and transported out to sea, however as the river was often the source of fresh water, contamination and the rise of water borne diseases such as cholera became an increasing problem.

In the summer of 1858, London experienced a combination of high temperatures and high flows of sewage into the sewer system due to the newly installed flush toilets in addition to a tidal condition that resulted in the accumulation of raw sewage in the Thames. The smell from the Thames was so great that the House of Commons was moved to rapidly enact a bill providing money to build a new sewer system.

The civil engineer Joseph Bazalgette subsequently designed and built a sewerage network over the next 16 years that took sewage from London. In building the new sewer Bazalgette built a system more than double the

capacity required and so provide a system that operated effectively into recent times. In designing such a system Bazalgette could be said to have operated under the prevention principle.

Similar problems were of course faced by all major cities around the World.

In 1871, in order to stop sending sewage into Lake Michigan, which was also the city's fresh water supply; the US city of Chicago in the State of Illinois dredged the Chicago River so that it emptied into the Des Plaines River rather than Lake Michigan. The sewage from Chicago subsequently flowed into the Mississippi River where it was expected that dilution would render it safe. The state of Missouri however sued Illinois based on concerns for the safety of the water supply for St Louis 300 miles down river. In this instance the courts rejected the suit as it was found that dilution had indeed eliminated any adverse health effects, although sewage treatment plants were later built in the 1920s.

In terms of environmental pollution disputes across international borders, a landmark case occurred in 1925 when smoke from a Canadian lead/zinc smelter in Trail, British Columbia was found to have damaged forests and crops across the border in the US State of Washington.

It was subsequently agreed that the Trail smelter (Figure 2.5.1) was responsible for the damage and was required to pay compensation. This case represented the first transnational decision regarding environmental responsibility and the establishment of controls on pollution across borders.

Figure 2.5.1   Trail smelter 1929

While recognising that potentially hazardous activities and products may be produced when undertaking legitimate activities such as mining, smelting and chemical processing the prevention principle requires the participants to undertake measures that will avoid environmental harm, such as:

- training of personnel

- use of pollution controls

- preparation for remediation

- notification of a pollution event

- creation of emission control limits

- environmental impact assessments

- performance of a HAZOP assessment

- independent monitoring of compliance.

Principle 18 requires that States shall immediately notify other States of any natural disasters or other emergencies that are likely to produce sudden harmful effects on the environment of those States. Every effort shall be made by the international community to help States so afflicted.

Principal 19 requires that States shall provide prior and timely notification and relevant information to potentially affected States on activities that may have a significant adverse transboundary environmental effect and shall consult with those States at an early stage and in good faith.

Principles 18 and 19 from the Rio declaration of 1992 also provides for international assistance in controlling environmental pollution and the notification of a transboundary pollution incident to those that might be affected.

Further reading

Manuele, F.A. (2010). *Acceptable risk: Time for SH&E Professionals to Adapt the Concept.* Professional Safety, pp 30-38. [Available online]

Manuele, F.A. (2008). *Prevention through Design: addressing occupational risks in the design & redesign processes.* Professional Safety, Vol 53 (10), pp 28-40. [Available online]

HSE. (2004). *Thirty Years on and looking forward: the development and future of the health and safety system in Great Britain.* Health and Safety Executive, UK.

The precautionary principle

Taking a broad view of the effects of the mining industry, a World Conservation Strategy (WCS) was developed in 1980 and introduced the concept of sustainable development. The World Commission on Environment and Development (WCED) issued a report in 1987, entitled *Our Common Future* that promoted the concept of sustainable development for the mining industry. This document has since also been known as *The Bruntland Report* after the Commission chairperson. The report suggested sustainable mining required developments to be undertaken at a rate consistent with the needs of future generations for resources and an unpolluted environment.

The concept of sustainable development was further strengthened at the United Nation's Conference on the Environment and Development (UNCED) in 1992, also known as the Rio Earth Summit. One of the most important outcomes of this conference was Principal 15, known as 'The Precautionary Principle'.

Principle 15 states, "In order to protect the environment, the precautionary approach shall be widely applied by states according to their capabilities. Where there are threats of serious or irreversible damage, lack of full scientific certainty shall not be used as a reason for postponing cost-effective measures to prevent environmental degradation."

The principle has been interpreted as meaning where there is uncertainty or doubt, act in favour of the environment. Critics of the Precautionary Principle, however, point out that most industrial activities can involve a risk of some sort and that the application of this interpretation of the principle would stop all development and technological progress. However, as written, the Precautionary Principle actually only relates to arguments against the introduction of 'cost effective' measures designed to prevent threats of serious or irreversible degradation. A comparison of the prevention and precaution principles is presented in Figure 2.5.2.

Further reading

Ahteensuu, M. (2007). *Defending the precautionary principle against three criticisms.* TRAMES, No. 4, pp 366-381. [Available Online]

European Commission (2012). *The Preventive and Precautionary Principle.* Workshop on EU Legislation: Principles of EU Environmental Law. [Available online]

The Precautionary Principle. (2010) [Available online at: www2.buildinggreen.com/print/article/precautionary-principle]

Prevention	Precaution
Knowledge based	Uncertainty
Risk can be assessed	Risk cannot be calculated
Danger	Risk
Occurrence of damage is probable if no measure is taken	Occurrence of damage is uncertain and cannot be predicted clearly
Regulatory emission framework defines substantial criteria (eg emissions thresholds)	Regulation through procedural requirements
Definition of acceptable risk is primarily science based	Social acceptance of the risk is considered

Figure 2.5.2   Comparison of the prevention and precaution principles

INTERNATIONAL MINDEDNESS

The enactment of environmental legislation generally

The ability and will of different countries to enact environmental legislation varies greatly.

© IBO 2014

requires some disruption to industry in terms of changing or improving the process in order to reduce environmental pollution. These changes are, not unexpectedly, often resisted with political campaigns mounted by industry to modify the impact of any legislation.

Depending on the size of the campaign and strength of political will to see the legislation enacted, the ability to introduce such legislation varies greatly.

The Australian election in 2010, leading to the defeat of the then Labor government, was largely fought and won by the Liberal party opposition on a promise to repeal a carbon pricing scheme introduced by Labor. The Carbon Tax as it became known, was seen to place Australian industry at a disadvantage as major trading partners had not introduced similar schemes and those that had been introduced were unstable and priced carbon at a significantly lower value.

THEORY OF KNOWLEDGE

Green issues are an area where experts sometimes disagree. On what basis might we decide between the judgements of experts if they disagree?

© IBO 2014

In answering this question students need to examine the question: what makes a person an expert? It is not unusual for experts to disagree. These disagreements can arise due to a wide variety of reasons; the validity of a test result, interpretation of new data in light of differing theories etc. The details of the disagreement are often complex and difficult for others outside the field in question to decide between them.

Occasionally we (as non-experts) are faced with information provided by experts and asked to decide who we believe. This situation exists presently with the debate over whether anthropomorphic climate change is real and the need to reduce greenhouse gas emissions. In examining the basis for deciding between experts we need to determine a number of things, each of which students might wish to expand upon.

- Does the expert have relevant education, experience, and reputation?

- Is the opinion within their field of expertise?

- Are their views consistent with majority of experts in the field.

- Is the expert opinion free of bias?

Students might also usefully examine the question from the point of view of how we form our opinions.

- Where do we get our information (newspaper, television, internet, friends)?

- Are both sides of the debate presented?

- How much do our personal biases influence our decision?

2.6–ECO-DESIGN

ESSENTIAL IDEA

Eco-design considers the design of a product throughout its lifecycle (from cradle to grave) using lifecycle analysis

© IBO 2014

NATURE OF DESIGN

Consideration of the environmental impact of any product, service or system during its life cycle should be instigated at the earliest stage of design and continue through to disposal. Designers should have a firm understanding of their responsibility to reduce the ecological impact on the planet. Eco design concepts currently have a great influence on many aspects of design.

© IBO 2014

AIM

The smart phone is an innovative example of converging technologies that combines two technologies in the kitchen into one space saving device. The resultant reduction of materials, and energy used in production and distribution has environmental benefits.

© IBO 2014

Timescale for implementing eco-design

Eco-design, also known as 'Design for the Environment', (DfE) represents a movement within the design community to adopt materials and processes that minimise the effects of production and construction on the environment.

In 2005 the European Union issued an Eco-Design directive (2005/32/EEC) that obliges manufacturers to reduce energy consumption and other environmental impacts that might otherwise occur throughout the product life-cycle. An Eco-design label (Figure 2.6.1) was to be applied to products meeting this criterion.

Figure 2.6.1   Eco-design label for life cycle energy reduction

Similarly, EU directive 2012/27/EU established measures for the improvement of energy efficiency to be obtained by 2020.

The 'cradle to grave' and 'cradle to cradle' philosophy

Life cycle analysis (LCA) is a method to assess the environmental effects of goods or services. When a life cycle assessment considers the environmental influence of a car, account is taken of not only the pollution by exhaust gas but also environmental effects associated with the manufacturing and scrapping of the car and production of its various components. In other words, LCA assesses environmental impacts from the extraction of the raw materials through to final disposal or "from cradle to grave". Many manufacturing industries have started to adopt this method of evaluation to measure the environmental performance of products.

The "cradle-to-cradle" philosophy extends the "cradle to grave"' concept to include recycling at the end of product life to reproduce the original product creating a closed circle. Such a situation can be seen to operate in the recycling of glass and PET bottles to produce new bottles.

Life cycle analysis (LCA)

Life cycle analysis is a tool to support decision making for manufacturers when assessing the impact a product or process has on the environment. Specifically, the process involves the consideration of all stages of product development including: extraction of raw materials, production, packaging, use, maintenance and ultimately disposal, relative to the environment.

LCA is a relatively young technique; it became popular in the early nineties. Initially many thought that LCA would be a suitable tool to support environmental claims that could directly be used in marketing. Over the years, it has become clear that this is not the best application for LCA, although, it is clearly important to communicate LCA results in a careful and well-balanced way.

In recent years, life cycle thinking (LCT) has become a key focus in environmental policy making. A clear example is the concept of IPP (Integrated Product Policy) as communicated by the EU, but also in Asia and the Americas many countries develop strategies that promote life cycle thinking as a key concept.

Another development is the sustainability reporting movement. "The majority of the Fortune 500 companies now report on the sustainability aspects of their operations." (PRé Consultants, Introduction to LCA with SimaPro, 2008)

Life cycle analysis is just one way companies are becoming more responsible for manufacturing-based emissions and retrieving product waste. It also forces designers to think about changing product design to favour the environment i.e. developing sustainable product designs considering energy, materials efficiencies, manufacturing processes, in-service use and finally product disposal.

LCA stages: pre-production; production; distribution including packaging; utilisation and disposal

The key stages in product life cycle analysis include: raw materials, manufacturing, distribution and end-of-life disposal. The purpose of the life cycle analysis process is to highlight areas where opportunities may occur to reduce energy or materials inputs and examines environmental consequences at every point in the product life cycle.

The process may be broken down into four component parts listed below and arranged graphically in Figure 2.6.2.

- Goal definition and scope – clearly specifying context, constraints and breadth of the review process.

- Inventory analysis – collecting and documenting data on energy, materials inputs and emissions.

- Impact assessment – analyzing environmental impacts associated with the above inputs and emissions.

- Interpretation – preparing interpretation of analysis for management.

N.B. LCA approaches are assistive devices in the decision-making process; the LCA itself makes no decisions.

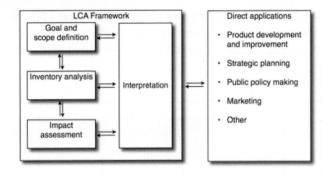

Figure 2.6.2   Phases of a LCA Study (ISO14040: 2006)

Environmental considerations

Every stage of product development has its own associated environmental impacts. These impacts can be broken down into inputs and outputs. Inputs include energy and raw materials, while outputs consist of energy, emissions and waste. The creation of these inputs and outputs can have a variety of direct and indirect environmental affects including, but not limited to: climate change, ozone depletion, soil contamination and erosion, loss of biodiversity and habitat, reduction in water quality, depletion of finite resources and noise pollution. A detailed life cycle analysis incorporates every stage of a product's life, the so-called 'cradle to grave' span. To be successful, the analysis must include an environmental assessment of the impacts associated with:

- pre-production; incorporating the mining of raw materials, processing and transportation

- manufacturing processes; including energy requirements, waste, cooling and lighting

- packaging and transportation; counting fuels, emissions, inks, size and density

- in-service use; encompassing power requirements, maintenance and in-use emissions

- end-of-life disposal; involving waste recovery, recycling, reuse and landfill.

Environmental impact assessment matrix

A matrix simply provides a way of assisting with organizing and presenting data for analysis. An LCA environmental impact assessment matrix allows researchers to identify, collect and value individual environmental impacts over the entire product life cycle.

A streamlined life cycle analysis (SLCA) is quicker and cheaper than a full LCA. Questions about each part of the life cycle are examined by the relevant teams throughout the life of the product and the environmental impacts noted in a matrix. A numerical scale (0-4) is used to record the degree of environmental impact associated with each variable.

In this scoring system 4 is good and 0 is poor. The simplified life cycle analysis matrix shown in Figure 2.6.3 identifies product life cycle stages for three different fuels on the vertical axis and the form of environmental impact on the horizontal.

	Material choice	Energy use	Solid residues	Liquid residues	Gaseous residues	Total score
Premanufacture						
Diesel	0	0	4	2	2	8
Biodiesel	2	2	4	3	3	13
Hydrogen	0	0	1	1	1	3
Manufacture						
Diesel	2	0	4	2	1	9
Biodiesel	3	2	3	3	3	13
Hydrogen	2	2	2.5	2.5	2.5	11
Delivery						
Diesel	3	1	4	4	3	12
Biodiesel	2	3	4	4	3	9
Hydrogen	0	0	0	3	2	10
Use						
Diesel	0	4	4	4	2	11
Biodiesel	3	3	4	4	3	11
Hydrogen	4	4	4	4	4	11
Disposal/recycle						
Diesel	N/A	N/A	N/A	N/A	N/A	N/A
Biodiesel	N/A	N/A	N/A	N/A	N/A	N/A
Hydrogen	N/A	N/A	N/A	N/A	N/A	N/A
Totals						
Diesel	5	5	16	12	8	46
Biodiesel	10	10	15	14	9	58
Hydrogen	6	6	7.5	10.5	9.5	39.5

Figure 2.6.3   SLCA matrix comparing three fuels, image from http://en.wikiversity.org/wiki/DFE2008_Internal_Combustion_Engines#Economic_Input_Output_Life_Cycle_ Assessment (Transferred from en.wikipedia) [CC-BY-SA-3.0].

Relative values in each category are awarded within the range of 0–4 (where the lower values signify a greater impact on the environment. The final numerical result is shown in the bottom right hand corner of the table.

The results of the streamlined lifecycle analysis show that biodiesel is the fuel of choice. However, the SLCA weighs the importance of each life stage equivalently, which cannot be the case in a real world scenario. The environmentally-harmful emissions in each life stage differ greatly, and so

life stages should be proportionally levied to account for this. If such were the case, and the use phase of the product were weighed to be of higher significance, Hydrogen fuel would have been the clear winner.

The complex nature of individual product requirements including: materials sourcing and processing, energy inputs, emissions, production techniques, transportation and in-service energy needs mean the nature and the number of elements in the matrix will vary wildly. The notion of a 'one size fits' all approach will not suffice.

In an effort to reduce the complexity of an LCA some of the minor components or indirect activities within a product's development may be removed from consideration when establishing the scope of the analysis. These components may however have a cumulative and significant impact on the environment. If omitted from the parameters for consideration when developing the scope of an LCA then the result can be misleading.

Many occasions will also require the weighting of the separate matrix elements to produce results truly reflecting the environmental impact of the product over its entire life-cycle. Life cycle analysis using a balanced equivalency for each of the matrix elements when analyzing motor vehicles could produce an extraordinarily skewed result.

An overwhelming majority of reports document the imbalance of environmental impact between production and in-service use. Clearly the weighting process must be carefully considered. If some elements of the life cycle are inappropriately prioritised and weighted then the final result can be even more distorted. Results obtained in this fashion could potentially change the emphasis for future product development from the in-service phase to the manufacturing phase or erroneously recommend one product over another.

In a document commissioned by the British Motor Industry, research showed a bias towards vehicle operation compared to manufacturing of 9 to 1, i.e. 90% of all energy consumed was in the operational phase. Although lower for vehicles such as the Toyota Prius, a 2006 study delivered a figure of 75% of energy use in the operational stage. The remaining 25% was derived from a combination of fuel production, manufacturing and end-of-life disposal. This type of information is critical to the construction of an accurate LCA matrix.

In contradiction to the previous example, when considering electronic equipment for environmental impacts, research identifies the in-use phase to be of lesser importance. Therefore assessments in this category, based only on energy use could lead to wrong or grossly inaccurate conclusions.

Product life cycle stages: the role of the designer, manufacturer and user

Designers are charged with the responsibility of bringing products all the way from the conceptual stage through to the consumer. They must precisely predict, target and capture market segments through the continued development of innovative designs. These designs all start with a clearly defined brief. The role of a product designer is to find the solution of best fit and encompasses many of the skills and characteristics associated with marketing, manufacturing, materials engineering, aesthetics and ergonomics. Constantly in search of a competitive edge, designers play a crucial part in differentiating their products from others in the market. Companies also require designers to trim costs by minimizing packaging and generating designs that use fewer materials, produce less waste and contain more recycled and recyclable materials. Research shows the overwhelming percentage (80% to 90%) of committed costs (including manufacturing, distribution and servicing) is locked-in at the design stage. Clearly the role of the designer is of paramount importance when considering the financial aspect of every stage of product development.

Manufacturers have an important role to play in the selection of production processes. They have responsibilities for both quality control and the speed at which products are produced. They must specify standards for components and outsourced sub-assemblies. They are also responsible for product warranties and may even provide after sales service or technical training in repair procedures. Manufacturers have a role to play in minimizing energy requirements, emissions, water contamination etc. through the adoption of waste management programs designed to recycle or reuse waste products. These measures reduce environmental impacts but can also make sound economic sense.

Users provide the demand for products. They have the right to purchase products that will perform as advertised. Their patterns of spending, determine whether a more durable product is purchased over a disposable device. Responsible use of products can also reduce power requirements through such facilities as the use of low power or sleep modes. Thoughtful disposal of products and packaging can increase recycling and reduce landfill. Consumers have the power to encourage designers and manufactures to pursue both creative and green developments of new and existing products through their buying patterns. Product sales clearly drive the process of design and innovation. Consumers also have opportunities to provide feedback to manufacturers and designers when completing warranty or product surveys on the purchase of a new product.

The major considerations of the United Nations Environmental Programme Manual on Eco-design

In 1996 the United Nations released an Eco-design manual also known as Design for Sustainability (DfS). The major concerns outlined in this document were to:

- increase recyclability.

- reduce energy requirements.

- maximise use of renewable resources.

- reduce creation and use of toxic materials.

- reduce material requirements of goods and services.

- increase product durability and reduce planned obsolescence.

Design for the environment software

A number of software products are available to assist designers in designing for the environment (DfE). The United States Environmental Protection Agency (EPA) offers one such resource although other packages are available.

Figure 2.6.4 Logo of the United States Environmental Protection Agency (EPA)

These packages allow the LCA of a product and the selection of materials and processes that minimise environmental effects. Using such software, designers can examine the environmental consequences of various decisions and optimise their designs to obtain a cost-effective environmentally sensitive outcome.

CAD software packages such as Solidworks™ have already incorporated LCA tools that can examine a final product's impact from 'cradle to grave'.

The analysis tool considers materials mining, production, manufacturing, product use and end-of-life disposal. Transportation impacts between all of these stages are also calculated. The evaluation in terms of air acidification, carbon footprint, total energy consumption and water eutrophication can all be manipulated within the software by changing various parameters such as materials selection, manufacturing process, plant sites and so on. This powerful tool allows designers to consider 'what if' scenarios before making any final product specification recommendations.

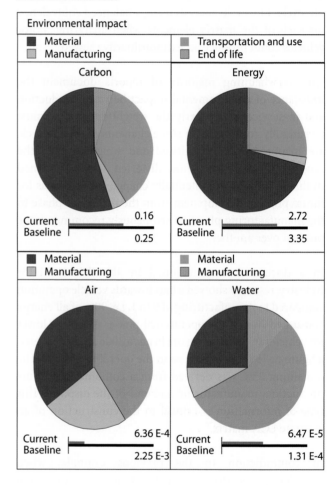

Figure 2.6.5 CAD environmental impact analysis

Converging technologies

Technological convergence is the amalgamation or merging of existing technologies into new forms that create innovative products and systems that may offer greater convenience, efficiencies or entirely new features and functions not currently in existence. Some examples of convergence are illustrated in the following fields.

Telecommunications

Modern communication systems increasingly provide greater personal access to communication, information and entertainment. In fact, the telecommunication industry has moved from a mere provider of communications channels to one of information provider with the advent of computer networks such as the internet.

Increasingly a multitude of technologies previously accessible only through separate devices are being made available in a single device or converging to allow access on a single platform.

This change is being seen perhaps most clearly in the mobile phone. Today there are more mobile phone connections than fixed line connections and mobile phones offer an increasing array of functions such as text messaging, MP3 player, digital camera, personal organiser, email, GPS directions, video player and internet access. This interconnectedness of telecommunications and computer technology is sometimes described as convergence.

Medicine

Drug delivery implants are becoming smaller and more accurate in dosing patients as increased computing power, sensing technology and wireless power supplies converge.

Mobile connected health devices such as watches and mobile phones that include applications to record, store and sometimes transmit data relating to exercise and sleep, blood pressure, heart rate, calorie intake, glucose levels and so on may be used to constantly monitor an individual's health.

Bio-robotics is a developing field in medicine merging biomedical and engineering technologies in the areas of remote robotic surgery, prosthetics and nanotechnology for drug delivery, exploratory diagnoses and even cardiovascular treatment.

Wearable technology

Wearable technology blends the field of fashion and multiple technologies to produce new and innovative embedded devices including 'google glass,' electronic contact lenses employing microchips and glucose sensors to monitor blood sugar levels, and temporary high technology tattoos made from flexible electronic circuits used to monitor patients, remotely transmitting information such as temperature, hydration and strain.

INTERNATIONAL MINDEDNESS

The differing stages of economic development of different countries/regions and their past and future contributions to global emissions is an issue.

© IBO 2014

The problem of anthropomorphic contributions of greenhouse gases is recognised as having a long history, dating back to the beginning of the Industrial Revolution. The economic development that occurred over the following 200 years or more, led to largely unrestrained greenhouse gas (GHG) emissions by those considered today to be developed nations. In response for calls to reduce GHGs, the developing nations called for the developed nations to take a lead in GHG reduction. This was justified based on the observation that most of the GHGs in the atmosphere were there because of the developed nations, and that to restrict developing nations as they attempted to meet their development needs would be unfair. This position was agreed to and mandated in the 2005 Kyoto Protocol. The phrase "common but differentiated responsibility" describes the position adopted, meaning that all parties/countries have a common responsibility to fight climate change but that this responsibility differs based on historical emissions. Notable exceptions to signing the Kyoto Protocol were the USA and Australia who held that because 80% of the World including India and China were exempted, due to the consideration of historical emissions that their economies would suffer.

THEORY OF KNOWLEDGE

There is no waste in nature. Should areas of knowledge look at natural processes beyond human endeavour?

© IBO 2014

Many developments in human technology owe their existence to the study of natural systems and how nature has solved certain design issues. In answering this question the student might speculate on whether it is possible to know what natural processes might be beyond human endeavour, considering that future activities are difficult to foresee.

SAMPLE QUESTIONS

1. Which of the following are features of incremental green design?

   A   Process streamlining, parts standardisation.
   B   Product optimisation, in-built obsolescence.
   C   Bold design change, improved reliability.
   D   competitor benchmarking, radical innovation.

2. Which of the following will assist with designing a new 'green' product

   A   Life cycle analysis
   B   Lean manufacturing
   C   Use of local materials
   D   Use of recycled materials

3. Which of the following factors would most determine a product's long term impact on the environment?

   A   Product cost
   B   Ergonomic issues
   C   Product durability
   D   Product aesthetics

4. Which of these combinations are not environmentally friendly?

   A   Reuse, recycle, repair
   B   Reduce, renovate, reclaim
   C   Replace, repurchase, re-make
   D   Refurbish, restore, recondition.

5. An environmentally responsible designer would do which of the following?

   A   Design using recycled materials.
   B   Attempt to change societal opinions.
   C   Develop new and innovative products.
   D   Analyse every stage of the product life cycle for environmental impacts.

6. Which of the following is the most important materials consideration for designers when developing sustainable designs?
   A   Strength.
   B   Durability.
   C   Recyclability.
   D   Supplied locally.

7. What green design strategies can designers employ to improve a product's in-service use?

8. Describe the role designers, manufacturers and consumers play in green product development.

9. Describe three factors affecting the rise of green design responses to product design?

10. Explain how "take back" legislation can assist designers and manufacturers.

11. Explain the advantages offered by technology convergence to designers.

12. Explain the difference between 'cradle to grave' and 'cradle to cradle' philosophies.

13. Explain how eco-labelling aids both consumers and the environment.

14, Outline the differences between end-of-pipe and clean technologies.

MODELLING

CONTENTS

3.1–CONCEPTUAL MODELLING

ESSENTIAL IDEA

A conceptual model originates in the mind and its primary purpose is to outline the principles and basic functions of a design or system.

NATURE OF DESIGN

Designers use conceptual modelling to assist their understanding by simulating the subject matter they represent. Designers should consider systems, services and products in relation to what they should do, how they should behave, what they look like and whether they will be understandable by the users in the manner intended.

AIM

The starting point for solving a problem springs from an idea developed in the mind. A detailed exploration of the idea is vital to it from the intangible to the tangible, along with the ability to articulate the idea to others.

The role of conceptual modelling in design

Conceptual modelling is defined by Preece et al, (2002) as, 'a description of the proposed system in terms of a set of integrated ideas and concepts about what it should do, behave and look like, that will be understandable by the users in the manner intended.'

Conceptual modelling contains all of the information required to describe a potential design solution that simulates the physicality of the design, functional features, performance, aesthetics, etc. At this stage designers can get a feel for how well the design meets the original design brief, specifications and user needs to maximise chances of product success in the identified target market.

To be effective, conceptual models should be as simple as possible incorporating concepts limited to those required for functionality.

Consulting Professor of Computer Science at Stanford University, David Little (1996) when commenting on the significance of conceptual models is quoted as saying, "The most important thing to design properly is the users conceptual model."

A conceptual model represents what the user is likely to think, and how the user is likely to respond. It is a high-level description of how a system is organized and operates. It specifies and describes:

- the major design metaphors and analogies employed in the design, if any.

- the concepts the system exposes to users, including the task-domain data - objects users create and manipulate, their attributes, and the operations that can be performed on them.

- the relationships between these concepts.

- the mappings between the concepts and the task-domain the system is designed to support.

It is vital to the success of the model that clear objectives are set before starting the process. Poorly defined modelling objectives may lead to overly complex, inaccurate models.

Like other aspects of the design cycle, conceptual modelling is an iterative process and thus the model evolves and improves over time.

Because it is the first step, conceptual designs affect all of the following stages in the design process. Decisions made during the conceptual design stage will determine the fundamentals of the design project. Poor choices may lead to failed or subpar design solutions.

If the designers take the trouble to design and refine a conceptual model for products and systems before they design it is more likely the end result will better fit the users requirements.

Conceptual modelling tools, skills and contexts

Conceptual models are mostly a way for designers to straighten out their thinking before physically starting to design. By its nature, conceptual modelling tools and skills vary with the design context.

Pencil sketches may be used to transform a mental conceptual model, laying out concepts, attributes and relationships.

Non-specific, commercial software packages such as Microsoft Word and Microsoft Powerpoint may be employed to make digital representations of conceptual models. The skill level associated with these is low as most computer users are familiar with the workings of this software. These packages are most probably only suitable for the most basic of conceptual designs and as the systems become more complex specific purpose built software is more appropriate.

A variety of software packages are available for digitising conceptual models, many of which are available free for on-line use and come equipped with standard symbol libraries.

Advantages and disadvantages of using conceptual modelling

Conceptual modelling seeks to verify that the root cause of the original brief is being met, that is the identified problem being solved.

A related advantage of conceptual modelling is the rigorous examination of the product requirements. Design features and product functions come under scrutiny. This examination may reveal characteristics previously thought to be essential as irrelevant. It may also indicate areas of deficit in the product requirements.

Conceptual design allows for truly creative and innovative thinking without the restrictions of specific technology. The design company 'Finish Line' best puts this as; 'Narrowly focused development teams who are not given an opportunity to think outside of their traditional technologies tend to generate the same kinds of solutions regardless of the problem or the requirements. As the old saying goes, "to a hammer, everything looks like a nail". ' www.finishlinepds.com/conceptual-design.html

One of the major advantages of conceptual modelling is its ability to save time further into the design cycle by eliminating costly false leads. Modelling may also be concurrently developed along with requirement generation.

Conceptual modelling has distinct advantages for designers, manufacturers and clients, including:

- opportunities for user trials

- client input into developing models

- speeding up product development cycles

- possibilities of testing production methods and materials prior to production tooling

- reducing development costs by avoiding costly mistakes and false starts in production runs

- functionality of the design becomes more obvious when reviewing physical models and prototypes

- testing proof of concept when examining interacting or moving components or internal mechanisms.

It should also be noted, however, that the exclusive use of conceptual modelling in the design process may cause problems in the form of:

- performance - models may not always be representative of the final product

- functionality - models are not always able to replicate in-service use

- predictions - models may not always provide a true indication of the final product; materials, performance or interaction with the environment.

Further reading

Johnson J and Henderson DA, *Conceptual Models: Begin by Designing What to Design*, Interactions, Jan-Feb 2002.

Johnson J and Henderson DA, *Conceptual Models: Core to Good Design*, Morgan & Claypool, 2011.

THEORY OF KNOWLEDGE

In the construction of a model, how can we know which aspects of the world to include and which to ignore?

© IBO 2012

Students should start with the consideration of the purpose of conceptual design. What are designers trying to achieve at this point in the design cycle? Who are they communicating with?

Careful consideration needs to be given to including or excluding components of a model particularly where issues of dependency may cause the model to fail or falter when evaluated under user test conditions.

If the primary function of a model is to foster the evaluation of initial ideas and lead to further iterative development of the design, then which aspects of the design specification are important for inclusion in the conceptual model? Who decides what is important and what may be left out at the modelling stage?

Is one model, of one style, sufficient to evaluate all of the design requirements or are multiple models using a variety of techniques and media incorporating different features required?

Exercise

Does the project under consideration have any bearing on the type of model produced?

3.2–GRAPHICAL MODELLING

ESSENTIAL IDEA

Graphical models are used to communicate design ideas.

© IBO 2012

NATURE OF DESIGN

Graphical models can take many forms, but their prime function is always the same—to simplify the data and present it in such a way that understanding of what is being presented aids further development or discussion. Designers utilise graphical modelling as a tool to explore creative solutions and refine ideas from the technically impossible to the technically possible, widening the constraints of what is feasible.

© IBO 2012

AIM

The development of ideas through graphical models allows designers to explore and deepen their understanding of a problem and context of use.

© IBO 2012

Product design starts with sketching and modelling. It is employed by designers to preview their ideas, prove concepts, develop iterations, detect errors, ergonomic assessments and make client presentations. Jay Jacobs (2010) comments on the value of modelling when he states, 'the cost of not modelling outweighs the investment to model an idea. Models exist to support decisions, they attempt to answer questions around 'what if.'

Models are also used to improve in-house communication between designers, engineers and non-engineering staff during the design phase. The process is fast, cheap and time efficient. Initially, sketches, photographs, doodles, verbal descriptions, etc. are often employed as a fast way of communicating fundamental design concepts that may be gradually developed and refined. The nature of this process encourages both freedom and creativity.

Early design models may be virtual or physical. Virtual models may be 2–D or 3–D, rendered, wireframe or orthographic, while physical models may be anything from cardboard mockups to fully functional prototypes. This creative first step represents the product concept for the first time in terms of appearance, form, fit size and if necessary function.

Mathematical models

Mathematical models typically offer convenience and cost advantages over the alternatives. They can be extremely powerful, enabling predictions to be made about a system or process. Predictions inform designers of possible developments that are worthy of further investigation or may be employed to optimise use of: materials, strength, materials choice, performance etc. Mathematical modelling allows for the testing and development of optimal solutions using simple mathematical processes or complex techniques such as matrix algebra. Manufacturers may use mathematical models to optimize profits through the calculation and manipulation of such variables as: inventory, production time, plant capacity, warehousing constraints and transportation timings. Unfortunately, mathematical models cannot be entirely reliable in predicting real world situations and are only as good as their programming allows. Graphs and tables could be classed as simple mathematical models and are often employed to document operations and processes or predict performance.

In the elite world of Formula One motor racing mathematical models are employed to design high performance fuel mixtures. Using data gathered from engine tests mathematical models of molecules are simulation tested in virtual engines to determine performance characteristics before field testing.

2–D and 3–D graphical models

As a part of their everyday operations, designers need to acquire the skills associated with graphical communication. The quick and easy nature of sketching as a tool provides the designer with a great deal of flexibility whether in the field or a design studio. The only tools required are paper and a pencil. Used in the early stages of the design process pencil sketches allow designers to quickly jot down ideas that may influence the final design. 3–D sketches provide designers with a sense of form, proportion and aesthetics while 2–D sketches are able to isolate and detail more structural features. At some later stage, these sketches

may need to be translated into a more formal and accurate representation.

Graphical models such as sketches and freehand drawings are quickly generated and useful for communicating initial design concepts. Drawings of a more technical nature take longer and require a degree of expertise not only to correctly construct but also to interpret. CAD drawings such as 3–D models, while requiring significant knowledge and skill to produce, are very user friendly when interpreting and manipulating.

In support of sketching as a design tool, Bouchard et al, (2006) commented in the *Journal of Design Research* that, "designers prefer to use traditional sketches for the earliest phases of conceptual design, because of their ability to fulfil their natural and intuitive needs during their activity. The effort-saving character of sketches allows the designers to concentrate more on the creative side of conceptual design." In the field of car design, sketching allows for the fast recording, communicating and development of abstract and high-level design ideas. It accommodates an amount of uncertainty to exist about specific physical attributes to exist while at the same time retaining important vehicle attributes such as form, proportion and spatial configuration.

The sketching process itself may be considered as a designer's communication with both themselves and the potential audience.

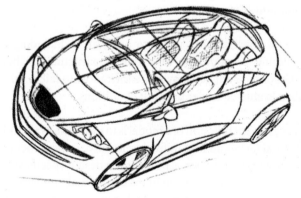

Figure 3.2.1   Car concept design sketch,

Annotations accompany drawings to improve the communication of information. They also help with the creative process documenting fleeting thoughts before they are forgotten. Designers use annotations in a variety of ways including the need to:

•   identify problems for future resolution

•   clarify obscure or difficult-to-sketch concepts

- note a range of related thematic variations or alternatives

- record their thoughts about particular features for later reference.

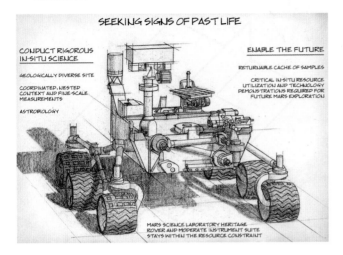

SEEKING SIGNS OF PAST LIFE

CONDUCT RIGOROUS
IN-SITU SCIENCE

GEOLOGICALLY DIVERSE SITE

COORDINATED, NESTED
CONTEXT AND FINE-SCALE
MEASUREMENTS

ASTROBIOLOGY

ENABLE THE FUTURE

RETURNABLE CACHE OF SAMPLES

CRITICAL IN-SITU RESOURCE
UTILIZATION AND TECHNOLOGY
DEMONSTRATIONS REQUIRED FOR
FUTURE MARS EXPLORATION

MARS SCIENCE LABORATORY HERITAGE
ROVER AND MODERATE INSTRUMENT SUITE
STAYS WITHIN THE RESOURCE CONSTRAINT

Figure 3.2.2   Artist's annotated concept of Mars 2020 Rover

Perspective, projection and scale drawings

Perspective drawing is based on observation from a single point, the eye, which produces images similar to that of a camera. Perspective drawings create the illusion of an object's size diminishing the further it retreats from a fixed viewpoint. Early artists employed the technique of perspective. A contemporary of da Vinci, German artist Albrecht Durer further perfected the technique of perspective in use at the time. Durer developed several machines designed to 'capture' an image that would maintain spatial relationships of objects, varying in distance from the observer. 'Durer's window' as shown in Figure 3.2.3 used a piece of glass acting as a picture plane to accurately create a perspective image. The concepts of picture planes, vanishing points and spatial relativity are equally relevant today.

Figure 3.2.3   1525 – Durer's perspective machine

The natural appearance of perspective drawings makes them popular choices with artists and architects. The receding lines give emphasis to objects in the foreground and less prominence to those in the background. The most important characteristics of perspective drawings are:

- objects appear smaller as their distance from the observer increases

- an object's dimensions are foreshortened along the line of sight compared with those dimensions across the line of sight

- objects appear as an approximate as if perceived by the eye.

Figure 3.2.4   Single point mechanical perspective drawing, image by Braindrain0000 CC-BY-SA-3.0 (www. creativecommons.org/licenses/by-sa/3.0) via Wikimedia Commons

Styles of perspective drawing are classified by the number of vanishing points employed.

- Single point perspective uses objects facing the viewer and receding to a single, often central vanishing point as shown in Figure 3.2.4 .

- Two point perspective shows all horizontal lines receding to one of two, (left and right) vanishing points situated on the horizon. This is the convention most often used in architectural drawings.

- Three point perspective incorporates a third vanishing point that appends to the vertical axis receding either upwards or downwards, depending on the viewer's standpoint.

Orthographic drawing uses lines of sight that are always perpendicular to the viewing plane to produce a projected image, hence the name orthographic projection (Figure 3.2.6).

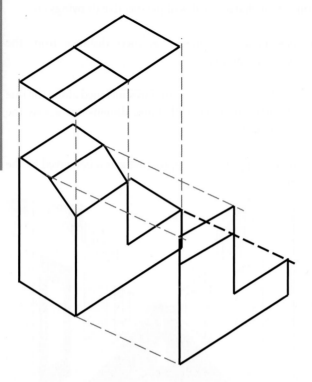

Figure 3.2.6   Orthographic projection

Varieties of different forms of orthographic projection are named depending on the positioning of the object and the observer in relation to the plane or planes of projection. Different styles, such as first and third angle projections are identified by the one of four quadrants or angles they enclose, (Figure 3.2.7).

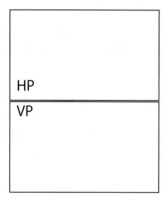

Figure 3.2.7   Drawing quadrants

In third angle projection, the front and horizontal planes of projection are perpendicular to each other, however, using the line of intersection of the two projection planes as a hinge, the top view is swung directly above the front view.

Frequently the folding line between the views is drawn on the paper. Above the folding line, an HP notation indicating a horizontal plane appears while below the folding line the letters VP may appear indicating a vertical plane (Figure 3.2.8).

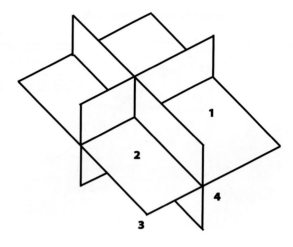

Figure 3.2.8   Third angle projection planes

First and third angle projections are both used extensively throughout the world. When the first quadrant is used, the lines of sight travel from the observer's eye to the object and then to the plane of projection.

When the third angle of projection is used, the lines of sight travel from the observer's eye through the plane of projection to the object (Figures 3.2.8 and 3.2.9). In each type of projection the views are obtained in a similar way but their relative positions vary.

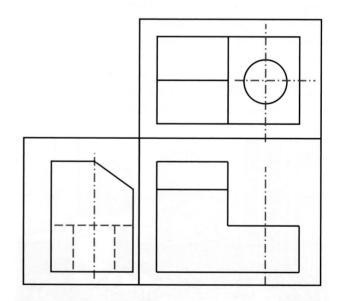

Figure 3.2.8b   Orthographic projection views

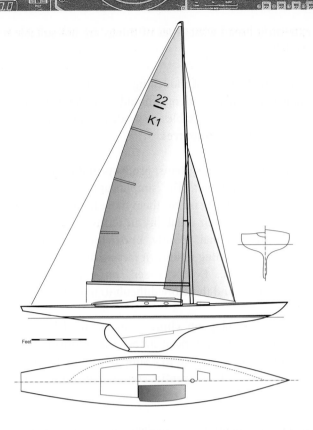

In first angle projection, the top view is on the bottom, drawn below the front view whereas, in third angle projection, the top view is drawn above the front view. Australia, Canada and the United States all use third angle of projection. The standard symbols identifying first and third angle orthographic projections appear as show in Figure 3.2.8.

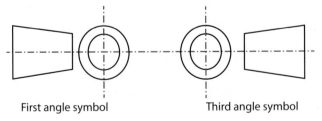

First angle symbol   Third angle symbol

Figure 3.2.10   Orthographic projection symbols

In a conventional third angle orthographic projection, the views will always appear in the positions shown. The top view is projected directly onto the horizontal plane of projection and shows the width and depth dimensions. The front view is projected directly onto the vertical frontal plane of projection and shows the width and height dimensions. The left-side view is projected directly onto the vertical left plane of projection. The side view of an object shows the depth and height dimensions. In most cases, three views convey all of the information to adequately

describe an object. In product design, orthogonal drawing usually refers to accurate line drawings used to convey dimensional and/or assembly details. These may be manually drawn using drawing equipment, or now, more commonly, using CAD software.

Orthogonal views are carefully selected, and sectioning and other conventional representations used to successfully communicate the complete design. Critical overall dimensions may be shown along with accompanying notes explaining details for overall assembly and function. Sub-assembly drawings are used for large or highly complex products. Product assembly may also have to be broken down into sub-assemblies to allow a sufficient level of detail to be shown. In this situation a hierarchy of assembly drawings may be required to relate each part to the functioning of the whole.

An orthographic drawing, (commonly referred to as an engineering or working drawing), shows precise details and dimensions. It is most often used as a workshop or production drawing. Generated in the final stage of the design process, and fully dimensioned, they provide valuable information to manufacturers and engineers relating to: dimensions, tolerances, construction methods, materials, surface finishes and assembly.

Scale drawings are constructed to a specific ratio relative to the actual size of the place or object. Various scales may be used for different drawings in a set. Ratios may be used to enlarge or reduce the appearance of the subject.

Commonly used ratios in the metric system for the purposes of reduction are 1:5, 1:10, 1:20, 1:50, 1:100, 1:200, 1:500, 1:1 000, 1:2 000 and 1:5 000.

Sketching versus formal drawing techniques

Sketch drawing and more formal drawing techniques each have their place in product design and manufacture. Sketches are used to quickly convey ideas, modify concepts and communicate with inside and outside design teams at the earliest stages of the design process. Drawing techniques such as isometric and perspective are employed in the later stages of the design process to communicate near complete design proposals to clients or marketing staff. In a user friendly pictorial form these drawings convey a closer approximation of the final appearance of a design. Technical drawing styles such as engineering or orthographic drawings are used in the manufacturing stage to define the exact size, fit, finish and appearance of the final product. While this type is drawing can be more time consuming than sketching, it contains and conveys significantly more information.

Part and assembly drawings

General assembly drawings are often orthogonal drawings that communicate the functional detail of a design by indicating the size and relative position of all parts, fastenings and functional relationships between parts.

Assembly drawings are required for any item consisting of more than one part. A table often accompanies these drawings identifying parts, the quantity of individual parts required and materials. Further instructions may document assembly and even surface finishes to be applied.

Assembly drawings may also be drawn in an exploded isometric style. Exploded isometric drawings display component parts displaced or exploded along an assembly axis. This type of drawing is more visually descriptive, showing actual assembly configurations and fastening details. Exploded drawings serve to clearly identify parts for both assembly and maintenance procedures.

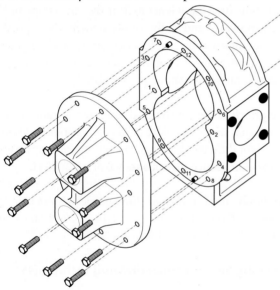

Figure 3.2. 11   Exploded assembly drawing, image by Napco_Rotary_Gear_Pump.gif: Reed T. Warnick derivative work: Cdang (Napco_Rotary_Gear_Pump.gif) CC-BY-SA-3.0 , via Wikimedia Commons

THEORY OF KNOWLEDGE

Are there aspects of the world that are not amenable to modelling?

© IBO 2012

Consider here the wide range of things that are appropriate for modelling including quantum mechanics, sales patterns, architecture and so on. While this field is extremely broad what types of things are not suitable to model?

While the benefits of modelling may have proven to be financially viable, students should consider if there are items that are not suitable for modelling and therefore a waste of time and resources.

Modelling complex systems, products and environments can be very difficult. The simplification of models by reducing complexity makes them more manageable but of course reduces their reliability in terms of predictability versus the original. Poorly understood systems and processes containing unknown factors may also generate unreliable data. Events based on randomness are unpredictable and therefore difficult to model accurately.

In its online blog on climate change models, science journal Scientific American states "The failure of a model can sometimes be traced to a simple inability to simulate the behaviour of an essential component of the system." [1]

When commenting on models, machine intelligence research expert David Cook (2014) proposes the following dilemmas for consideration.

- Mathematically, "it is extremely difficult to model the real world totally inside of code."

- "All models are inaccurate (yet) some models are useful anyway."

- "It's hard to model unforeseen circumstances."

The following questions may also clarify the role of models and their suitability.

Are models that fail unsuccessful?

What can we learn from the failure of a model?

Can failure of a model actually be the targeted result?

Is it possible to model human feelings, emotions or intangible concepts such as good and evil?

Consider why the social sciences involving people, such as psychology, sociology, or economics are difficult to model. Data gathered is based on observations but is this data reliable enough for future predictions?

The question here may be rephrased to examine whether graphical communication does in fact limit communication and in what ways has it enhanced knowledge.

Some of the earliest forms of communication date back to cave art. Students should examine what form these communications took and the type of knowledge conveyed.

More developed ancient societies such as the Greeks and others used complex pictograms to convey complex information and record daily events. How widespread was this type of communication and how if it all was it limited? These societies also used more traditional drawings and plans to build some of the most complex and awe-inspiring feats of engineering.

In more recent times the expression "a picture is worth a thousand words" is often used. How does this common expression spread light on the initial statement?

Exercise

Investigation could be made into cultures such as the Australian Aborigine that have never developed a formal written language but continued to record their culture, history and religion first through rock art and later through paintings. Are there other cultures who continue to solely use graphic forms of communication?

Figure 3.2. 12 - Australian Aboriginal Rock Art, Kakadu, NT.

3.3–PHYSICAL MODELLING

ESSENTIAL IDEA

A physical model is a three-dimensional, tangible representation of a design or system.

© IBO 2012

NATURE OF DESIGN

Designers use physical models to visualize information about the context that the model represents. It is very common for physical models of large objects to be scaled down and smaller objects scaled up for ease of visualization. The primary goal of physical modelling is to test aspects of a product against user requirements. Thorough testing at the design development stage ensures that an appropriate product is developed.

© IBO 2012

AIM

Physical modelling not only allows designers to explore and test their ideas, but to also present them to others. Engaging clients, focus groups and experts to interact with physical models of products allows designers to gain valuable feedback that enable them to improve the design and product-user interface.

© IBO 2012

Once a design has been fully realised in sketch form, designers may move to virtual or physical models for further review. Depending on the context, the style, tools and media used for conceptual models vary considerably. Application of one particular rigid model can never be suitable in all contexts. Depending on the desired outcome, various components of the process require more attention, time or repeated cycling to provide a suitable solution.

Physical models of consumer products may be constructed from a range of materials including, but not limited to, cardboard, balsa wood, acrylic, high density polyurethane, moulding silicone and urethane.

Scale models

As a design tool, architectural conceptual models are a quick and inexpensive way for architects to visualise space, consider the relationship between buildings and landscape/ environment and assist when discussing revisions with clients. Landscape models of large developments may use a scale of about 1:100 while, for individual buildings (requiring greater detail), a scale of 1:20 would be more appropriate. Models such as the one shown in Figure 3.1.2 may use a variety of materials including: illustration board, foamcore, medium density fibreboard, corrugated cardboard, balsa wood and acrylic.

Figure 3.3.2   Clay model, image by By DineshAdv (Own work) CC-BY-SA-3.0 (http://creativecommons.org/ licenses/by-sa/3.0) via Wikimedia Commons

Aesthetic models

Aesthetic models may be physical or digital and are used to assess the appearance or visual appeal of a design. How individuals view aesthetics can be a matter of perspective based on emotional responses, cultural influences, previous experiences and so on. The characteristic principles of aesthetic design include line, form, colour, patterns and proportion. Elements of style, fashion trends, personal taste and originality all contribute to the aesthetic.

Figure 3.3.1   Architectural model, Image by Wasily at nl.wikipedia [Public domain], from Wikimedia Commons

In the auto industry clay modelling is a very traditional technique used by car designers to produce physical models. Some design studios have transferred their modelling activities to the CAD department while others maintain that clay is still the best way to visualise the development of 3–D designs. Clay scale models such as the one shown in Figure 3.1.1 may be produced to examine aesthetics, while full-size models allow for wind tunnel testing, fitting of hardware and components such as door handles, glass etc. Physical models can also be digitised using 3–D scanners. The process of 3–D scanning allows engineers to virtually manufacture panels, add powerplants and drivetrains towards the development of a simulated working prototype.

Mock-ups and prototypes

The terms mock-up and prototype are often used interchangeably but can be distinguished in the ways outlined below.

A mock-up generally refers to three dimensional, full-size or scale product models. These are often made from materials other than those which will make up the final product and are designed to save the money and time involved in developing more accurate prototypes. Mock-ups are produced to catch design flaws at the earliest stage. They do not replicate functionality but may be used for aesthetic and ergonomic assessments. Multiple iterations of mockups may be required before proceeding to the next stage.

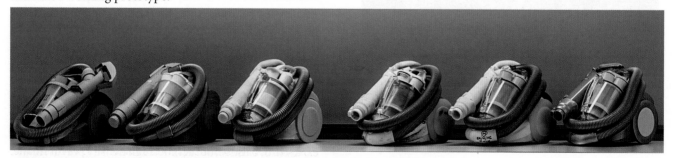

Figure 3.3.3   Range of models from mock-up to prototype, image by Dyson Australia

Prototypes are models that also include the functionality aspects of a design. Prototypes look and feel like the real production item but are produced as a one off to provide a final full evaluation before mass production. At this point changes are still able to be affected but because prototypes look and feel like the real product they allow marketing departments start advertising campaigns and demonstrate the product to distributors before manufacturing starts.

Mock-ups and prototypes apply equally to digital design as much as product design. Wire frame mockups of web pages have all the layout features and visual appeal of the further developed fully interactive prototype.

Instrumented models

Fully instrumented models are produced to extract performance data across a range of criteria for the purposes of verification and validation.

Validation is 'the process of determining the degree to which a model is an accurate representation of the real world from the perspective of the intended uses of the model' (AIAA, 1998).

Verification is 'the process of determining that a model implementation accurately represents the developer's conceptual description of the model and the solution to the model' (AIAA, 1998).

Instrumented models may be used in a wide variety of situations. Some specific examples include:

- feedback from prosthetic devices to provide data on both loading and ground reaction forces

- architectural models to study critical design decisions and alternatives

- instrumented wheelsets for the continuous assessment of multi-planar forces

- product development and reverse engineering.

THEORY OF KNOWLEDGE

Models that only show aspects of reality are widely used in design. How can they lead to new knowledge?

© IBO 2012

The initial investigation should centre around models and the variety of purposes they may serve. It should consider the nature of change and how models play a part in enacting that change. Students should consider how the iterative process of design can be applied to the continued development and evolution of new models. Comparisons may be made between the development of innovative products and the new knowledge generated by constantly evolving models.

- What do models do?

- What makes a good model?

- How may they be used?

Models are basically used to observe explain and predict patterns or behaviours. Models are judged to be acceptable or not based on how well they can explain and predict data and how consistent they are with what is already known about the world. The value of modelling lies in its ability to combine known pieces of information in a range of ways to produce predictions that better inform decision making. Models may be physical constructions, mathematical, graphs, computer simulations and so on. Even though data input may be based on existing knowledge, as model parameters are changed and manipulated the interaction of the various components may produce previously unseen results. It is this ability of prediction that makes models so valuable.

"Models are constantly being used to ask more questions about the world and when new data are gathered, models are revised or discarded altogether. Scientific knowledge is not static, but is always changing." [1]

www.teachers.oregon.k12.wi.us/sundstrom/Physical%20 Science/Measurement/Scientific%20Modeling%20 Reading.pdf

Exercise

Historically, many scientific models have changed a great deal in light of new data and new ideas. Identify an example of a model that has changed over time. Why was the new model adopted over the previous one?

3.4–COMPUTER-AIDED DESIGN (CAD)

ESSENTIAL IDEA

A computer-aided design is the generation, creation, development and analysis of a design or system using computer software.

© IBO 2012

NATURE OF DESIGN

As technologies improve and the software becomes more powerful, so do the opportunities for designers to create new and exciting products, services and systems. Greater freedom in customization and personalization of products has a significant impact on the end user. The ability to virtually prototype, visualize and share designs enhances the whole design cycle from data analysis through to final designs.

© IBO 2012

AIM

The use of CAD to simulate the conditions in which a product will be used allows the designer to gain valuable data at low cost. For example, simulating the flow of air across a car exterior negates the need for a car and wind tunnel.

© IBO 2012

Types of CAD software

There is a variety of different types of CAD software depending on the application to which it is being applied. Each of these systems applies its own form of internal logic that must be understood by designers

2-D CAD

2-D CAD software operates in the *x* and *y* axes. Drawings are constructed line by line or through the creation of basic shapes. This type of CAD was used in place of traditional drafting techniques and while relying on two dimensions only could also be used for the construction of pictorial drawings in the isometric or oblique style.

Wire frame modelling

Wire-frame models are constructed, surface-by-surface, to produce a three-dimensional representation of the object. Software features include the ability to rotate the object in space to examine the drawing from a variety of perspectives. Orthographic drawings are also able to be generated automatically at the click of a mouse. Features such as holes or keyways had to be added as lines as the software did not recognise shapes nor their relationships to each other.

3-D modelling

Solid modelling software produces 'solid' representations of objects that may be further manipulated. Because these objects have 'mass', calculations may be performed on the object within the software, such as volume and centre of gravity. Changes made to parts or segments within the drawing are automatically translated throughout the model allowing for modifications to be made without the need for a new drawing. This makes the software suitable for the fast testing of new design iterations and problem solving. Materials properties may also be allocated to allow for virtual testing of physical and engineering properties.

Advantages and disadvantages of using computer-aided modelling

CAD drawing packages allow users to design in 3–D to give designers the opportunity to view models as they would appear in real life. No longer are complex orthographic drawings created and converted into 3–D figures. These 3–D models can quickly be viewed as wire-frame or solid. They are able to rotated and viewed from any direction, as well as be resolved into oblique, isometric or perspective views. 3–D models such as the one shown in Figure 3.1.10 instantly provide recognition and realism for designers, clients and consumers. Notice how the features in the CAD drawing (upper), are instantly recognisable in the final manufactured part (lower).

The ability to sketch directly in 3–D has also enhanced the designer's ability to perceive potential design flaws. This process known as virtual design is increasingly used in industry to generate computer models of real components or assemblies. Animation of moving and mating components can show areas of non-alignment or 'clashing'. Flow simulation software can analyse effects, such as turbulence and drag, without recourse to expensive models and wind tunnel tests. Stress analysis can also be performed on these virtual products to identify weaknesses and make modifications before the first physical component is produced.

While 3–D CAD design software has revolutionised product design, manufacturers still require engineering drawings for production purposes. CAD packages allow for the easy transformation of 3–D graphics into detailed workshop drawings, with all the attendant documentation. Specifically the advantages of CAD drawings may be summarised as their ability to be:

- stored in a variety of formats

- corrected or altered very quickly

- created as 2–D or 3–D representations

- rescaled, zoomed, cropped etc. for detail

- presented as paper printouts, virtual models or rapid prototypes

- electronically distributed for collaboration as part of a group project used in conjunction with numerical control machinery for CAD/CAM production.

The disadvantages associated with CAD drawings include:

- levels of staff training required to be competent

- initial cost and upgrading of software

- compatibility between software and hardware

- skills constantly require upgrading as software updates

- steep learning curves associated with early stages of uptake.

Surface and solid models

Surface modelling software shapes the surface or 'skin' of a CAD object. It enables very complex geometries and produces a more detailed view than wireframe modelling. The aim of surface modelling is to produce as realistic an effect as possible, however, no information is recorded about the object's interior detail.

Solid modelling contains the most geometric information of all CAD model types. Solid models contain all the wire frame and surface information to fully define faces and edges of models, as well as associative information known as topology.

Based on external appearance, there may seem to be little difference between surface and solid models. Surface modelling is used to quickly generate complex shapes and is extensively employed in the consumer product design industry. These shapes however, possess no thickness or interior information therefore they cannot be cut to provide interior details or used as the basis for rapid prototyping. Conversely, solid modelling is often used in conjunction with rapid prototyping technologies to build a physical 3–D model. Solid modelled objects contain more information in the form of primitive geometry (planes, cones, cylinders etc.).

Data modelling including statistical modelling

Matthew West and Julian Fowler, (1999), define a conceptual data model as being "developed based on the data requirements for the application that is being developed, perhaps in the context of an activity model. The data model will normally consist of entity types, attributes, relationships, integrity rules, and the definitions of those objects. This is then used as the start point for interface or database design."

The flowchart shown in Figure 3.4.1 illustrates the way data models are developed and applied.

Data models structure data through the use of a variety database models or templates. These determine the way in which data is stored, organised and processed. Common logical data models for databases include: flat file, hierarchical, relational, object-oriented and network database models. The following explanations of database models accompanies the database images and is courtesy of the Data Integration Glossary, U.S. Department of Transportation.

Flat file models use a file structure involving data records that have no structured interrelationship. A flat file takes up less computer space than a structured file but requires the database application to know how the data are organised within the file.

Hierarchical models do not link records together like a family tree, but each record type has only one owner (e.g., a purchase order is owned by only one customer). Hierarchical data structures were widely used in the first mainframe database management systems. However, due to their restrictions, they often cannot be used to relate structures that exist in the real world.

Relational models organise data as a set of formally described tables from which data can be accessed or reassembled in many ways without having to reorganize the database tables. Each table (sometimes called a relation) contains one or more data categories in columns. Each row contains a unique instance of data for the categories defined by the columns.

The object-oriented model defines a data object as containing code (sequences of computer instructions) and data (information that the instructions operate on). Traditionally, code and data have been kept apart. In an object-oriented data model, the code and data are merged into a single indivisible thing—an object.

Network models are a special case of the hierarchical data model in which each record type can have multiple owners (e.g., purchase orders are owned by both customers and products).

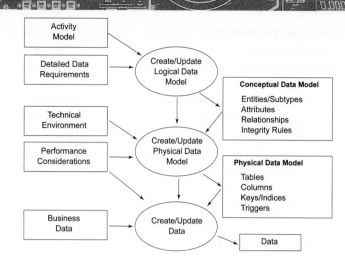

Figure 3.4.1 Data_modelling_today.jpg: Matthew West and Julian Fowler derivative work: Razorbliss (talk) - Developing high quality data models, Source: EPISTLE

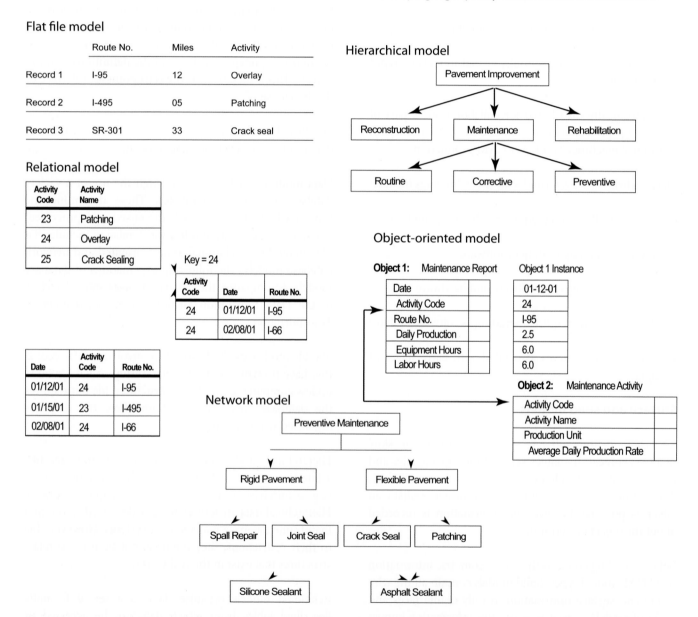

Figure 3.4.2 Collage of five types of database models, images by U.S. Department of Transportation vectorization: own work [Public domain], via Wikimedia Commons

Virtual prototyping

Virtual prototyping is a software-driven modelling process that simulates products and environments by mimicking real world behaviours. It is finding increasing application in the development and testing and assessment of products. Due to the lack of a need for a physical product, virtual prototyping has on occasions replaced rapid prototyping for the iterative development of new products or those requiring renewal.

Designers and engineers are able to simulate visually and mathematically the design, assembly and in-service use of complex products in a range of environments and work scenarios. Modifications may also be quickly evaluated in a time-effective manner involving multiple designers, clients, and business managers. Not only is the process faster than traditional methods, but costs are reduced, materials use minimised and design cycle times shortened.

Researchers at the University of Hong Kong, Choi and Cheung, (2012), see virtual prototyping and virtual manufacturing technologies as critical to the success of product development companies wishing to compete in global markets. They offer the opportunity to reduce lead times, minimise product development costs, eliminate costly errors and maintain quality. 'Virtual prototyping and virtual manufacturing integrate virtual reality simulation techniques with design and manufacturing processes to fabricate digital prototypes for subsequent stereoscoic visualisation, validation and optimisation of product designs, as well as for evaluation of product assemblability and producability.'

Virtual prototyping finds application across a wide range of industries including carmaking, white goods, yellow goods, aerospace and consumer products.

In an entirely different use of virtual prototyping, NASA (1999) notes the importance of carbon nanotubes in composites and the role virtual prototyping plays in their development when it states "carbon nanotubes are of interest as constituents-reinforcements for composites, probes for scanning microscopy, quantum wires for electronics, and building blocks for nanomachinery. Their small size makes direct experimental measurements difficult. Therefore, the critical answers about their properties should be obtained based on adequate modelling, virtual prototyping, using the methods of classical molecular dynamic, in combination with the analytical methods and continuum mechanics."

In 2003, NASA's Virtual Prototype Facility software was used to simulate the assembly process of the Stardust spacecraft. Components were assembled in a variety of combinations to optimise the assembly process and check on any conflicts arising under simulated operational conditions. Maintenance procedures were also checked in the virtual environment to make certain repairs and adjustments could be easily made to any area of the spacecraft.

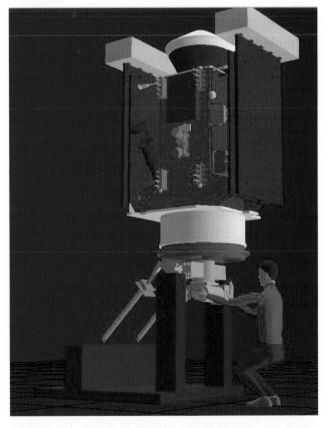

Figure 3.4.4   A view of the spacecraft in its vertical (launch) configuration image by NASA (http://stardust.jpl. nasa.gov/mission/assembly.html) [Public domain]

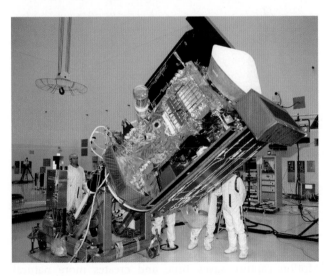

Figure 3.4.3   A view of the physical Stardust spacecraft in the Payload Hazardous Servicing Facility, image by NASA (http://stardust.jpl.nasa.gov/photo/ksc990111.html) [Public domain]

Bottom-up and top-down modelling

'Bottom up' design involves creating parts before joining (mating) them together to form an assembly. These parts may be: constructed from scratch, imported from established libraries or downloaded designs from third party suppliers of standard components. Each of these parts contains independent geometry and any modifications to individual components will not be distributed to others that may be affected. Overall, the process can be time consuming particularly when one change may affect a variety of other components that must first be identified then modified manually.

'Top down' design relates to the use of a hierarchy involving locking-in information critical to a design at the earliest stage and relying on this structure to inform the design at later or lower levels of product design. Top-down design, involves the addition of new parts to assemblies through the application of relationships. As a simple example– two cylindrical parts may be mated around their centres using the relationship of concentricity. This maintains the alignment of the two parts regardless of changes to circle diameters. This automatic modification of related components saves considerable time throughout the evolution of a design and reduces the chance of error in complex assemblies.

Digital humans: motion capture, haptic technology, virtual reality (VR), and animation

Digital humans are computer-based models designed to assist researchers to simulate human biomechanics and predict how a real human body would react in a variety of situations and environments. The use of digital humans allows for the gathering of information relative to the range of human motion, forces, fatigue, potential injury etc.

Motion capture has been employed to assist with the understanding of human factors, physical limitations of users and product evaluation.

Motion capture technology is used to record, track and analyse movement. The process records movement through a series of snapshots generated many times per second. Special markers may be applied to strategic points of a moving human body to identify key pieces of geometry. The resultant changes in position of the figure(s) are recorded and easily digitised for playback or analysis.

Figure 3.4.5 shows such a process in action. The capture and transference of data points through an intermediary digital skeleton into a digital human construct is clearly demonstrated.

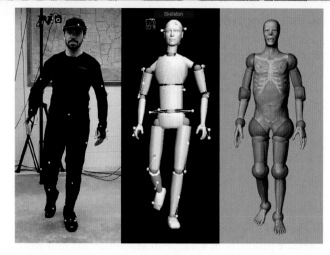

Figure 3.4.5a   Motion capture process image by Vazquez88 (own work) [CC-BY-SA-3.0 (http:// creativecommons.org/licenses/by-sa/3.0)], via Wikimedia Commons

A motion capture session records the movements of the actor, not his or her visual appearance. The captured movements are mapped to a 3–D human virtual model created by a computer artist. This process allows the computer model to replicate the movements and actions of the original human model.

Once recorded, motion animation such as in filmmaking, (as shown in Figure 3.4.6a), may be generated. The information may also be used directly for the purposes of motion study, or the interaction of human motion with the natural or built environments.

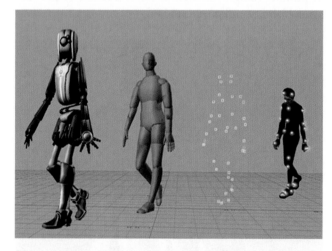

Figure 3.4.6a   Motion capture manipulation

Motion capture saves time and creates more natural movements than the alternative, manual animation, but is limited to motions that are anatomically possible. Motion capture can reduce the cost of animation, which otherwise requires the animator to draw either each frame or key frames, that are then interpolated.

Digital humans, using software with an underlying physics engine may be used to replicate and calculate muscle force, efficient muscle action or fatigue. They may also identify effects of clothing on performance, model the dynamics of walking patterns and utilize the mathematical relationships between energy produced, heart rate and oxygen uptake. It is also possible to derive physiological indices such as the heart rate, breathing rate, carbon dioxide production rate and core temperature.

All of this data can be gathered automatically and simultaneously in a range of simulated environments, 'what if' scenarios or hazardous situations that would be either too expensive or dangerous to reproduce using a human model.

Using statistics and data gathered from anthropometric tables and motion capture, digital humans employ complex algorithms to generate motion, posture, joint force etc. to predict responses to new situations or environments, previously untested.

Digital human models are increasingly used early in product design to reduce product development time and costs. Manufacturing industry demands that products be designed for the comfort and accessibility of consumers as well as workplaces and the health and safety of employees. Digital human models assist manufacturers to examine designs from an ergonomic perspective. They allow designers to test virtual models and evaluate the performance of future products prior to the construction of a prototype.

Using digital humans early in the design cycle, designers can:

- save time and expensive resources

- test and evaluate products based on ergonomic factors

- take into account the range of sizes and shapes of users

- consider user safety factors in a range of environments

- establish physical use requirements and product serviceability

- review human factors in design before building physical prototypes.

Digital human modelling can reduce the need for the production of physical prototypes. A range of parameters may be modelled and tested during product development, not only to optimise individual design factors, but to allow for the evaluation of the complex interplay between multiple modifications and their 'knock-on' effects. DHM and simulation in product design enable products to be developed more quickly, i.e. more design iterations in less time. This results in higher product quality, and meets human requirements more accurately. Products are safer as a result of more thorough analysis of safety aspects and improved productivity results from enhanced automation of the development process. Digital prototypes are also cheaper and faster to produce, test and modify than physical prototypes.

Digital humans enable manufacturing plants to be developed more quickly and manual workflow to be optimised. They improve worker safety and reduce compensation costs resulting from accidents. Machines and other equipment can be positioned to optimise cycle time and avoid hazards. Manufacturing processes can be designed to eliminate inefficiencies and ensure optimal productivity. They can be used to ensure that people can access the parts and equipment needed to assemble products; check that workers can effectively use any hand tools needed to perform manual tasks; and check that all tasks can be performed safely without requiring inordinate strength or exposing people to risk of injury.

Using digital humans enables designers to ensure that there is sufficient space to perform maintenance tasks, including space for hands, arms and tools, as well as space to install and remove parts. Designers can check that technicians can see the subject when they do specific maintenance tasks and that they can use the requisite hand tools. Digital humans enable people to be trained in multiple locations without the need for physical prototypes or actual equipment, and so reduce the cost of training manufacturing and maintenance personnel.

Digital humans can be used in e-commerce to model clothing products. A customer can produce a model corresponding to his or her body shape, size and look. The model can then try on clothing so that the customer can see what it might look like, for example, www.landsend.com.

Virtual Reality and animation

Computer animation is a way of automating the process of linking graphic elements that change slightly over time and, when played consecutively, simulate motion. Animation and virtual reality presentations add realism to CAD models. The animation of the complex engine and crankshaft assembly shown in Figure 3.4.5 illustrates the benefits associated with animation. Not only does the graphic show a great degree of detail but, through animation, shows the complexity of movement associated with each rotation of the shaft.

Figure 3.4.5 Engine animation, image by Freeformer [GFDL CC-BY-SA-3.0 (www.creativecommons.org/licenses/by-sa/3.0/), via Wikimedia Commons

CAD-generated virtual models can be reviewed, modified, and altered as required. Computers may perform virtual machining operations allowing designers to choose the optimum manufacturing process and sequence of operations. Full size physical prototypes may then be machined identical to the virtual construct.

Virtual or augmented reality can range from a simple arrangement of elements on a computer desktop to a more immersive experience. Virtual reality simulates environments and may give the user an opportunity to interact with the environment. Walk-through or fly-over simulations are an example of this type of digital material where the user is able to 'walk around' digital models or environments and view them as if they existed in a three dimensional space. They are designed to provide an off-site viewer with an in-context impression of projected designs that may not even exist. These digital constructs provide detail, perspectives and interaction not necessarily available with a physical model without any of the costs associated with physical models or transport to remote sites. Virtual technologies are used to test vehicle aerodynamics, train astronauts and even simulate road conditions for learning drivers.

In applications where assembly instructions or movement of parts is required, these are best supplied visually though a staged/timed assembly presented through an animation. This type of presentation would also be the fastest to produce, generate the smallest file size and be the least expensive option.

The required outcome of the initial brief and anticipated returns will often determine whether the considerable

time and costs associated with generating a realistic and effective virtual environment can be justified.

The ability of computers to either convert 2–D drawings or 3–D models into virtual reality environments has enhanced the designer's ability to perceive potential design flaws, test for materials suitability, examine ergonomic compatibility and make modifications before the first physical component is produced. Recent developments see CAD programs incorporating 'assessment of sustainability algorithms' that can determine and compare the environmental impact of a range of viable alternatives.

Virtual reality technologies generating computer models of real components or systems are finding application in architectural modelling, remote control of robotics, machining, ergonomic design and vehicle prototyping.

Virtual reality can be used to simulate the interaction of components on-screen, without incurring the costs of physical prototypes. Static or dynamic loads may be modelled to analyze the performance of a particular design or modification. Virtual reality constructs also allow designers to predict how the model will perform in use and when exposed to a variety of real world forces.

Virtualisation of products allows designers to evaluate efficacy of design in a responsive, immersive environment. It is often employed in conjunction with computer-based testing such as finite element analysis. In the transport industries, (air, sea and land), designers are able to use virtual tests to examine fluid dynamics and review the efficiency and viability of their designs. Both time and money are saved in these virtual 'proof of concept' simulations. Designers are able to test a variety of factors such as lift, drag, turbulence, fluid flow patterns, heat transfer fields, momentum etc. All of this is done using the CAD package's embedded mathematical modelling and is driven by a physics engine maintaining the laws of physics. In a practical, consumer-based application, Japanese customers of Matsushita can submit architectural plans for processing into a virtual simulation of a range of kitchen design alternatives.

All of these operations save costs, allow for real-time training, testing and development at considerable cost savings and reductions in time compared with traditional approaches to model making, testing and evaluation.

Virtual reality technology has the potential to:

- advance real-time training

- reduce product development cycles

- save resources by removing reliance on physical modelling.

Figure 3.4.6 shows a 3-D CAD simulation of a robotic car body inspection and measurement machine. The pre-programming of robotic movements, cycle times, interactions with humans and anti-collision paths can be constructed to reflect real time operations and viewed as an animation. In this situation, the animation process saves time and expensive errors. It may also be conducted off-site and programmed off-line without access to any expensive robotic hardware.

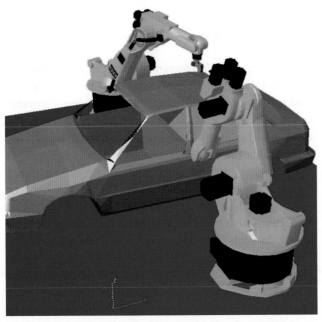

Figure 3.4.6   Simulated robot production line, image by L. Beyer at the English Wikipedia project CC-BY-SA-3.0 (www.creativecommons.org/licenses/by-sa/3.0/), via Wikimedia Commons

The Rensselaer radiation measurement and dosimetry group of New York are currently developing a virtual nuclear power plant for the calculation of effective dose equivalent data. Digital humans are inserted into the CAD generated virtual reality environment to simulate movement of workers and assess potential radiation exposures using pre-calculated dose databases. The package is used to assess potential hazards and to school workers in effective, safe and efficient work practices.

Finite element analysis (FEA)

Most often used for stress calculations, finite element analysis or FEA is a tool used to test virtual models under a variety of load conditions. It may be used to test the design of new products or analyse existing products in new situations.

A number of FEA software packages are available. Some include components to measure thermal, electromagnetic, fluid and structural dynamics.

Using the structural assessment component, FEA can simulate how an object would react under service loads or conditions. Under the FEA process, a virtual model shows how loads would be distributed within the object. These reactive forces may be in response to loads generated by: expansion due to temperature variations, external loads, pressures or vibration. Through the action of dividing the model up into a series of simple but discrete elements joined through nodes, the program is able to analyse a complex object by considering it as a series of resolvable units. Observations are then made as to how the object may perform under a variety of conditions. When assessing a structure FEM may be employed to generate stiffness and strength visualisations. This data may in turn assist with weight minimisation, materials selection, manufacturing process choices and costing.

FEA can be used to study the interactions of assembled components on-screen, before incurring the costs of physical prototypes. Static or dynamic loads may be simulated to evaluate a design's performance under extension, bending and twisting to evaluate stress, strain, and displacement. FEA thus allows design simulations to evolve before manufacturing. FEA often finds applications in the car industry, where simulated collisions using components, assemblies or whole-of-vehicle designs can show the result of various crash scenarios. The data would show distributed forces, twisting, buckling, movement and even failure of various elements of the design.

Figure 3.4.7   Finite element analysis of an asymmetrical collision

FEA is very cost and time effective. Manufacturing and physical testing costs far outweigh those of producing and testing a computer simulation. It substantially decreases the time from design concept to product reality. FEA analysis, however, can only inform designs to a point where physical testing may be required to confirm the specifications of the final product.

3.5–RAPID PROTOTYPING

ESSENTIAL IDEA

Rapid prototyping is the production of a physical model of a design using three-dimensional CAD data.

© IBO 2012

NATURE OF DESIGN

The growth in computing power has had a major impact on modelling with computer-aided manufacture. Rapid software and hardware developments allow new opportunities and exciting new technologies to create dynamic modelling of ever-greater complexity. Models can be simulated by designers using software, tested and trialled virtually before sending to a variety of peripheral machines for prototype manufacture in an ever-increasing range of materials. The ease of sending this digital data across continents for manufacture of prototypes has major implications for data and design protection.

© IBO 2012

AIM

The increasing effectiveness of rapid prototyping techniques in terms of both cost and speed enables designers to create complex physical models for testing.

© IBO 2012

Rapid prototyping

The importance and potential of rapid prototyping is summed up in statements that proclaim it as the next Industrial Revolution. Essentially, it is a group of technologies that are used to construct physical models (prototypes). Often referred to as '3–D printers' most of the technologies involving rapid prototyping are additive in nature but CNC milling machines such as the Roland MDX series have coined phrases such as 'subtractive rapid prototyping' to describe their systems.

The basic process for additive rapid prototyping consists of five steps:

- create a CAD drawing of the object

- convert the CAD file into an STL format

- transfer the STL file to the rapid prototyping machine of choice

- manufacture the product

- clean-up/assemble the final product

Stereo lithography

Stereo lithography (as shown in Figure 3.5.1) is just one rapid prototyping technology employed to build physical models, using only CAD data. In this process, computer software sections a 3D computer model into thin slices (0.05 mm–0.15 mm) before a computer-controlled laser beam 'builds' the model layer by layer.

The model building process involves the reaction between a bath of liquid photopolymer and a directed ultraviolet laser beam that 'prints out' the gradually solidifying object. As each layer is complete, the object, mounted on a moveable table, moves downwards to expose more photopolymer ready to create the next layer. This technique allows the production of objects that may be too costly, time consuming or difficult to create, using traditional methods.

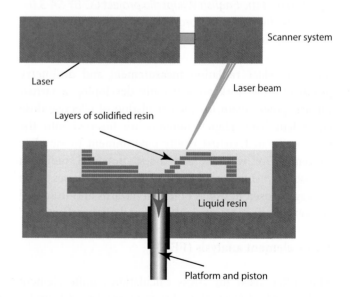

Figure 3.5.1   Stereo lithography, image by Materialgeeza [CC-BY-SA-3.0 (www.creativecommons.org/licenses/by-sa/3.0) or GFDL (www.gnu.org/copyleft/fdl.html)], from Wikimedia Commons

Laminated object manufacturing (LOM)

Using a laser cutter, LOM technologies cut sheet material (pre-glued paper or plastic) based on data provided by CAD software that has sliced the original CAD model into layers. Once cut, these layers are glued together to form a physical model. Assembly of these layers may use locating pins or an automatic process conducted on a moveable table directly under the laser, (Figure 3.5.2). Kraft paper, backed with a polyethylene-based, heat sensitive adhesive, is often used as the modelling material. This product is both cost-effective and environmentally friendly. Paper models are regularly sealed to prevent damage from moisture and improve their overall strength. Other modelling materials include acrylic, metal and ceramic 'felt'.

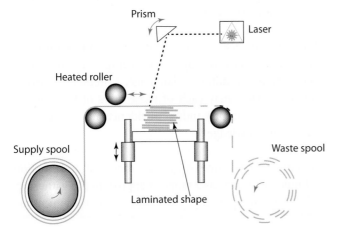

Figure 3.5.2   Layered object manufacturing, image modified from Laurensvanlieshout CC-BY-SA-3.0 (www. creativecommons.org/licenses/by-sa/3.0)

Fused deposition modelling (FDM)

Fused deposition modelling works on a principle similar to a hot-melt glue gun, (Figure 3.5.3). FDM uses ultra thin filaments, stored on a spool. These filaments are extruded through a heated chamber that converts them into a semi-liquid form, before being deposited. The fusion head travels horizontally across a moveable machine table.

FDM modelling filaments include investment casting wax, polycarbonate, polyphenylsulfone, and durable polyester. Accuracies of +/– 0.15% can be achieved. A second printer head delivers the support material in a different colour to allow for differentiation and ease of removal. Models may be manufactured in wax or, more commonly, ABS plastic.

Surface finish of these models is not as accurate as some other processes, but models are strong and may be cleaned up later.

Figure 3.5.3   Fused deposition modelling, image by Bart Dring GFDL 1.2, via Wikimedia Commons

Select laser sintering has its name derived directly from the manufacturing processes involved. A CO_2 laser selectively focuses on a section of a moveable table covered in a heat-fusible powder. The power of the laser is set to bind the powder without it melting (sintering). Repetitive scans of the table with the laser, build up the model in layers. Support structures are not required in this process. As each layer scan is complete, a new layer of powder is deposited over the top and pressed flat with a roller. The act of compressing the powder allows the model to be constructed without supporting structures. Models may even be manufactured with moving parts. Once complete, the model is dusted off, with excess powder recycled. SLS powders can be manufactured from thermoplastics, polystyrene, sand, wax, ceramics, steel and even stainless steel.

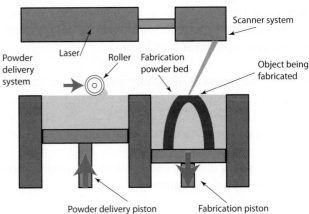

Figure 3.5.4   Selective laser sintering, image modified from Materialgeeza - own work CC-BY-SA-3.0 (www. creativecommons.org/licenses/by-sa/3.0)

Within the range of rapid prototyping processes available, stereo lithography, selective laser sintering and fused deposition modelling are the most common technologies employed.

FDM and SLS, (as opposed to LOM), are selected when functionality of the model is a consideration. FDM modelled components are similar to injection moulded components.

SLS offers the ability to form complex geometries, is faster than FDM and has greater flexibility in its range of materials selection including investment casting wax, metals and thermoplastic composite materials. Recent advances provide materials that even simulate glass-reinforced nylon. Improvements in the technology have secured greater dimensional accuracy and see parts produced to finer tolerances. If necessary, minimal post-processing such as sanding may be adopted.

INTERNATIONAL MINDEDNESS

> The high cost of some new processes does not allow for their rapid dissemination globally.
>
> © IBO 2012

Leading-edge technologies that bring new ways of manufacturing and innovative use of materials come at a premium. The cost of new technologies and processes is often driven by the need to recover expensive research and development costs and the fact that manufacturers want to maintain a competitive edge by not licensing the technology widely.

Several factors determine the ultimate 'cost' of adopting new technology. High costs for firms to invest in new technology limit its adoption. The following may impact on the viability of introducing new technology making purchases of equipment prohibitive.

- Staff training, skill upgrading and extended learning times.

- National import rules, trade restrictions and tariffs.

- Geographical distance and its effect on transportation costs of capital equipment.

THEORY OF KNOWLEDGE

> Which ways of knowing do we use to interpret indirect evidence gathered through the use of technology?
>
> © IBO 2012

When interpreting this question students need to consider the differences between the different types of evidence, that is, direct, indirect and negative evidence. Indirect and negative evidence are sometimes grouped under the heading of circumstantial. The importance of indirect evidence should also be examined and the supporting or corroborating role it plays.

Students must also consider how we acquire knowledge through the various ways of knowing: emotion, faith, imagination, intuition, language, memory, reason and sense. How may each of these ways of knowing be employed to interpret indirect evidence across the range of areas of knowledge?

Students should investigate the range of information technologies as well as a range of approaches to gathering, managing, manipulating, processing and communicating.

CORE

CASE STUDY

Fender Musical Instruments Corporation is recognised as one of the world's foremost manufacturers of guitars, basses, amplifiers and related equipment with a history dating back to its establishment in 1946.

In recent times they have successfully embraced rapid prototyping and integrated it into the design process for the development, testing and pre-marketing of new products.

Senior model maker Shawn Greene (electronics division) explains that through the use of computer aided design, coupled with additive rapid prototyping technologies such as 3D printing, the company has developed systems and processes that allow them to continue to be competitive in a highly contested marketplace.

Fender has employed a Direct Digital Manufacturing (DDM) process to rapidly prototype and test its latest development in professional studio monitor speakers, the Passport Studio®. The process not only allows for the rapid production of prototypes for visual and aesthetic evaluations but when fitted with the appropriate mouldings, hardware and electronics the speakers are nearly indistinguishable from production models and allow for near production-quality performance testing.

The advantages speak for themselves. The use of rapid prototyping at Fender has led to:

- the ability to evaluate in prototype form before tooling setups commence cost effective, fast design cycle and product iteration (example - Passport ®)

- Studio monitor speakers - sketch to prototype in 90 days while exploring 20 different concepts at minimal cost - prototyping costs reduced by up to 50% compared with previous materials and manufacturing costs multiple iterations of design quickly in a cost effective fashion including factors such as look, feel, function, performance verification.

- tooling costs being cut in half (through the eradication of false starts and design modifications) a product brought to market 40% faster compared to traditional approaches, early delivery of fully functional prototypes to marketing before production runs start.

While the Passport Studio® monitor speaker development process is considered here, Fender also uses rapid prototyping to test the development of many of its other products including the world famous Stratocaster® electric guitar.

SAMPLE QUESTIONS

1. Rapid prototyping systems may use:

   A   Liquids.
   B   Solids.
   C   Powders.
   D   Any of the above.

2. This type of CAD modelling allows a designer to add new parts to assemblies through the application of relationships, reducing the chance of error in complex assemblies.

   A   Solid.
   B   Surface.
   C   Top down.
   D   Bottom up.

3. When choosing between SLS, LOM and FDM rapid prototype processes. SLS may be chosen due to its:

   A   low cost and larger model options.
   B   flexibility in materials selection and speed.
   C   absence of the need for support structures.
   D   production of parts requiring no additional finishing.

4. Digital human modelling allows human factors designers to improve products by:

   A   reducing product lead times.
   B   using motion capture technology.
   C   producing product animations for consumers.
   D.   simulating human biomechanics in a range of environments.

5. Describe the advantages of rapid prototyping to designers, manufacturers and consumers.

6. Discuss the relative merits of sketching and CAD for design development.

7. Explain the difference between virtual reality and animation.

8. Explain how liquids are converted to solids during processes such as stereo lithography.

9. Discuss how virtual reality and motion capture technologies may be used to inform human factors investigations.

RAW MATERIALS TO FINAL PRODUCTION

CONTENTS

4

CORE

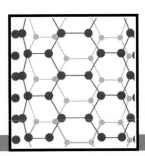

4.1–PROPERTIES OF MATERIALS

ESSENTIAL IDEA

Materials are selected for manufacturing products based on their properties.

© IBO 2012

NATURE OF DESIGN

The rapid pace of scientific discovery and new technologies has had a major impact on material science, giving designers many more materials with which to choose from for their products. These new materials have given scope for 'smart' new products or enhanced classic designs. Choosing the right material is a complex and difficult task with physical, aesthetic, mechanical and appropriate properties to consider. Environmental, moral and ethical issues surrounding choice of materials for use in any product, service or system also need to be considered.

© IBO 2012

Materials are often developed by materials engineers to have specific properties. The development of new materials allows designers to create new products which solve old problems in new ways. For example, the explosion of plastic materials following World War II enabled products to be made without using valuable metals.

© IBO 2012

AIM

Physical properties

The physical properties of a material are those properties that can be determined without damage or destruction and relate to the interaction of the material with energy and matter in its various forms. Some examples of physical properties are indicated below.

Mass

Mass (m) of a body is a measure of the amount of matter a body contains and is a constant. The SI unit for mass is the kilogram (kg).

Weight

Weight is a force and represents the mass of an object acted upon by gravity and is expressed by Newton's second law as:

$$\text{Force (weight)} = m \times a_g$$

Where a_g is acceleration due to gravity. On the Earth's surface a_g has a value of approximately 9.8m/s^2 while on the Moon its value would only be 1.6m/s^2. Weight is therefore a variable quantity.

Because it is a force, the SI units for weight are Newtons (N) where

$$1 \text{ Newton} = 1 \text{kg.m/s}^2$$

Confusion between mass and weight is seen every day in the use of bathroom scales. When we stand on a set of these scales we exert a force on them. The read-out of weight should therefore be expressed in Newtons, but a value of kilograms is indicated.

This is because a_g is a constant for any particular location, and these scales are typically used on the Earth's surface. The read-out is therefore adjusted to take this constant into consideration and give us a reading of our mass in kilograms which we colloquially refer to as our weight. To obtain our actual weight we would need to multiply the result by 9.8m/s^2.

Electrical resistivity

Electrical conductivity (σ) and electrical resistivity (ρ) are measures of the ease with which free electrons move through a material and are inherent properties of a material. As might be expected, conductivity is inversely related to resistivity as indicated below:

$$\sigma = 1/\rho$$

This relationship is strictly true only when applied to metals. The values of resistivity and conductivity for a variety of common materials are presented in Figure 4.1.1.

Material	Electrical conductivity (σ)	Electrical resistivity (ρ)
Silver	6.29×10^7	1.59×10^{-8}
HC copper	5.98×10^7	1.67×10^{-8}
Gold	4.26×10^7	2.35×10^{-8}

Material	Electrical conductivity (σ)	Electrical resistivity (ρ)
Aluminium	3.77×10^7	2.65×10^{-8}
Tungsten	1.85×10^7	5.40×10^{-8}
Iron	1.02×10^7	9.76×10^{-8}
Platinum	9.43×10^5	10.6×10^{-8}
Titanium	2.38×10^7	42.0×10^{-8}
Graphite	10^5	10^{-5}
Magnetite	10^2	10^{-2}
Germanium	2.13	4.7×10^{-1}
Limestone	10^{-2}	10^2
Silicon	2×10^{-4}	5×10^3
Window glass	2×10^{-5}	5×10^4
Granite	10^{-6}	10^6
Marble	10^{-8}	10^8
Bakelite	10^{-9} to 10^{-11}	10^9 to 10^{11}
Borosilicate glass	10^{-9} to 10^{-15}	10^9 to 10^{15}
Mica	10^{-11} to 10^{-15}	10^{11} to 10^{15}
Polyethylene	10^{-15} to 10^{-17}	10^{15} to 10^{17}

Figure 4.1.1   Electrical resistivity and conductivity of selected materials

Resistivity in metals has been described in terms of resistance to the free flow of electrons. This resistance to motion was postulated to arise from the scattering of the electrons due to collisions with the positive ions of the metal lattice. According to this theory, resistivity arises from any phenomenon that disturbs the motion of electrons, such as:

- collisions with lattice imperfections (e.g. caused by cold working)

- collisions with solute atoms (e.g. impurities)

- collisions with thermally-induced lattice vibrations (e.g. temperature).

Temperature has the greatest effect on resistivity. As temperature increases, thermally-induced lattice vibrations increase, raising the chance of interaction with electrons. Therefore, as temperature increases, so does resistivity.

When the temperatures approach absolute zero, (0°K), thermally-induced lattice vibrations also approach zero and resistivity becomes a function of temperature-independent factors such as impurity content and microstructural effects such as lattice imperfections, precipitates and inclusions.

The SI unit for resistivity (ρ) is ohm-metres (Ω-m), while the SI unit for electrical conductivity (σ) is siemens per metre (S/m).

Thermal Conductivity

When a temperature gradient is present in a material, heat will flow from the region of higher temperature to the region of lower temperature. Thermal conductivity (K) is a measure of the efficiency with which thermal energy will travel through a material.

The higher the thermal conductivity the greater is the rate at which heat will flow. Thermal conductivity is therefore a physical property because temperature flow can be measured using thermocouples without damage to the material under test. The SI units for thermal conductivity are Weber/metre/°K ($Wm^{-1}K^{-1}$).

Metals typically have high thermal conductivity, while polymers and ceramics have a low thermal conductivity and are insulators rather than conductors of heat. The thermal conductivity of a number of materials at room temperature is provided in Figure 4.1.2.

Note, values are indicative only. For purposes of translation of values:

$$1\ Wm^{-1}K^{-1} = 0.00239 \times Cal\ cm^{-1}\ s^{-1}\ K^{-1}$$

Material	Thermal conductivity ($Wm^{-1}k^{-1}$)	Thermal conductivity ($Cal\ cm^{-1}\ s^{-1}\ k^{-1}$)
Graphite	2 000	4.8
Silver	429	1.03
Copper	380	0.91
Gold	310	0.74
Aluminium	230	0.55
Brass	109	0.26
Grey cast iron	55	0.13
Mild steel	54	0.13
Ferritic stainless steel	25	0.6
Austenitic stainless steel	15	0.4
Alumina	20	0.05
Glass	1	0.002
Oak	0.16	0.0004
Plywood	0.13	0.0003
Polyurethane	0.02	0.00005
Nylon 6,6	0.25	0.0006
PTFE	0.25	0.0006
PVC	0.19	0.0005
Bakelite	0.23	0.0005

Figure 4.1.2   Thermal conductivity of selected materials at room temperature

Thermal expansion

When a material is heated, the thermal energy gained, results in an increase in atomic vibrations. This leads to an increase in atomic separation and an increase in the dimensions of the material overall. This increase in dimensions is typically quantified as the change in length per unit length per degree ($m.m^{-1} K^{-1}$) for the coefficient of linear thermal expansion (α). Figure 4.1.3 shows α values for a number of materials from 20° to $100^{\circ}C$.

Material	Mean coeficient of thermal expansion ($10^{-1} K^{-1}$) at $20^{\circ}C$
Graphite	7.9
Silver	19.5
Copper	18
Aluminium	24
Gold	14.2
Brass	18.7
Mild steel	11
Grey cast iron	10.8
Glass – Pyrex	4
Glass – plate	9
Bakelite	80
Polyurethane	57.6
Nylon 6,6	80
PVC	50.4

Figure 4.1.3   Thermal expansion of selected materials from 20° to $100^{\circ}C$

Hardness

Hardness refers to the resistance of a material to scratching or abrasion. It may also refer to resistance to indentation, penetration or cutting. The number of definitions for hardness, indicates that hardness may not be a fundamental property of a material, but rather a composite one including yield strength, work hardening, true tensile strength, modulus of elasticity, and others. Because of this, and the fact that the process of obtaining a hardness involves some surface damage, hardness is often listed as a mechanical property. The limited damage produced, however, and the utility of the measurement as an indicator of material condition sees hardness testing employed widely as a non-destructive quality control test.

As indicated above, hardness is routinely used as an indication of material condition. For example, increased hardness is often interpreted as a general indication of greater resistance to deformation and wear. As might be expected, a variety of tests have been developed to measure hardness. These tests fall into three broad groups, consisting of:

- scratch hardness (e.g. Mohs, Bierbaum, Pencil)

- static indentation hardness (eg Brinell, Rockwell, Vickers, Knoop, Janka, Durometer)

- dynamic hardness (Scleroscope, Leeb).

A selection of commonly used hardness tests are described below. The requirements for surface preparation vary but all necessitate some preparation of the surface to ensure it is clean and free of debris.

Scratch Hardness

As the name implies scratch hardness tests involve the scratching of the test surface with a stylus/indentor.

The German mineralogist Friedrich Mohs developed one of the earliest measures of material hardness in 1812. The Mohs hardness as it has come to be known is defined by how well a substance will resist scratching by another substance of known or defined hardness and a ranking from 1 to 10 assigned.

The scale contains ten minerals that Mohs proposed as exemplars of each position on the scale, starting with the mineral talc at position 1, which can be scratched by a fingernail, to diamond at 10, see Figure 4.1.4.

Mohs hardness	Mineral
1	Talc
2	Gypsum
3	Calcite
4	Fluorite
5	Apatite
6	Orthoclase
7	Quartz
8	Topaz
9	Corundum
10	Diamond

Figure 4.1.4   Mohs hardness scale

The Mohs scale therefore is not linear; that is, each increment in the scale does not indicate a proportional increase in hardness. For instance, the progression from calcite to fluorite (from 3 to 4 on the Mohs scale) reflects an increase in hardness of approximately 25%, while the progression from corundum to diamond, on the other hand, (9 to 10 on the Mohs scale), reflects a hardness increase of more than 300%.

For this reason, the Mohs test, while greatly facilitating the identification of minerals in the field, is not suitable for accurately gauging the hardness of most materials, particularly industrial materials such as steel or ceramics.

The Bierbaum test uses a standardised diamond indentor that is dragged across the test surface and the width of the scratch produced measured. This test is suited to a variety of materials, particularly plastics.

The pencil test uses a set of twenty pencils ranging from grades 9B to 9H. A pencil is placed in a holder at an angle of 45° to the test surface and the holder moved across the surface under a fixed force of 7.5 N. The test is repeated until a pencil grade that just scratches/indents the surface is found and that grade recorded as the hardness. This test has found use in the testing of polymer coatings.

Static Indentation Hardness

Static hardness tests typically involve the penetration of an indentor into the test surface using low loading rates.

The Barcol hardness test uses a cone shaped steel indentor that is pushed into the test surface until a spring is completely depressed, resulting in the application of a fixed load. The depth to which the indentor has penetrated the surface is then read off a dial gauge calibrated from 0 to 100 and recorded as the Barcol number. This test is often used to determine the degree to which plastic resin has cured.

Brinell tests use a hardened steel or tungsten carbide ball typically of 10mm diameter to produce an indentation in the surface of the material using a standard load. The diameter of the impression is measured with a small portable microscope and the Brinell hardness read from a conversion table.

Rockwell tests use either a small steel ball or a diamond indentor ground to form a cone of 120°, to form an impression. Several Rockwell hardness scales are available (A, B, C, etc) using various combinations of indentor and applied load, depending on the material to be tested, The depth of the impression is related to a Rockwell hardness that is read off a dial gauge or LCD.

Vickers tests use variable loads and a diamond pyramid indentor. Because the same indentor is used and only the applied load varied, a comparable hardness is obtained when testing a range of materials. Because of this, the Vickers test is the standard method for the reliable measurement of metal and ceramic hardness. The impression diagonals are measured and related to a Vickers hardness number by reference to a table selected based on the applied load used in the test.

Knoop tests explore microhardness by making rhombohedral indentations, (one long and one short diagonal), with a pyramidal diamond indentor. The aspect ratio of the impression diagonals allows impressions to be placed closer together without concerns of previous impressions affecting later hardness results.

The Brinell, Rockwell, Vickers and Knoop hardness testers use a standardized indentor and fixed load to determine hardness and are used extensively in the testing of metals. Their indentors are shown in Figure 4.1.5.

Figure 4.1.5   Commonly used indentors for hardness testing: Brinell (top), Rockwell (middle), Vickers (bottom)

The Janka hardness test is used for the testing of wood and is similar to the Brinell test in that a steel ball, this time of 11.28 mm is impressed into the surface to a depth of 5.64 mm (half the indenter diameter), leaving an impression of 100 mm^2. The force required to create this impression is measured in kN and is reported as the Janka hardness (JH).

The Durometer hardness test (Figure 4.1.6), is principally undertaken on polymers and involves the pressing of an indenter (consisting of a hardened steel rod) into the surface of the test piece and is similar to the Barcol test.

The indentation hardness is read from a dial gauge on the body of the instrument. If the indenter completely penetrates the sample, a reading of 0 is obtained, and if no penetration occurs, a reading of 100 results. This test is not a good predictor of other properties such as tensile strength, abrasion resistance or wear resistance and is generally used in concert with other tests for product specification.

Figure 4.1.6   Durometer Hardness tester

Dynamic Hardness

Dynamic hardness tests are rebound tests in which an indentor falls from a standard height and the change on rebound measured. These tests depend on elastic recovery of the test surface and use high rates of loading.

The Scleroscope or Shore Scleroscope tests measure the loss in kinetic energy from a falling diamond-tipped metal 'tup'. The tup is enclosed within a glass fronted graduated column and the bottom of the column placed against the surface to be tested. When the tup is released from the top of the column the tup falls, hits the test surface and rebounds. The height of rebound is recorded as the hardness (HSc). The test equipment is light and portable but must be held vertically and test access is restricted by the height of the column, see Figure 4.1.7

Figure 4.1.7   Scleroscope Hardness tester

The Leeb hardness test (Figure 4.1.8) uses a small pen-shaped device containing a spring-loaded impact body. During testing a small permanent magnet within the impact body passes through a coil in the impact device inducing a voltage proportional to the velocity. The hardness calculated is a ratio of the velocities before and after rebound. Values can be displayed as Leeb hardness (HL) or more usually displayed as a Vickers, Rockwell or Brinell equivalent.

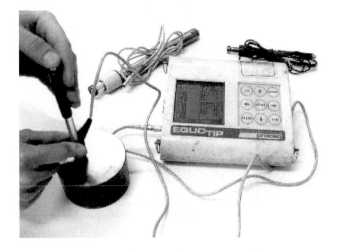

Figure 4.1.8   Equotip™ Hardness tester used to determine Leeb hardness

Many conversion tables are available that allow hardness measurements, undertaken with one method, to be compared with hardnesses obtained with a different method and to be equated approximately with tensile strength. These tables are developed from test data for a particular material such as steel or aluminium and cannot be extrapolated to include other materials not tested.

Mechanical properties

Mechanical properties are those properties that relate to the way in which the material responds to the application of a force.

Tensile and Compressive strength

Tensile strength is a measure of a material's resistance to plastic deformation from a tensile or stretching type load. When the tensile strength of a material is quoted it is the maximum tensile strength known as the ultimate tensile strength (ultimate tensile stress). This is one of the most often quoted mechanical properties for a material.

The ultimate tensile strength (UTS) represents the maximum applied tensile load that a material can sustain, divided by the material's original cross-sectional area. The tensile strength is therefore typically measured in kN/mm^2 or Mega Pascals (MPa), where $1Pa = 1N/m^2$.

On the engineering stress-strain curve the tensile strength is represented by that position where the maximum stress is achieved as illustrated in Figure 4.1.9.

Determine the Ultimate Tensile Stress (UTS) of a 15 mm diameter rod if the maximum load it can withstand is 70 kN.

$$\text{Load} = 70 \times 10^3 \text{N}$$

$$\text{Diameter} = 15 \times 10^{-3} \text{m}$$

$$\text{Area} = \pi (15 \times 10^{-3})^2 / 4$$

$$= 1.767 \times 10^{-4} \text{m}^2$$

$$\text{UTS} = \text{Load / area}$$

$$= 70 \times 10^3 / 1.767 \times 10^{-4}$$

$$= 396 \text{ MN/m}^2$$

$$= 396 \text{ MPa}$$

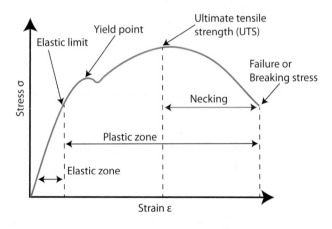

Figure 4.1.9   Engineering stress-strain diagram

Stiffness

Stiffness is the resistance of an elastic body to deflection by an applied force. There are several measures of material stiffness depending on the stress state imposed. These include the modulus of elasticity (also known as Young's modulus), the shear modulus (also known as the Modulus of Rigidity), and the Bulk Modulus.

The most commonly quoted measure is the modulus of elasticity or Young's modulus which is a measure of stiffness when a body is subjected to axial tensile or compressive stresses and is visible on the stress strain diagram as a straight line. The angle of the line (gradient) indicates the relative stiffness of the material, such that a stiff material will have a high Young's modulus. Young's modulus is represented by the capital letter E and typically is expressed in Gigapascals (GPa).

The gradients typical of a number of materials are presented in Figure 4.1.10. In this Figure, it can be seen that a brittle material displays linear elastic behaviour and fails with little strain e.g. ceramics and glasses (1). A soft and tough material, on the other hand, exhibits a very small initial slope, but strain hardens and withstands larger strains before failure e.g. low carbon steel (2).

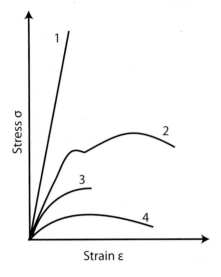

Figure 4.1.10   Typical Stress–strain curves for (1) ceramics and glasses, (2) low carbon steel, (3) Aluminium, (4) natural and synthetic rubbers.

The Young's modulus for a selection of common materials is presented in Figure 4.1.11.

Material	Young's modulus (GPa)
Rubber	0.01–0.1
Nylon	2–4
Oak (along the grain)	11
Glass	50–90
Aluminium	69
Copper	110–130
Carbon fibre reinforced plastic	150
Structural steel	190–210

Figure 4.1.11   Young's modulus for a selection of common materials (Adapted from ASM Handbook).

Toughness

Toughness is the ability of a material to resist the propagation of cracks. A material's stress-strain curve can be used to give an indication of the overall toughness of the material. The area under the stress-strain curve, within the plastic range, is a measure of a material's toughness as illustrated in Figure 4.1.12. The greater the area under the graph, the tougher the material, and the greater the amount of energy required to cause it to fail.

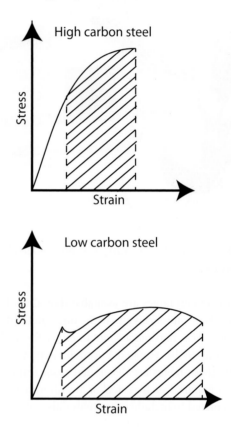

Figure 4.1.12   Comparison of stress-strain curves for low (above) and high (below) toughness materials

A commonly employed method of testing the toughness of a material is to measure its resistance to impact. A number of standard tests are available, such as the Izod impact test or the Charpy impact test for metals. In these tests, a test piece of standardised dimensions is obtained from the material to be evaluated and a notch machined into the surface to a 'V' or 'U' profile. The sample is subsequently fractured by impact with a pendulum and the swing height the pendulum attains following the sample fracture is used as a measure of the energy absorbed.

Metals that are tough will generally undergo a ductile fracture in which plastic deformation occurs during crack propagation. Ductile fractures typically exhibit dull fibrous surfaces with obvious plastic deformation. An illustration of the test piece used for the Charpy V-notch test is provided in Figure 4.1.13.

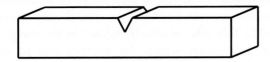

Figure 4.1.13 Illustration of a Charpy V-notch impact test piece.

The more plastic deformation required to advance the crack, the more energy required and hence a tougher material. Low toughness metals will generally fracture in a brittle manner in which the crack is able to propagate without the absorption of additional energy. Little work is done in brittle fracture and hence the material fails catastrophically. Brittle fractures are usually characterised by bright crystalline features with no evidence of plastic deformation.

The toughness of a material will vary depending on the temperature. If tested at elevated temperatures, a material will show ductile fracture behaviour and consequently may be considered to have good toughness. If tested at low temperature the same material may fracture in a brittle manner and may be considered to have poor toughness.

Typically, a plot of absorbed energy versus test temperature for metals will produce a graph with a sigmoidal profile, in which the absorbed energy levels off past a certain temperature into what is known as the upper shelf energy (ductile) or the lower shelf energy (brittle). The inflection point between these two regions is known as the transition temperature and marks the position where one form of fracture begins to dominate over the other. Because of this, the appearance of the fracture can also be used to measure toughness by assessing the fracture appearance in terms of % crystallinity or % fibrosity. A typical ductile-brittle transition curve obtained by Charpy V-notch testing of steel is presented in Figure 4.1.14. Representative fractures from each region are shown.

Historical note

The British metallurgist Constance Tipper pioneered research into brittle/ductile transitions. Investigating the failure of Liberty ships during WWII, she discovered that there was a critical temperature below which fractures in steel change from ductile to brittle mode. The 'Liberty Ships' in the North Atlantic were subjected to such low temperatures that they would have been susceptible to

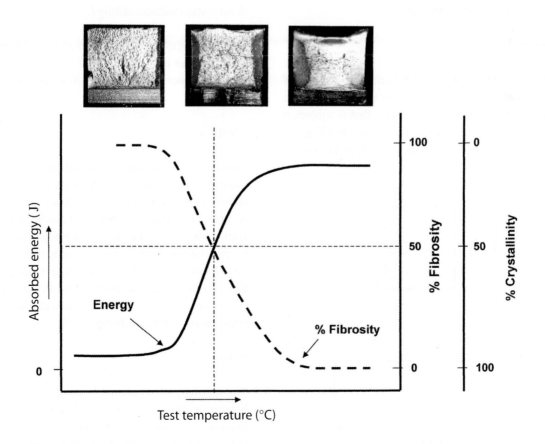

Figure 4.1.14   Ductile-brittle transition curves determined by impact testing of steel

brittle failure, see Figure 4.1.15. These ships were the first all-welded, mass produced, prefabricated cargo ships produced by the United States to assist in the war effort. The sudden and catastrophic failure of these vessels was a major problem for the Allies. Tipper demonstrated that the type of steel used, rather than the fact that the ships had been welded, was the cause of the fractures. The 'Tipper test' soon became the standard method for determining this form of brittleness in steel, although the test has now been largely superseded by the Charpy impact test.

Figure 4.1.15   Fractured Liberty ship

Fracture toughness

The fracture toughness of a material relates to the size of crack that may be present before fracture will occur. Testing is performed using a notched specimen that is subjected to cyclic loading in tension or three point bending, in order to create a short fatigue crack as illustrated in Figure 4.1.16.

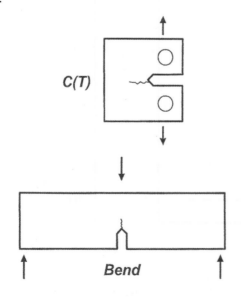

Figure 4.1.16   Fracture toughness test pieces

This pre-cracked sample is then fractured to determine a material constant known as the critical stress intensity or K1C. This value is directly related to the energy for crack propagation within the material and to other material constants such as Young's modulus and Poisson's ratio. In this sense the K1C value provides a more fundamental measure of material toughness compared to the Charpy test, which includes not only the energy of crack propagation to fracture but also the energy of crack initiation from the notch.

The limiting factor in the general use of fracture toughness tests lies in the difficulty and cost involved in producing a pre-cracked specimen compared with the ease of producing Charpy test pieces.

Ductility

Ductility is the ability of a material to undergo plastic deformation by extrusion or the application of tensile forces. Ductility should not be confused with the related concept of malleability, which is the ability of a material to be shaped plastically, generally by compressive forces. The amount of cold work that individual metals can withstand without failure therefore depends on their ductility. Conversely, a material that is unable to undergo plastic deformation without failing is described as being brittle.

Both elongation and reduction of area determined from measurement of the length and cross-section respectively of the tensile test piece after fracture are measures of ductility.

Elasticity

Elasticity of a material is a measure of its ability to stretch under load and then return to its original dimensions following the removal of that load. When a material is uniaxially loaded within its elastic region a linear relationship is obtained in which elongation is found to be proportional to load. This relationship is known as Hooke's Law, named after the 17th Century English Scientist Robert Hooke. This relationship is often restated as stress is proportional to strain and is the straight portion of the stress strain curve, see Figure 4.1.9.

Plasticity

The plasticity of a material is associated with elongation behaviour that exceeds the elastic region. Continued deformation past the elastic limit leads to more complex deformation where the relationship between stress and strain is no longer linear. On removal of load the material no longer returns to its original dimensions but instead retains some permanent deformation.

Plastic deformation of metals occurs as a result of atoms moving relative to each other along crystallographic planes of the metallic lattice by a process called 'slip'. This process will be discussed further in section 4.2a on Metals and metallic alloys.

Young's modulus

As indicated previously Young's modulus is a measure of a material's elasticity. It is an intrinsic property of the material as it is closely related to the bonding force between the constituent atoms. The atoms of a material with a high Young's modulus are therefore more difficult to separate resulting in greater stiffness and higher melting point. It indicates the elasticity of the material regardless of design.

Stress and Strain

Stress is a measure of the force being applied per unit area, ie Stress $(\sigma) = F/A$.

Stress can be divided into two classifications engineering stress, which uses the original cross sectional area (A_o) of the test piece as a constant, and true stress which uses the instantaneous (true) cross sectional area as it changes throughout the test.

Strain is a measure of the change in length occurring when under stress, divided by the unit length. Strain can also be divided into two classifications, engineering strain, which uses the original length of the test piece as a constant, that is:

$$\text{engineering strain } (\varepsilon) = (l - l_o) / l_o$$

and true strain which uses the instantaneous (true) length as it changes throughout the test. This results in a slightly more complicated relationship where:

$$\text{true strain } (\varepsilon_t) = l_n \times (l / l_o)$$

Engineering stress-strain relationships such as those shown in Figure 4.1.9 are most commonly used as they are easier to measure.

Aesthetic characteristics

Aesthetic characteristics might be defined as those features that have an appeal to human senses of beauty and pleasure. These features in turn are evaluated based on the social and cultural background of the individual and our five senses: taste, smell, hearing (sound), sight (appearance), and touch (texture). Our appreciation of products is therefore often a complex interplay of a number these features as Aradhna Krishna points out in her book *'Customer Sense: How the five senses influence buying behaviour'*.

Because aesthetic appeal can be an important part of a decision to purchase goods, designers often manipulate the various characteristics of their designs, particularly when dealing with consumer products, to appeal to the aesthetic tastes of the proposed user group. Such considerations also help with product differentiation.

Taste: thousands of tiny receptors, known as taste buds, are distributed over the upper surface of the tongue, the soft palate, upper oesophagus and epiglottis, through these sensors we can distinguish 5 basic flavours, sweetness, sourness, bitterness, saltiness and umami. Our sense of taste is, however, an example of how the interplay of a variety of aesthetic properties such as colour, texture, appearance and smell can have a profound affect on our senses. The experience of having difficulty in identifying the taste of various common foods and drinks when pinching the nose and blindfolded, in order to eliminate input from smell and sight is a commonly performed science class experiment and party game.

Another example of the power of this interaction is indicated by an experiment described by Dr Krishna, in which subjects were asked to use a straw to drink a sample of water from a sturdy disposable cup and from a flimsy disposable cup and to rate the taste. The water from the flimsy cup was subsequently rated as significantly worse even though in both cases lips only touched the straw and the only contact with the cups was through touch.

Chefs such as Heston Blumenthal attempt to provide a multi-sensory experience that engages all the senses to enhance taste. Using cooking techniques associated with molecular gastronomy, Blumenthal uses scientific principles to modify the texture and appearance of food. In addition to the plating of the food, presentation is aimed at enhancing emotional connections for the diner, and may involve the playing of background sounds and the use of a spray or dry ice to deliver a scent, as accompaniments to a meal.

The food industry goes to great lengths to create packaging and processing techniques that will increase shelf life of foods while maintaining nutritive value and taste.

Hearing: our ability to hear relies on the detection of sound waves entering our ears and which stimulate the vibration of the ear drum and bones of the middle ear. These vibrations are subsequently transferred to the snail shaped Cochlea of the inner ear. Within the Cochlea is the Organ of Corti which contains small hair cells that transfer signals to the auditory cortex of the brain. We interpret these signals in terms of their pitch, timbre, tone, clarity, volume, frequency and decay.

The sound produced by a material when struck depends in part on its modulus of elasticity and density.

Smell: we owe our sense of smell to the presence of approximately 10 million olfactory receptors consisting of 350 different receptor types situated in the olfactory mucosa at the top of the nasal cavity. Impulses are sent to the brain from these receptors, where the smell is identified, providing sufficient odour molecules were present. Our response to a scent appears to be largely learned or culturally determined having been associated with life experiences and emotions. Because of this, smells that may be considered pleasant in one culture may be considered unpleasant in another. Aradhna Krishna notes that the new car smell prized by many in the West, and created by the release of volatiles from the upholstery, is found to be objectionable by the Chinese who often attempt to remove it by drying tea leaves in the car. Similarly, the smell of pine, eucalyptus and sandalwood are commonly used as air fresheners because of their association with a clean fresh outdoor environment.

Appearance

Colour: photoreceptor cells in the retina allow us to see. There are two types of photoreceptors present in the retina, these are the rod cells and cone cells.

The rod cells contain a single pigment molecule known as rhodopsin. This pigment is very sensitive to light and is responsible for our vision in low light conditions. However, because only one pigment is present it cannot differentiate colours. By contrast the cone cells contain three different pigment molecules known as photopsins, each of which detects different frequencies of light. It is the cone cells of the retina that are responsible for our colour vision.

Because of the differences in the rod and cone cells, as the light level decreases the cone photoreceptors become less activated, until in very low light conditions only the rods are stimulated. This is why colours cannot be discerned in low light conditions.

Colour and our reactions to it have been studied widely by psychologists and marketers. Our reaction to colour is in large part culturally determined, but businesses spend considerable time on the colour pallet of products and packaging. In some instances certain colours are strongly associated with a product or manufacturer and in such cases the relationship is jealously guarded. This has led to a number of legal disputes around colour as intellectual property. Two examples are given below.

Because it was found that farmers liked to match the colour of their tractors and loader attachments, in 1982 John Deer attempted to trademark their colour green to stop a competitor (Farmhand) from using the same colour on their loaders. This application was disallowed because it was found that awarding exclusive use would disadvantage competitors for reasons unrelated to price or quality. A similar dispute erupted between Cadbury and Nestle regarding the colour purple. In this instance, Cadbury were denied registration of their colour after a ten year battle that went as far as the UK court of appeal.

Colour is of course only one aspect of a materials appearance. A wide variety of processing techniques are available to change the appearance of materials.

While metals are opaque, they can be polished to a high reflective surface or textured to a matte finish. By contrast many polymers and ceramics can be produced in a multitude of forms from opaque to transparent. Similarly, most materials have a natural colour that can be modified by the addition of alloying elements or pigments. Each metal for example has a distinctive natural colour of grey, silver, yellow, or orange, however a still greater colour variation is possible if metals are processed to form a tightly adherent surface oxide.

Colours have strong cultural ties and differences in meaning. The colour white, for example, in some cultures conveys images of purity and peace while in others it is associated with death and mourning. Similar cultural differences can be found with most colours either individually or in combination.

Further reading

Cousins, C. (2012). *Color and Cultural Considerations* http://www.webdesignerdepot.com/2012/06/color-and-cultural-design-considerations/

Shape: features such as symmetry/asymmetry, textural balance, proportion, complexity/simplicity, curvature and size all contribute to aesthetic appearance.

Sharp angular features are often associated with masculine attributes while rounded shapes are associated with more feminine ones. While this is translated into designs aimed at specific groups, products with some curves are generally preferred by consumers.

Touch (or haptics): Our sense of touch and texture conveys not only feelings of rough, smooth, hard, soft, but perceptions of strength, delicacy, sensuality, etc., and is closely integrated with our other senses.

Sensations of touch arises from the presence of haptic sensors located over the outer surface of the body and in some internal locations such as the mouth. A number of sensors with different functions make up the haptic system. These include sensors for temperature (thermoreceptors), pain (nociceptors), and texture (mechanoreceptors).

There are four types of mechanoreceptors, each of which provides a different function as indicated in Figure 4.1.17. An important property of these receptors in determining texture is their rate of adaptation or the rate at which they react to external stimuli and return to normal:

Pacinian corpuscles – act rapidly or are said to exhibit fast adaptation, they fire at the onset/offset of stimulus, typically returning to normal in less than 0.1 seconds. These sensors are situated some distance below the surface and therefore have large receptor fields. Because of their rapid adaptation they transmit high-frequency vibrations and assist in discriminating fine surface textures. These receptors are also responsible for the extension of our perception field to the end of a hand held tool.

Meissner's corpuscles – exhibit moderate adaptation, they typically return to normal in approximately 1 second. These receptors are situated close to the surface in the dermal ridges of the finger and therefore have small reception fields. They act to transmit low-frequency vibrations and are particularly sensitive to edges and corners.

Merkel's discs - exhibit slow adaptation and are situated close to the surface being aligned with the dermal ridges of the finger. Because these sensors are slowly adapting, they continue to act as long as pressure is applied. They allow the detection of light pressure required for the maintenance of a grip and the discrimination of fine textural detail, being particularly sensitive to edges and corners.

Ruffini's corpuscles – exhibit slow adaptation and are situated some distance below the surface and therefore have large receptor fields. They also assist in the maintenance of a grip.

| | | Adapting rate | |
		Slow	Rapid
Vibration frequency	Low	Merkel	Meissner
	High	Ruffini	Pacinian

Figure 4.1.17   The four mechanoreceptors

The physical properties of materials such as thermal conductivity, ductility and hardness result in a wide range of features we discern through touch. Some materials such as metals and ceramics are typically hard and cold to the touch while materials such as wood, leather and rubber are often described as warm. Our sense of touch actually provides us with a wide range of descriptors we use for materials every day as shown in Figure 4.1.18.

Warm	Cold
Hard	Soft
Stiff	Flexible
Rough	Smooth
Heavy	Light

Figure 4.1.18   Range of sense descriptors

Properties of smart materials

Smart materials have one or more properties that can be dramatically altered, for example, transparency, viscosity, volume, conductivity. The property that can be altered influences the application of the smart material. Smart materials include piezoelectric materials, magneto-rheostatic materials, electro-rheostatic materials, shape memory alloys. Some everyday items are already incorporating smart materials (coffee pots, cars, eye-glasses, tennis racquets), and the number of applications for them is growing steadily.

Piezoelectricity

Piezoelectric material is a material that responds to the application of an applied stress by producing a small electrical discharge. Similarly, when an electric current is passed through a piezoelectric material a shape change occurs in response. By reversing the polarity of the electrical signal the shape again changes. An AC current can therefore produce a shape change about the rest state of the material as illustrated in Figure 4.1.19. Piezoelectric materials are widely used as sensors in different environments. Quartz (SiO_2) is a commonly used piezoelectric material, and has been extensively used in watches. A number of ceramics are also used such as barium titanate ($BaTiO_3$) and lead zirconate titanate ($Pb[Zr_xTi_{1-x}]O_3$), known as PZT.

Piezoelectric materials are widely used for the thickness testing of pipes and vessels and the detection of internal flaws by ultrasonic testing as illustrated in Figure 4.1.20.

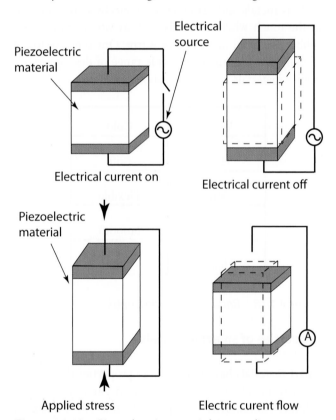

Figure 4.1.19   *Piezoelectric material responding to an electric potential (top), and an applied stress (bottom)*

In ultrasonic testing, an alternating voltage is supplied to a probe containing a piezoelectric crystal. The voltage stimulates the crystal to change dimensions (vibrate) producing sound waves of a defined frequency. When the probe is placed on the test surface, the sound waves travel into the material and are reflected back from the other side of the test piece and from any internal discontinuities.

When these returning sound waves reach the probe surface, the vibrations stress the piezoelectric crystal sufficiently to produce an electrical voltage in response. The initial sound pulse and the returning signal are recorded on an oscillograph screen allowing visual interpretation by a technician.

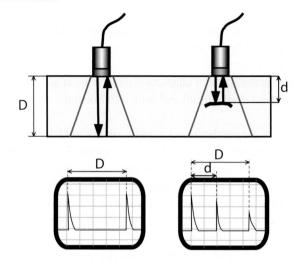

Figure 4.1.20   *Ultrasonic testing*

Shape memory

SMAs are metals that exhibit pseudo-elasticity and shape memory effect due to rearrangement of the atomic lattice. Discovered in the 1930s the shape memory alloys represent a group of materials that are capable of changing shape or size in a predetermined manner by undergoing a solid-state phase change at a defined temperature. Despite creating a great deal of interest, these alloys remained largely a laboratory curiosity until the 1960s when the NiTi alloy Nitinol (an acronym of the Nickel and Titanium Naval Ordinance Laboratory) was produced. Due to its excellent mechanical properties and biocompatibility Nitinol has since become one of the most widely used shape memory alloys. Nitinol is nonmagnetic and consists of almost equal amounts of Ni and Ti in a simple cubic lattice arrangement. If a shape memory alloy is in the stable lattice arrangement of the austenite phase, and is exposed to a mechanical stress, slip can occur leading to distortion of the lattice and the formation of martensite. Normally a reduction in temperature would be required to achieve this change, but under the influence of an applied stress, martensite formation can occur without the involvement of a temperature change and is referred to as deformation martensite. This change in structure is accompanied by an apparent non-linear deformation, typically associated with plastic deformation.

When the applied stress is removed, however, the atomic lattice returns to the austenite phase and the material returns to its original shape. Figure 4.1.21 illustrates this phenomenon in which an applied stress essentially increases the temperature at which martensite will form and shows the reversible change back to austenite on the removal of the applied stress. Ms and Mf refer to the start and finish transformation stages of martensite formation, while As and Af refer to the start and finish transformation stages of austenite formation.

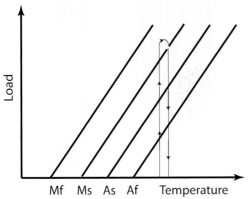

Figure 4.1.21   Load diagram of the pseudo-elastic effect

This ability to undergo plastic deformation and still return to its original shape is one of the defining characteristics of the shape memory alloys and is known as pseudo elasticity. Pseudo elasticity can be expressed symbolically as:

Austenitic structure + force (stimulus)

leads to

Martensitic structure - force (stimulus)

leads back to

Austenitic structure

Shape memory alloys (SMA) also exhibit pseudoelasticity by way of a reversible temperature induced martensite transformation. In this case, however, removal of the applied stress does not result in the material returning to the austenite phase and its original shape. This change requires moderate heating up to approximately 100°C. At elevated temperatures these alloys have an austenitic structure that is relatively strong. On cooling, these alloys undergo a phase transformation to martensite, which is relatively soft. The unique character of these alloys is seen when the alloy is formed to shape in the austenitic condition and then cooled to martensite. If another forming operation is then performed while it is in the martensitic condition, changing the shape of the material, it will maintain that shape until reheated to austenite, at which time the alloy reverts to its previous shape. Some alloys even have the ability to change back when the temperature has again been reduced, resulting in a two-way memory effect. These alloys can therefore cycle between shapes with changes in temperature.

Alloy	Transformation range °C	Transformation hysteresis °C
Ag–Cd	–190 to –50	~ 15
Cu–Al–Ni	–140 to –100	~ 35
Cu–Zn	–180 to –10	~ 10
Ni–Al	–180 to 100	~ 10
Ni–Ti	–50 to 110	~ 30
FeMnS	–200 to 150	~ 100

Figure 4.1.22   Transformation temperature ranges for a selection of SMA's (ASM Handbook)

A number of shape memory alloys have been developed, which operate at a variety of different temperatures, as indicated in Figure 4.1.22. Precise control of the material composition is required to ensure the reliable reproduction of the transformation temperatures.

The shape memory affect can be illustrated as shown in Figure 4.1.23 in which the phase changes have been represented at each stage along with the changes that would be seen with an arterial stent made from the shape memory alloy Nitinol. SMAs are considered to be passive response type devices, as they do not require separate sensors to operate, but rather react directly in response to the external stimulus, as opposed to the ER and MR fluids and piezoelectric materials that can be considered active response devices. In this capacity of passive response, the pseudoelastic properties of the shape memory alloys have been used in products such as electrical connectors, eyeglass frames and antennas for mobile phones.

Shape memory alloys have been used in products such as electrical connectors, safety taps to prevent hot water scalding children, vascular stents to repair blocked arteries, airflow controls, orthodontic arch wires and components of eyeglass frames. The excellent biocompatibility of Nitinol combined with its non-magnetic nature and excellent mechanical properties have resulted in its extensive use in biomedical applications such as coronary stents.

Some use of SMAs has been made in passive dampening systems to mitigate earthquake damage. The roof of the St Francis Basilica in Assisi has been joined to the wall with Nitinol anchors consisting of wire bundles that stretch in response to vibrations, dissipating the seismic loads.

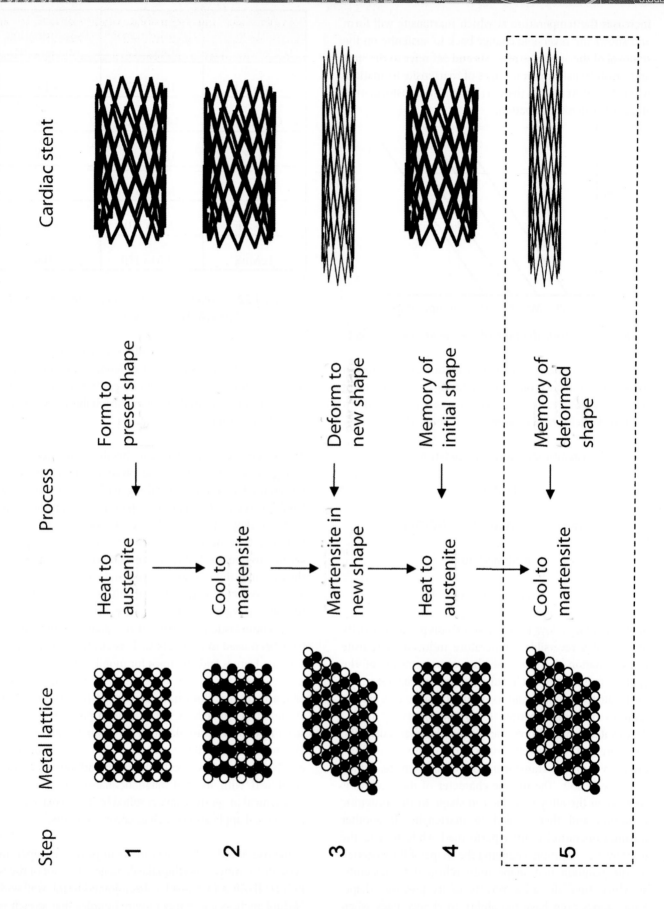

Figure 4.1.23   Illustration of the stages of transformation in an SMA. Stages 1 to 4 represent a one-way shape memory, while the addition of stage 5 represents a two-way shape memory

Photochromicity

Photochromic materials undergo a reversible photochemical reaction that results in darkening proportional to the level of exposure to Ultra Violet (UV) light. These materials are most commonly seen in photochromatic (also known as transition) lenses and may be made from glass or polymer such as polycarbonate. An example of this effect is shown in Figure 4.1.24 in which one lens was initially covered and the other exposed to sunlight for 30 seconds.

Figure 4.1.24   Photochromatic lenses

Glass lenses have molecules of silver chloride (AgCl) within the silica crystal structure of the glass. The presence or otherwise of UV light determines the direction in which a reversible oxidation-reduction reaction, representing a Le Chatelier type chemical reaction of the type indicated below, will proceed.

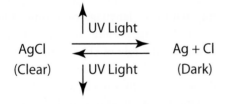

$$\text{AgCl} \underset{\text{UV Light}}{\overset{\text{UV Light}}{\rightleftharpoons}} \text{Ag} + \text{Cl}$$

$$\text{(Clear)} \qquad \text{(Dark)}$$

When the level of UV radiation exposure is low, light passes through largely unimpeded. When exposed to UV light, however, the reaction proceeds to the right forming colloidal silver that acts to absorb up to 80% of the incident light and leading to the observed darkening of the lens. On removal of the lens from exposure to the UV light, the reaction reverses direction and the silver recombines with the chloride ions to form AgCl and the glass clears.

The photochromatic lenses made from polycarbonate by contrast have a coating of an organic molecule, which changes shape on exposure to UV light leading to darkening of the lens and which reverses when exposure to UV light decreases.

Magneto-rheostatic and Electro-rheostatic

Electro-rheostatic (ER) and magneto-rheostatic (MR) materials are fluids that can undergo changes in their viscosity, becoming semi-solid when exposed to an electric or magnetic field respectively. When the applied field is removed the materials return to their original fluid state.

These materials are most commonly colloidal suspensions within oil. Because of this, one of many considerations in their use is the length of time the particles remain in suspension. As a general rule, as the particle size decreases time in suspension increases.

The shear yield strength of an ER fluid is determined by the strength of the applied electric field, such that varying the field strength can control the viscosity. Similar to electro-rheostatic fluids, the shear yield strength of magneto-rheostatic (MR) fluids is determined by the strength of the applied magnetic field, such that varying the field strength can control the viscosity.

The ER and MR fluid must satisfy a number of criteria:

- low toxicity

- non-abrasive

- non-corrosive

- long storage life

- long working life

- high boiling point

- low freezing point

- particles must remain as a colloidal suspension and not settle out settle.

An example of an ER fluid is one containing lithium polymethacrylate particles in paraffin or silicon oil, while small ferromagnetic particle such as particles of carbonyl iron have been used in MR fluids.

The major advantage of MR fluids is that they can resist large forces, while ER fluids have the advantage that relatively small actuating elements can be developed.

The control over viscosity has allowed the ER and MR fluids to find uses in clutches, hydraulic valves and shock absorbers. The 2002 Cadillac Seville STS and second generation Audi TT automobiles have used MR fluids in the suspension system, while the National Museum of Emerging Science in Tokyo, Japan has installed MR fluid devices throughout the building to reduce shock loading from high winds and seismic activity.

Potential uses include suggestions for medical devices to prevent sleep apnea, in which the wind-pipe closes during sleep, and devices to deliver cardiac massage. Haptic applications such as a Braille Tablet and gloves providing tactile stimulus to accompany computer generated scenarios.

Thermoelectricity

Thermoelectric materials exhibit the features that when exposed to a temperature differential, an electric potential is created and, conversely, when exposed to an differential electric potential a change in temperature occurs.

These devices offer the prospect of developing power generators, cooling systems and waste heat recovery systems with no moving parts or polluting waste.

INTERNATIONAL MINDEDNESS

> Smart materials are likely to be developed in specific regions/countries and their benefits can be limited globally in the short term.
>
> © IBO 2012

Most smart materials have been discovered and developed in laboratories undertaking high technology pure or applied research. Such research is typically expensive and requires sophisticated equipment and specialist scientists and engineers. Such resources are generally only available in highly industrialised nations. The availability of smart materials can, therefore, be limited, at least initially.

Added to this is the difficulty in finding a use for such materials. Many smart materials begin their commercial life as curios in novelty stores before a practical use is found.

Shape memory alloys today find widespread use in the aerospace, military, communications, transport, leisure and medical fields. Applications range from fuel control and temperature relief valves, eyeglass frames, and mobile phone antennas, to orthodontic wires and as stents in vascular surgery. These materials however struggled to find an application for many years following their discovery in 1932.

THEORY OF KNOWLEDGE

> Through their specialised vocabularies, is it the case that shaping of knowledge is more dramatic in some areas of knowledge than others?
>
> © IBO 2012

Language helps us define concepts and communicate these concepts to others. A large vocabulary helps us communicate with others and fully explore meaning. As human knowledge has grown over the centuries areas of knowledge have grown in which specialized vocabularies have developed. It has been suggested that without language there cannot be thought (Sapir-Whorf hypothesis). This is the underlying principle of 'Newspeak' used by George Orwell in his novel *Nineteen-Eighty-Four*, in which it was suggested that by controlling the language, the thoughts of the populous could be controlled. Students should be cautious in quoting novels as examples as they are not necessarily based in reality and the Sapir-Whorf hypothesis remains contentious.

By contrast, increasing a vocabulary should allow a greater capacity for the creation and expression of ideas, if such a position is examined, students will need to provide suitable examples. Some general exploration of the changing nature of language over time might also be considered. During periods of rapid increases in human knowledge, the rate of change and specialisation of vocabularies would be expected to increase. While specialized vocabularies may have increased the precision of meaning within some areas of knowledge, it could also be argued that these vocabularies can become a barrier to understanding between various areas of knowledge and certainly the general public. In 1959, the British scientist CP Snow delivered a famous lecture entitled '*The Two Cultures and the Scientific Revolution*' in which he suggested that the Sciences and Humanities operated like two cultures with little understanding of each other.

In addressing the aspect of the shaping of knowledge being more dramatic the student will need to take a temporal view, that is, vocabulary would be expected to change in response to advances in any area of knowledge, and those advances may not occur at the same time throughout all areas of knowledge. Vocabulary changes could be cited within art history movements such as classicism or abstract impressionism, Luther and the Reformation, and feminist theory as readily as concepts such as space-time and gene splicing.

4.2a–METALS AND METALLIC ALLOYS

ESSENTIAL IDEA

Materials are classified into six basic groups based on their different properties.

© IBO 2012

NATURE OF DESIGN

Typically hard and shiny with good electrical and thermal conductivity, metals are a very useful resource for the manufacturing industry. Most pure metals are either too soft, brittle or chemically reactive for practical use and so understanding how to manipulate these materials is vital to the success of any application.

© IBO 2012

AIM

Design for disassembly is an important aspect of sustainable design. Valuable metals, such as gold and copper, are being recovered from millions of mobile phones that have gone out of use following the end of product life. Some laptops and mobile phones can be disassembled very quickly without tools to allow materials to be recovered easily.

© IBO 2012

Extracting metal from ore

Most metals are not naturally found in their pure form but rather as an ore consisting of a carbonate, oxide or sulphide and often in combination with other metals. Figure 4.2a.1 shows samples of iron ore from the Hamersley ranges region of Western Australia.

The ore is comprised of several minerals of iron oxide consisting primarily of hematite (Fe_2O_3), but with smaller amounts of magnetite (Fe_3O_4), goethite ($FeO(OH)$),and limonite ($FeO(OH)_n(H_2O)$).

A process of metal extraction must therefore be undertaken in which the constituent metals are separated. The heating (roasting) of carbonate and sulphate ores in air can be performed to obtain the oxide.

$$2PbS + 3O_2 \longrightarrow 2PbO + 2SO_2$$

Metals are then separated from their oxide in a process known as smelting in which the ore is heated in combination with a reducing agent such as carbon.

$$PbO + C \longrightarrow Pb + CO$$

A catalysing or fluxing agent such as lime (Calcium oxide) is also often included to help remove impurities into a slag that can be discarded.

Evidence of the smelting of some ores such as lead can be traced back to at least 6 500 BCE. The details of these early practices are however few. One of the earliest records of the processes of mining and metal extraction is found in the *De Re Metallurgica* (Latin for *On the Nature of Metals*) published in 1556 by the German physician and botanist Georgius Agricola. This book detailed the techniques being practiced in the Middle Ages and remained a standard text on mining and metallurgy throughout Europe for over 150 years. Published in Latin, the language of scholarship at the time, it was translated into German in 1557 and Italian in 1563. The first English translation, however, had to wait until 1912 and was undertaken by the mining engineer Herbert Clark Hoover and his wife Lou Henry Hoover. Seventeen years later Herbert Hoover was to become the 31st President of the USA.

It is probably unremarkable that tin and lead were the first metals to be smelted given that the heat of a wood fire is sufficient to separate them from their ores. The separation of other metals however, while basically the same process, required higher temperatures than those obtained from a wood fire. The injection of air into the furnace using a bellows, replacement of wood charcoal by coke derived from coal and increasingly sophisticated furnace designs were required to smelt other ores, to increase batch size and to increase yields by reducing metal loss in the slag.

"When the ore is smelted, those things which were mixed with the metal before it was melted are driven forth, because the metal is perfected by fire in this manner. Since metalliferous ores differ greatly amongst themselves, first as to the metals which they contain, then as to quantity of the metal which is in them, and then by the fact that some are rapidly melted by fire and others slowly, there are, therefore, many methods of smelting" *De Re Metallurgica* 1556.

In Figure 4.2a.2 a woodcut print from *De Re Metallurgica* is reproduced showing the smelting of tin ore in which two sandstone hearths can be seen. The hearth on the right has been lined with wood logs ready for charging. The hearth on the left is in operation. In it have been placed tin bars known as cakes which are still high in impurities and have been returned for further refining. A dipping pot placed at the end of the hearth collects the molten tin as it flows from the hearth. Having taken molten tin from the dipping pot with a ladle, the master furnace man (left foreground) pours the molten tin over copper plates to cool the tin and form it into bars. A worker in the background is seen checking the bars for purity by hitting them with a hammer. Those that are impure are brittle and crack and are returned to the smelting process as cakes.

A—Hearths. B—Dipping-pots. C—Wood. D—Cakes. E—Ladle. F—Copper plate. G—Lattice-shaped bars. H—Iron dies. I—Wooden mallet. K—Mass of tin bars. L—Shovel.

Figure 4.2a.2   Woodcut from De Re Metallurgica showing the smelting of tin

Grain size

When most solids form, (with the exception of glass and some polymers), they generally do so by arranging themselves in a regular three-dimensional pattern of atoms. This regular 3–D arrangement is known as a crystal structure and all metals solidify as collections of crystals (also known as grains). If special care is taken, a metal can be made to solidify as a single large crystal although metals are more commonly produced containing many crystals, being termed polycrystalline.

Three commonly encountered crystal structures for metals are shown in Figure 4.2a.3 and represent the body centred cubic (BCC), face centred cubic (FCC) and close packed hexagonal (CPH) structures (shown left to right repectively).

The crystal structure adopted by a metal will be the structure that results in the lowest energy state for the atoms of that metal. The crystal structure or lattice arrangement therefore reflects the properties of the metallic element.

During the solidification of metals the atoms begin to arrange themselves in the crystal lattice.

Because of variations in temperature and the presence of inhomogeneities of the mould surface and within the liquid, crystal growth will usually initiate (nucleate) at a number of positions, each of which has a different orientation from its neighbours. As solidification continues and each of these crystals (or grains) grows, a time arrives at which neighbouring crystals intersect. Because each crystal has initiated at a different position there will be a mismatch in the stacking order along the boundary between the crystals as shown in Figure 4.2a.4. This region of mismatch is known as the crystal or grain boundary.

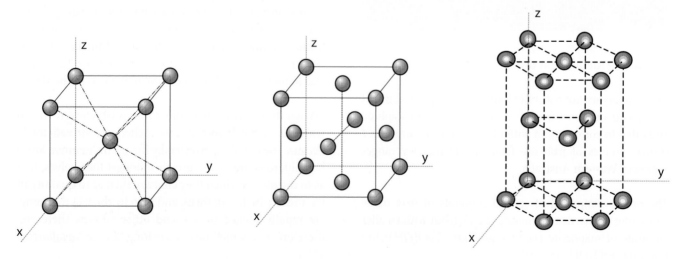

Figure 4.2a.3   Common crystal structures

CORE

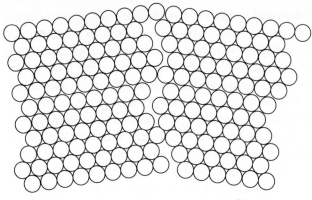

Figure 4.2a.4   Schematic representation of lattice mismatch at a boundary between two grains

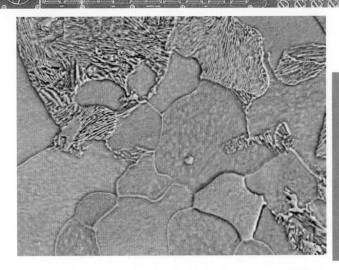

Figure 4.2a.5   Photomicrograph of the etched surface of a low carbon steel taken using a Scanning Electron Microscope and showing the different levels of attack obtained

If a finely polished metal surface is etched with an appropriate acid solution, the grains can be revealed. This occurs because the grain boundaries are selectively attacked. Etching is in essence a controlled corrosion process. Similarly, various phases within the grains will also undergo differing rates of attack to reveal structure within the grains. The study of microstructural elements of metals and alloys is known as metallography.

When a metal is etched in an acid, atoms are chemically removed from the surface; the rate of removal of atoms from the surface depends on the orientation of the crystal that is facing the acid. Because each grain presents a different orientation, each grain etches down at a different rate as can be seen in Figure 4.2a.5 where the surface of a low carbon steel with a structure of ferrite and pearlite is shown following etching.

The variation in level of attack of the various grains of ferrite, and differential attack of the cementite and ferrite lamella of the pearlite phase is clearly evident. Having revealed the grains in such a way, their size can be measured and may be reported in a number of ways, such as number of grains per unit area or average diameter.

Figure 4.2a.6   A selection of microstructures, conforming to the indicated ASTM grainsizes 3, 4, 6 and 8 (below)

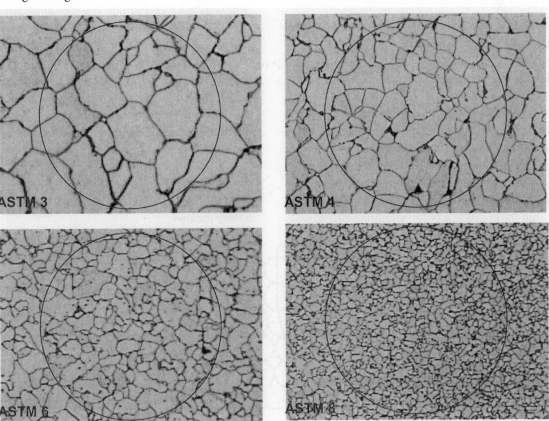

A simple rating of grainsize, standardized by the American Society for the Testing of Materials (ASTM), and known as the ASTM grain size number, is often quoted when assessing grain size. In simplified form, this number is obtained by recording the number of grain boundaries that are intercepted by a line when viewing the microstructure at a magnification of ×100. The simple formula shown below is then used to produce the ASTM number. The grainsize decreases as the grainsize number increases.

$$N = 2^{n-1}$$

Where N = the ASTM grain size number
n = number of grains per square inch at a magnification of ×100.

Standardised reference charts are available showing the grain size equivalent to each of the ASTM grain size numbers from 0 to 9, allowing an estimated grainsize to be given without time consuming measurement. A selection of microstructures, conforming to the indicated ASTM grainsizes, is illustrated in Figure 4.2a.6 and represents the grainsize when viewed at ×100 magnification.

Grain size is one of the most important characteristics of a material. In metals, the grainsize influences the yield strength, impact toughness, elongation and creep resistance. The grainsize of a metal can be influenced in a number of ways, the most common of which involves plastic deformation followed by heat treatment to encourage recrystallisation.

Modifying mechanical properties by alloying, work hardening and tempering

Work Hardening

Work hardening (also known as strain hardening) is the phenomenon in which the material is strain hardened during cold work. In a stress-strain curve the region of work hardening can be seen in the increasing stress required to continue deformation after exceeding the yield point. This effect is considered to be the result of increasing resistance to slip within the grains of a polycrystalline material.

Slip occurs within the metal lattice when planes of atoms are able to move past each other. This movement of crystallographic planes is believed to be assisted by the movement of defects in the stacking order leaving local vacancies known as dislocations. Effectively, dislocations represent regions in which the regular lattice order has been locally disrupted. A number of different types of dislocations have been identified that help explain the different forms of plastic deformation encountered. This is outside the requirements of the IB and will not be treated further. In Figure 4.2a.7 an illustration of a dislocation is presented. As can be seen the lattice is distorted and a stress field is associated with the dislocation.

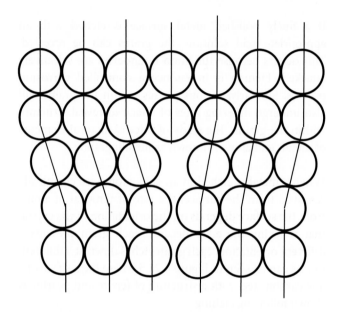

Figure 4.2a.7   Dislocation in lattice arrangement

These dislocations can move through the metal lattice and will do so freely until they meet an obstacle. As dislocations pile up at grain boundaries, a back pressure is created that restricts the motion of dislocations in the lattice making further deformation more difficult. A higher stress is therefore required to continue plastic deformation, which we identify as work hardening.

Figure 4.2a.8   Dislocation movement through metal lattice (below)

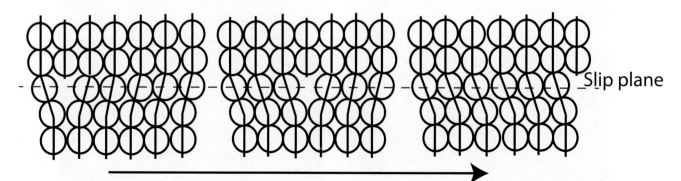

Slip plane

The surface of a polished and etched sample of austenitic stainless steel is shown in Figure 4.2a.9, in which lines of slip can be seen within different grains.

Figure4.2a.9   Photomicrograph of plastically deformed austenitic stainless steel revealing slip lines

Alloying

Alloying of a metal is the phenomenon in which metallic elements other than those of the base metal are intentionally incorporated into the crystal lattice of the base metal. Through the process of alloying, changes are effected either throughout the crystal lattice or locally, resulting in the presence of more than one crystal structure at a time. By alloying a metal with one or more additional metallic elements changed properties can be obtained, such as increased yield strength and tensile strength.

Element	Atomic radii (pm)
H	37
C	77
B	88
S	102
Fe	124
Cu	128
Zn	133
Al	143
Ti	145

Figure 4.2a.10   Atomic radii SI Chemical Data 6th Edition

The position occupied by the alloying element(s) within the base metal crystal lattice depends on the relative atomic sizes (as measured by their atomic radii), see Figure 4.2a.10.

In those instances where the atomic radius of the alloying (solute) element, differs by no more than 15% from that of the base (solvent) metal, a substitution of one for the other can occur within the metal lattice. Such an alloy addition forms what is known as a substitutional solid solution, see Figure 4.2a.11.

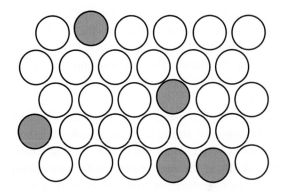

Figure 4.2a.11   Illustration of a metal lattice containing substitutional alloying elements (shaded)

As the size difference between the substitutional atom and the lattice increases, an increasing strain is created in the lattice. This lattice strain acts as an impediment to dislocation movement leading to an increase in strength, although above a difference of 15% substitutional solubility is limited. Therefore the larger the mismatch in atomic radii the greater is the strengthening effect of the alloy addition.

By contrast, if the atomic radii of the base (solvent) metal is greater than approximately 60% that of the alloying (solute) element, the alloying element will be located in the spaces or interstices between the lattice positions of the base metal. Such an alloy addition forms what is known as an interstitial solid solution, see Figure 4.2a.12.

Figure 4.2a.12   Illustration of a metal lattice containing interstitial alloying elements (shaded)

As the size of the element taking up an interstitial site increases relative to the size of the vacancy within the lattice, an increase in lattice strain occurs. As may be seen from Figure 4.2a.10, hydrogen, when present, would be an interstitial addition in most alloy systems. Hydrogen, nitrogen, oxygen, carbon and boron are present as interstitial additions in iron, with most of the other elements being present as substitutional alloy additions. Lead (Pb) does not have any solubility (interstitial or substitutional) in the iron lattice due the exceptional difference in their atomic radii.

By introducing strain into the lattice, both substitutional and interstitial alloying hinders the movement of dislocations and as a result increases the yield and tensile strength of the metal. This phenomenon is known as solution hardening.

Increasing the percentage of the alloying element leads to an increase in strength by increasing the number of regions of lattice strain, up to the point at which the solid solubility of the alloy is exceeded. At this point the excess atoms often form in groups or clusters at the grain boundaries by diffusion, leading under conditions of slow cooling to the formation (precipitation) of a second phase consisting of a fine intermetallic compound.

Substitutional and interstitial solutes can also interact leading to the formation of this second phase precipitation. The result is that some of the solute atoms are removed from the lattice and a decrease in solid solution hardening occurs but a process known as precipitation hardening can occur.

As indicated previously, dislocation movement through the crystal lattice allows atoms to move past one another, or slip, along crystallographic planes during plastic deformation. By restricting the movement of dislocations, alloying elements restrict the degree of plastic deformation that can take place before fracture as measured by a decrease in malleability and ductility.

Tempering

When metals such as steel undergo a hardening heat treatment, in which an item is raised to an elevated temperature (typically >800°C) and cooled rapidly by plunging it into a suitable quenching medium, hardness and strength are significantly increased. With this increased hardness, however, is an accompanying decrease in ductility and impact toughness. The metal can be said to be brittle. In order to regain some ductility, a low temperature tempering heat treatment is often employed immediately following the quench hardening operation.

This tempering treatment reduces strength slightly while also reducing internal stresses and increasing ductility and toughness. The degree to which ductility is recovered (and strength reduced) depends on the tempering temperature used, with greater ductility being achieved as the tempering temperature is increased. If tempering is performed on a steel sample with a machined surface the temperature used is often reflected in the colour of the surface oxide formed during tempering and is known as the temper colour, see Figure 4.2a.13.

Temper Colour	Temperature (°C)
Pale straw	230
Dark straw	240
Brown	250
Brownish-purple	260
Purple	270
Dark purple	270
Blue	300

Figure 4.2a.13   Temper colour chart

Design Criteria for Superalloys

The group of metal alloys known as superalloys all feature excellent high temperature strength and resistance to thermal shock along with high temperature oxidation resistance. The superalloys are therefore particularly known for their ability to operate at high temperatures while maintaining strength even at temperatures approaching a high fraction of their melting point. A measure of this is known as the homologous temperature T_H, where T_H represents the ratio of operating temperature to melting temperature, expressed in degrees Kelvin. The superalloys typically have a $T_H > 0.7$.

The superalloys all exhibit a face centred cubic (FCC) structure and typically fall into three groups:

* Iron-Nickel based alloys

* Nickel based alloys

* Cobalt based alloys.

Most of the superalloys have a significant chromium addition, which plays an important part in the formation of a tightly adherent oxide layer that restricts access of oxygen to the alloy surface, impeding further oxidation. Strengthening occurs by a combination of solid solution strengthening, precipitation hardening or dispersion hardening. The iron-based grades are generally cheaper than the nickel and cobalt based alloys. Examples of several superalloys are provided in Figure 4.2a.14

Alloy Group	Common Name	% C	% Fe	% Co	% Ni	% Cr	% Mo	% W	% Ti	% Al	% Other
	Solid solution										
Iron-nickel alloys	Incoloy 800	0.5	Bal.	—	32	21	—	—	0.4	—	
	Incoloy 900	0.5	Bal.	—	43	13	6	—	—	—	2.9 Ti, 0.2 Al
	Precipitation										
	Altemp A286	0.5	Bal.	—	26	15	1.25	—	2.5	0.2	0.003 B
	Solid solution										
Cobalt base alloys	HS 21	0.25	1	Bal.	3	27	5	—	—	—	
	HS 25	0.1	3	Bal.	10	20	1.5	15	—	—	
	Elgiloy	0.15	25	Bal.	15	20	7	—	—	—	0.4 Be
	MAR M322	1.00	—	Bal.		21	—	9	0.75	—	2 Zr, 4.5 Ta
	MP35N	—	—	Bal.	35	20	10	—	—	—	
	Solid solution										
	Hastelloy C276	0.02	5	2.5	Bal.	15	16	3.5	—	—	1 Mn
	Iconel 625	0.25	5		Bal.	22	9	—	—	—	3 (Nb + Ta)
	Precipitation										
	Iconel 601	0.5	14	—	Bal.	23	—	—	—	1.4	0.2 Cu
	Udimet 500	0.08	—	18	Bal.	19	4	3	3	3	0.005 B
	Waspaloy A	0.07	10	13	Bal.	19	4	—	3	1.5	0.006 B, 0.9 Zr
	Nimonic 90	0.1	3	18	Bal.	19	—	—	2.5	1.5	1.5 Si
	Rene 41	0.09	—	11	Bal.	19	10	—	3	1.5	0.01 B

Figure 4.2a.14   Selection of superalloys and an indication of the strengthening mechanism

Alloy additions made to the superalloys contribute to strength and oxidation resistance in a number of ways, summarised in Figure 4.2a.15. As can be seen from this table, carbide and gamma prime (γ') precipitation play a major role in the strengthening of the superalloys. The gamma prime phase represents an intermetallic precipitate such as γ'-Ni$_3$Al or γ'-Ni$_3$(Al,Ti).

Through an understanding of the effects of the various alloying elements on the structure and properties of materials, such as the superalloys, metallurgists and materials engineers are able to design alloys for certain tasks.

Alloy additions	Solid solution strengtheners	γ' formers	Carbide formers	Grain boundary strengtheners	Oxide scale formers
Chromium	X	—	X	—	—
Aluminium	—	X	—	—	—
Titanium		X	X	—	—
Molybdenum	X	—	X	—	—
Tungsten	X	—	X	—	—
Boron	—	—	—	X	X
Zirconium	—	—	—	X	X
Carbon	—	—	—	X	X
Niobium	—	—	X		
Hafnium	—	—	X	X	X
Tantalum	—	—	X	X	X

Figure 4.2a.15   Role of alloying elements in superalloys

Creep resistance: elevated temperature creep resistance is one of the principle characteristics of super alloys. Creep is a process in which a material subjected to an applied load, lower than the yield strength, will over time, elongate or undergo strain. The rate at which creep will occur is dependent on both the applied stress and the operating temperature.

Creep occurs as a result of thermal vibrations of the metal lattice, which over time allow obstacles to plastic flow to be overcome. This plastic flow typically occurs at the grain boundaries. In advanced stages of creep, grain boundary sliding leads to the development of cavities at grain boundary junctions, eventually resulting in fracture.

Oxidation resistance: due to the presence of additions such as chromium, a tightly adherent oxide film is formed on the surface. This film restricts further access of oxygen to the metal surface so that unless the oxide barrier is damaged the rate of oxidation is severely reduced.

Superalloy applications

Superalloys find particular application in high temperature service such as jet and rocket engines and chemical plants where mechanical strength at elevated temperature, and resistance to corrosive atmospheres and oxidation resistance is necessary.

The high corrosion resistance and biocompatibility of the cobalt based alloys has also seen them used in biomedical applications. Some uses of a selection of superalloys are indicated in Figure 4.2a.16. General applications of superalloys based on sub groupings are shown following.

Iron-nickel based superalloys find applications in:

- cryogenics

- jet engine components

- petrochemical processing machinery.

Alloy group	Common Name	Applications
Iron - nickel	Incoloy 800	Applications requiring resistance to high temperature oxidation and carburization, e.g. Carbonizing equipment, heating element sheathing, heat treatment baskets, chemical and petrochemical processing equipment e.g. heat exchangers and piping equipment.
based	Incoloy 901	Gas turbine parts including: rotors and compressor discs, high temperature fasteners, and cryogenic equipment.
alloys	Altemp A286	Jet engine nacelles, parts and fasteners. Belleville springs and washers in oil-field and racing applications as well as cryogenics.
	HS21	Turbine blades and vanes, biomedical implants.
Cobalt	HS25	Turbine blades and vanes, combustion chambers, afterburner parts and biomedical implants.
based	Elgiloy	Springs for oil-field applications and orthodontic wires.
alloys	MAR M322	Jet engine turbine blades and vanes.
	MP35N	Aircraft fasteners, biomedical devices, chemical and food processing equipment, springs for oil-field applications.
	Hastelloy C276	Petrochemical processing equipment, heat exchangers, air scrubbers, flue-gas desulphurization equipment and cryogenic applications.
	Inconel 625	Heat exchangers and gas turbine components, reaction vessels and heat exchangers, valves, marine applications and cryogenics.
Nickel	Inconel 601	Chemical processing radiant tubes, steam superheater tube supports and heat treatment fixtures.
based	Udimet 500	Gas turbine components e.g. vane guides.
alloys	Waspalloy A	Gas turbine components e.g. discs, blades, seals and shafts. Missile components
	Nimonic 90	Gas turbine components e.g. valves, discs and blades. Hot working tools. High temperature springs.
	Rene 41	Jet and rocket engine parts: afterburner parts, turbine casings, wheels and fasteners. Space shuttle turbo pump seals.

Figure 4.2a.16   Selection of specific superalloys

Cobalt based superalloys are employed in:

- turbine blades

- orthodontic wires

- biomedical implants

- food processing equipment.

Nickel based superalloys appear in:

- air scrubbers

- marine applications

- gas turbine components.

Recovery and disposal of metals and metallic alloys

The recovery and disposal or recycling of metals and metallic alloys is now an important part of the material life cycle. It is often defined as the series of activities, including collection, separation, and processing, by which products or other materials are recovered from the solid waste stream for use in the form of raw materials in the manufacture of new products.

From the standpoint of energy consumption, the manufacture of metal from its scrap is much more advantageous than manufacture based on the smelting of the metal ore, and well established avenues exist for the recovery and reuse of the commonly used metals such as steel, aluminium and copper.

Recycled steel (Figure 4.2a.17) can be used in place of virgin iron thus reducing iron ore extracted from mines, which results in about 60% energy saving and reduction in environmental impact. Structural members from decommissioned bridges as well as car bodies and steel reinforcing recovered from concrete can easily be recycled into new steel. Steel-making technologies such as the basic oxygen furnace and the electric arc furnace contribute to high rates of steel reusability. Typically the BOF uses 25% recycled steel while the EAF accepts 100% scrap steel.

Similarly, by many measures, aluminium remains one of the most energy intensive materials to produce. Aluminium production is the largest consumer of energy on a per-weight basis and is the largest electrical energy consumer of all industries.

Energy reduction in the aluminium industry is the result of technical progress and the growth of recycling.

Recycled aluminium requires less than 6% of the energy needed to produce aluminium from mined materials and thus provides significant cost and environmental benefits.

Figure 4.2a.17   Scrap yard, image by Roger Graeme

Metal recovery and disposal is now a significant problem associated with modern electronics, with an estimated 20 to 50 million tonnes of e-waste from discarded televisions, computers and mobile phones created every year.

Many countries now operate recycling schemes directed specifically at this electronic waste or e-waste. A large trade has developed in e-waste recycling in which consumer electronics are exported to developing countries for disassembly, as shown in Figure 4.2a.18. In these countries, recovery of metals is often performed without the environmental and health safeguards expected in developed countries.

Figure 4.2a.18   Ghanaians working in Agbogbloshie, a suburb of Accra, Ghana

Many of the materials found in e-waste are expensive such as, platinum and silver, and their recovery offers a considerable cost saving. Still others such as mercury, lead, arsenic and cadmium can pose health problems if allowed to leach into the environment from landfills.

E-waste contains varying proportions of metals such as aluminium, manganese, lead, copper, nickel, cobalt, tin, titanium, tantalum, zinc, chromium, silver, cadmium, antimony, beryllium, iridium, germanium, gallium, yttrium, terbium, vanadium, mercury, platinum, gold, palladium, barium, ruthenium, selenium, and rare earths. A cathode ray tube (CRT) monitor can alone contain up to 4 kg of lead. The recycling industry is not without its own environmental and health problems however.

INTERNATIONAL MINDEDNESS

Extraction takes place locally with added value often occurring in another country.

© IBO 2012

The mining of raw materials today, as in the past, often occurs in locations remote from large established population centres in both developed and developing countries. This means that following the mining of an ore, that ore is often shipped to a larger industrial centre for further processing and value adding. In this context value adding represents the increased value that the material is seen to gain as the material is increasingly refined and concentrated, removing unwanted waste. That is to say, as the material undergoes each stage of processing, the amount that it can be sold for increases reflecting both the costs of processing undertaken by the supplier and the convenience offered to the buyer of a more concentrated material.

The chain of activities leading from the initial mining of an ore through its beneficiation, and subsequent smelting to produce a metal suitable for further processing into a finished product can involve a complex inter-relationship of governments, financial institutions, and local and international mining and industrial interests. This chain of transportation along the route from raw material to final product is called the global value chain (GVC). As shown in Figure 4.2a.19 the GVC can span a number of countries as it is processed. In each country the contribution to the Gross Domestic Product (GDP) grows such that the country in which the resource was originally mined actually receives the lowest direct income in dollar terms. Despite this, mining of natural resources is often an important step for developing countries to obtain much needed foreign investment for public works and the establishment of an industrial sector. Today mining is a largely capital intensive activity in which mechanisation has resulted in highly efficient and safer means of material extraction. With mechanisation also comes the need for a number of highly trained equipment operators and maintenance personnel. Transportation systems such as road and rail are required, in addition to a local service industry supplying everything from equipment repair, food, accommodation, security and unskilled labour.

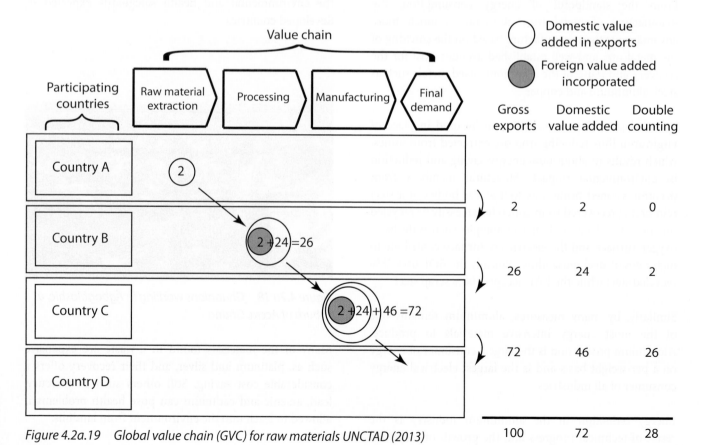

Figure 4.2a.19   Global value chain (GVC) for raw materials UNCTAD (2013)

THEORY OF KNOWLEDGE

How does classification and categorisation help and hinder the pursuit of knowledge?

© IBO 2012

The need to classify and categorize the world around us appears to be a natural attribute of human nature. These processes allow us to group and organise knowledge into a form that allows us to recognise connections and simplify information.

The Greek philosopher Aristotle (384-322BCE), classified human knowledge into the following three categories.

- Theoretic–knowledge pursued for its own value.

- Productive–knowledge involved in making things pursued by artists and craftsmen.

- Practical–knowledge involved in judgements associated with ethical enquiry and political life.

Aristotle's interests ranged wide and included writings on physics, zoology, and biology as well as ethics and logic. Because of these contributions many consider him the first scientist.

His reputation, however, was such that many of his pronouncements about the physical world went unchallenged until the 17th century. Aristotle's reputation therefore, although laying a foundation for enquiry, hindered the later advancement of knowledge.

Students will be able to find many examples in which the classification and categorization of information has helped guide the pursuit of knowledge, Mendeleev and the Periodic table, the Linnaeus biological classification system, Dewey Decimal system, etc.

Language itself can influence the way we categorise things as indicated in Figure 4.2a.20.

Could this help or hinder the pursuit of knowledge?

English	German	Danish	French	Italian	Spanish
Tree	Baum	Trae	arbre	albero	Árbol
Wood	Holz			legno	Leňa
			bois		Madera
Woods	Wald	skov		bosco	Bosque
Forest			forêt	foresta	Selva

Figure 4.2a.20   Cultural relativity in word meanings. Hjorland, B. (2006). Knowledge representation. [Available online at: http://arizona.openrepository.com/arizona/bitstream/10150/105281/1/Knowledge_Representation_Lifeboat.pdf]

Classification systems can of course also have a darker side as history has repeatedly shown.

Classification by nationality, religious belief, political affiliation, social status, physical and mental health, IQ and gender have all at one time or place been used as justification for discrimination and prejudice and hindering the pursuit of knowledge. In this sense the pursuit of knowledge could be defined as educational opportunities of the individual and the rights to pursue knowledge in any of its forms or that of human advancement in general.

4.2b–TIMBER

ESSENTIAL IDEA

Materials are classified into six basic groups based on their different properties.

© IBO 2012

NATURE OF DESIGN

Wood is a major building material that is renewable and uses the Sun's energy to renew itself in a continuos cycle. Whilst wood manufacture uses less energy and results in less air and water pollution than steel or concrete, consideration needs to be given to deforestation and the potential negative impact the use of timber can have on communities and wildlife.

© IBO 2012

AIM

Designers have great influence over the materials that they specify for products. The move towards using timber from sustainably managed forestry gives consumers confidence that rare species found in rainforests have an opportunity to recover.

© IBO 2012

Characteristics of natural timber: hardwood and softwood

As timber comes from a living organism it is perhaps not surprising that the classification system is not related purely to physical or mechanical properties but to biological functions related to the way the tree grows.

Timber is therefore classified into two basic groups: hardwoods or softwoods.

These terms are perhaps unfortunate because they suggest a relationship with the physical property hardness, which is not intended. As may be seen in Figure 4.2b.1, the hardness ranges of the softwoods and hardwoods, as measured by the Janka hardness, overlap. This is perhaps best illustrated by the soft, light timber Balsa wood which

is classified as a 'hardwood' and has one of the lowest Janka hardnesses, while the hard, heavy timber Yew is a 'softwood' and has a moderately high Janka hardness.

	Timber	Janka dry hardness kN
Softwood	Western red cedar	1.6
	Californian redwood	2.0
	White fir	2.1
	Eastern hemlock	2.2
	Douglas fir	3.2
	Radiata pine	3.3
	Western larch	3.7
	Eastern red cedar	4.0
	Cyprus pine	6.5
	Pacific yew	7.1
Hardwood	Balsa	0.4
	American chestnut	2.4
	Silver maple	3.1
	Dark red meranti	3.5
	American mahogany	3.6
	Teak	4.4
	Black walnut	4.5
	Yellow birch	5.6
	White ash	5.9
	Jarrah	8.5
	Turpentine	12.0
	Indian Rosewood	14.1
	Ebony	14.3

Figure 4.2b.1 Janka hardness of selected softwoods and hardwoods

The difference between hardwoods and softwoods lies in their structure. Softwoods have a simpler structure principally containing one type of cell, consisting of long pores approximately 3 to 5 mm long and 20 to 80×10^{-6}m in diameter, known as tracheids, and which act as fluid transport.

Hardwoods by comparison contain two cell types, consisting of fibres and vessels. In hardwoods the fibres are similar to tracheids but smaller being less than 20×10^{-6} m in diameter, and do not contribute to fluid transport. The vessel cells have a significantly larger diameter and thinner walls than pore cells and support fluid transfer. Images produced from a scanning electron microscope (SEM), (Figure 4.2b.2), show the presence of vessels in hardwoods (Oak, top) and tracheids in softwoods (Pine, bottom).

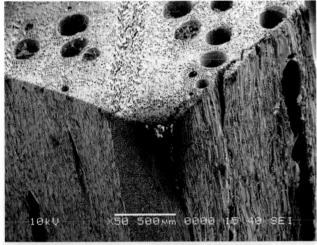

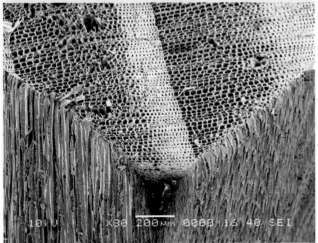

Figure 4.2b.2   SEM showing hardwood (top) and softwood structures (bottom), image by Mckdandy CC-BY-SA-3.0 (www.creativecommons.org/ licenssoftwood climatees/by-sa/3.0/) via Wikimedia Commons

Softwoods are typically Conifers, meaning that they form a seed cone and have narrow needle like leaves, (Figure 4.2b.3), compared to hardwoods that typically have broad leaves. In softwoods, the cells are connected such that they allow the movement of nutrient throughout the length

of the tree. Because of this, softwoods grow much faster than hardwoods, which do not have this arrangement. Classified as Gymnosperms they are also called non-pored timbers based on elements in their structure. The trees grow in cooler climates and the timber is often light in colour.

Figure 4.2b.3   Conifer seed cone and needle-shaped leaves, image by John Haslam from Dornoch, Scotland CC-BY-2.0 (www.creativecommons. org/licenses/by/2.0), via Wikimedia Commons

Hardwoods are produced by broad leaved trees whose seeds are enclosed in fruit e.g. acorns. They have a variety of grains and a multitude of colours.

Hardwoods can originate from trees that are either the evergreen type, keeping their leaves all year round, or of the deciduous type and lose their leaves in winter. Hardwoods grow in all climatic conditions, wherever trees are found and bear seed-containing fruit. Classified as Angiosperms they are also called pored timbers based on elements of their structure. The evergreen varieties are typically found in the tropical and sub-tropical regions of the world, such as South and Central America, Africa, India and South East Asia. The deciduous varieties are typically found in the temperate regions such as Britain, Europe, Japan, USA and New Zealand.

While the classification of timbers as hardwood or softwood cannot be used as an indication of hardness, the differing structures do have a significant effect on many of the characteristic properties. Some of the factors affecting the strength of timber (although by no means exclusive) are:

- moisture content

- duration of loading

- defects – knots, splits, shakes etc – act to reduce mechanical properties because they introduce a disruption to direction of grain flow

- chemical treatment – many chemical treatments have an adverse effect on mechanical properties although the effect is greatest for water-based preservatives compared to oil-based.

Many of these factors are related to the growth rate of the wood rather than classification as hardwood or softwood

Softwoods generally have a faster growth rate than hardwoods and consequently exhibit a lower density and lower hardness, although as indicated by the example of Balsa wood and Yew earlier this is not universal.

Characteristics of man-made timbers

Man-made timbers sometimes called engineered timber are composite products that use wood lengths, fibres and veneers along with an adhesive binder and combined under heat and pressure to produce a product. These products find widespread use as structural members such as I-beams in wood frame construction. Examples of man-made timbers include plywood, glued laminated timber (Glulam), laminated veneer lumber (LVL) and parallel strand lumber (PSL).

Characteristics of man-made timber are:

- dimensional stability

- uniformity of properties

- greater availability of product sizes

- lower cost compared with solid natural timber of same dimensions.

Treating and finishing timbers

Green timber contains a high percentage of moisture (~85%) within its cells. Once cut, green timber will begin to lose moisture. The commercial drying of timber is called seasoning and is directed toward the controlled removal of moisture.

Before timber can be used commercially, moisture must be removed in such a way that the structural integrity and yield strength of the timber is not affected by splitting or warping. Similarly, if moisture is not reduced to a level below about 20% the timber will be subject to decay and

attack by fungus often referred to as dry rot. The drying of timber is not intended to remove all moisture but to achieve equilibrium with the environment, known as the equilibrium moisture content or (EMC). There are two primary methods used to season timber: air-drying and kiln-drying. Both methods involve the stacking of the sawn timber in such a way that movement is restrained during the drying process, while allowing air to freely circulate throughout the stack. In air-drying, the stack is exposed to the general atmosphere, either in the open or stored in large sheds (Figure 4.2b.4). In this situation there is little control over the drying process. Kiln drying, in contrast, places the stacks in a kiln, within which the drying environment is closely controlled. Temperatures within the kiln are typically controlled between 70° and 100° C.

The moisture within timber is contained either in the cells walls and is known as absorbed moisture, or within the cell cavities and intercellular spaces which is known as free moisture. During the initial drying of wood, only the free moisture is removed and no structural changes occur. Once the free moisture has been removed the loss of absorbed moisture begins. It is at this stage when the moisture is below about 30% that structural changes associated with shrinkage begin.

Figure 4.2b.4   Timber seasoning, image by Richard Young [CC-BY-SA-2.0 (www. creativecommons.org/ licenses/by-sa/2.0)], via Wikimedia Commons

Drying proceeds from the surface into the centre. If the humidity is not controlled during the seasoning process, stresses develop between the surface of the timber and the centre that can lead to warping and splitting. Some of these effects are shown in Figure 4.2b.5.

Figure 4.2b.5   Common timber shrinkage, image by MPF Creative Commons Attribution-Share Alike 3.0 Unported license

Softwoods are generally kiln-dried while hardwoods, which can be subject to degradation during kiln drying, are usually air-dried.

Correctly seasoned timber exhibits the following features:

- strength

- stability

- resistance to decay

- easy to paint glue, nail, screw, and machine

- timber preservation processes require the removal of free water from wood.

Timber is a natural product. Once the wood is taken from the natural protection of the bark, it is prone to attack from poor weather conditions, insects, fungus and moisture. To protect timber from these attacks it would be prudent to either treat the timber or apply a finish. Treatment can involve using solutions, which make the wood poisonous to insects, fungus and marine borers as well as protecting it from the weather. Finishes can also be applied but, generally speaking, timber that will be positioned outdoors should be treated, while an adequate finish should be applied to timber that will be positioned indoors.

Finished timber requires sanding, (to close up the grain leaving smaller gaps), with abrasive paper and the application of one of the following:

- oil

- stain

- paint

- shellac

- wax polish

- french polish

- plastic varnish.

Recovery and disposal of timbers

Reforestation is the process of restoring tree cover to areas where woodlands or forest once existed. If this area never returns to its original state of vegetative cover the destructive process is called deforestation. In order to maintain a sustainable forest industry reforestation is necessary.

Reforestation may take a variety of forms. In many temperate zones such as the eastern United States, reforestation occurs quite naturally as the native hardwood forests are so resilient that these, given any opportunity, quickly re-establish themselves. However, urban sprawl and agriculture requires a permanently deforested land that is leading to forest reduction. Artificial reforestation is required where poor logging practices and/or nutrient deficient soils generate erosion-prone environments.

In various arid, tropical, or sensitive areas, forests cannot re-establish themselves without assistance due to a variety of environmental factors. One of these factors is that, once forest cover is destroyed in arid zones, the land quickly dries out and becomes inhospitable to new tree growth. Other critical factors include overgrazing by livestock, especially animals such as goats, and over-harvesting of forest resources by native populations or outside businesses. Together these forces may lead to desertification and the loss of topsoil. Without soil, forests cannot grow until the very long process of soil creation has been completed (if erosion allows this).

In some tropical areas, the removal of forest cover may result in a duri-crust or duri-pan that effectively seals off the soil to water penetration and root growth. In many areas, reforestation is impossible because the land is in use by people. In these areas, reforestation requires tree seedling or tree planting programs. In other areas, mechanical breaking up of duripans or duricrusts is necessary. Careful and continued watering may be essential, and special protection, such as fencing, may also be required.

One debatable issue in artificial reforestation is whether the succeeding forest will have the same biodiversity as the original forest. If the forest is replaced with only one species of tree and all other vegetation is prevented from growing back, a monoculture forest similar to agricultural crops would be the result. However, most reforestation involves the planting of different seed lots of seedlings taken from the area. More frequently, multiple species are planted as well. Another important factor is the nature of the wide variety of plant and animal species that previously occupied a clear-cut. In some regeneration areas the suppression of forest fires for hundreds of years has resulted in large single aged and single specie forest stands.

Reforestation need not be only used for recovery of accidentally destroyed forests. In some countries, such as Finland, the forests are managed by the wood products, pulp and paper industries. In such an arrangement, (like other crops), trees are replanted wherever they are cut. In such circumstances, the cutting of trees can be carefully controlled to allow easier reforestation. In Canada, the wood product, pulp and paper industries systematically replace many of the trees it cuts, employing large numbers of summer workers for tree planting.

Figure 4.2b.6   Young Scots Pine stand (ca. 25 years of age) after the first thinning, image by MPorciusCato [CC-BY-SA-3.0 (www. creativecommons.org/licenses/by-sa/3.0)], from Wikimedia Commons.

INTERNATIONAL MINDEDNESS

The demand for high quality hardwoods results in the depletion of ancient forests in some regions/countries impacting on the environment in multiple ways.

© IBO 2012

Many of the World hardwood forests are found in tropical environments such as the rainforests of South America, India, South East Asia and Indonesia. Timbers such as mahogany, teak and meranti found in these locations are highly prized for furniture.

Due to the stresses placed on areas such as rainforest from the development of farms, animal grazing and mining in addition to logging, the continued availability of a sustainable timber resource is under threat in many areas. One of the most serious threats to the sustainability of this resource is the use of clear cutting operations rather than selective logging. Clear cutting results in the removal of all trees from an area resulting in habitat destruction and loss of bio-diversity, while selective logging, as the name implies, takes trees selectively from the forest causing minimal destruction that quickly regrows. Illegal logging operations are particularly concerning in this regard. In order to combat illegal logging, a system of forest certification has been introduced intended to sustainably manage such resources by encouraging customers to only source timber that carries a stamp such as that shown in Figure 4.2b.7 that indicates it was legally logged.

Figure 4.2b.7   Certified legally logged timber

The pressure of hardwood logging is not exclusive to tropical rainforest regions of course and old growth forests are under threat in many more temperate locations around the world including North America, Europe and Australia. While many of these old growth forests are preserved in national parks others remain at risk particularly from mining interests.

THEORY OF KNOWLEDGE

Designers are moving from exploitation of resources towards conservation and sustainability. Is the environment at the service of man?

© IBO 2012

In answering this question the student should consider how widespread the move from exploitation to conservation and sustainability is, and what the driving force for such a move might be; concern for cost, biodiversity, resource availability, marketing?

What does sustainable mean? To act in a sustainable manner suggests that the availability of the resource is known and a holistic assessment of the impacts of exploitation has been determined and can be controlled. It also assumes that all parties will adhere to guidelines of sustainable development. Unfortunately, many of the arguments between industry and the environmental movement revolve around disagreements over these very issues. What, for instance does sustainable mining mean? Once extracted from the ground and processed, the resource is no longer available and a new source of raw materials must be found. Assuming a finite world, the economic recovery of mineral resources at least, must decrease.

As for the question of the environment being at the service of man, this suggests linguistically at least a religious view that the environment has been created for our use as found in the Old Testament admonition in Genesis: 1:28.

And God blessed them [Adam and Eve], and God said unto them, Be fruitful, and multiply, and replenish the earth, and subdue it: and have dominion over the fish of the sea, and over the fowl of the air, and over every living thing that moveth upon the earth.

Through most of recorded history it can be argued that the environment has been at the service of man. Resources have been plentiful and when problems have arisen technology has generally provided new efficiencies and options.

From time to time, however, societies have been unable to find a solution to over exploitation of resources and have failed, as Jared Diamond points out in his 2005 book *Collapse: How societies choose to fail or survive.*

On a different scale, James Lovelock's Gaia hypothesis proposes that the Earth can be considered as a closed system in which the organisms on Earth interact with the inorganic components of the environment to form a self-correcting complex system. In such a system the environment is not at the service of man. Man is just one component within the system.

From this viewpoint, failure to take due consideration of the effects of exploitation and pollution on the environment threatens the future of mankind.

Exercise

Examine two different manufactured items. One that flagrantly uses resources either by it's construction or usage and another that is designed to be environmentally friendly throughout its lifecycle.

Further reference material

McShane, K. (2007). *Why environmental ethics shouldn't give up on intrinsic value.* Environmental Ethics, Vol.29(1), pp 43-61. [Available online at http://www.umweltethik.at/download.php?id=441]

Sandler, R. (2012). *Intrinsic Value, Ecology, and Conservation.* Nature Education Knowledge, Vol.3(10):4. [Available online at http://www.nature.com/scitable/knowledge/library/intrinsic-value-ecology-and-conservation-25815400].

Younkins, E. (2004). *The Flawed Doctrine of Nature's Intrinsic Value.* [Available online at http://www.quebecoislibre.org/04/041015-17.htm]

4.2c–GLASS

ESSENTIAL IDEA

Materials are classified into six basic groups based on their different properties.

© IBO 2012

NATURE OF DESIGN

The rapid pace of technological discoveries is very evident in the manufacture and use of glass in electronic devices. Different properties have been presented in glass for aesthetic or safety considerations for many years but the future of glass seems to be interactivity alongside electronic systems. The structure of glass is not well understood, but as more is learnt, its use is becoming increasingly prominent in building materials and structural applications.

© IBO 2012

AIM

The earliest found examples of glass objects come from the 3rd millennium BCE and up until the 1850s, glass was considered a luxury item. Since then, glass has permeated and revolutionised many aspecs of human life and culture in diverse fields such as the arts, architecture, electronics and communication technologies.

© IBO 2012

Characteristics of glass

Glass represents a group of non-crystalline (amorphous) ceramics, in which the constituent atoms are stacked in an irregular, random pattern i.e. there is no long-range order.

The main constituent of commercial glass is silica sand (SiO_2), and sand by itself can be fused to produce glass, although temperatures of the order of 1700°C are required. In order to reduce the energy requirements, other materials are added to sand to reduce the temperature of fusion, that is, the addition of soda ash reduces the temperature of fusion to about 800 - 1 000°C.

Glass of this composition is relatively soft and water-soluble and is known as water glass. In order to give the glass stability and hardness, other materials such as limestone ($CaCO_3$) and Dolomite ($MgCO_3$) are added. In addition, scrap glass is added to make the process more economical.

There are many different types of glass with different chemical and physical properties. Each can be made by a suitable adjustment to chemical compositions, but the main types of glass are:

- glass fibre

- lead glass

- commercial glass also known as soda-lime glass

- borosilicate glass (low coefficient of thermal expansion for example Pyrex®).

Glasses may be devised to meet almost any imaginable requirement. For many specialised applications in chemistry, pharmacy, the electrical and electronics industries, optics, the construction and lighting industries, glass, or the comparatively new family of materials known as glass ceramics, may be the only practical material for the engineer or designer to use.

Like other ceramics, glasses are brittle. The majority of the glass we see around us in our everyday lives is in the form of bottles, jars and flat glass for windows. This type of glass is known as commercial or soda-lime glass, as soda ash (sodium carbonate Na_2CO_3) is used in its manufacture. The addition of soda ash reduces the melting point of silica from approximately 1700°C to 874°C.

Most commercial glasses have roughly similar chemical compositions of:

70% - 74% SiO_2 (silica)

12% - 16% Na_2O (sodium oxide)

5% - 11% CaO (calcium oxide)

1% - 3% MgO (magnesium oxide)

1% - 3% Al_2O_3 (aluminium oxide)

Commercial glass is normally perceived as colourless, allowing it to freely transmit light although in thicker sections a green colouration can be noticed due to contamination by a small amount of iron oxide.

The presence of impurities in glass produces various colours, as indicated below in Figure 4.2c.1.

Metal oxide	Colour
Antimony oxide	White
Cadmium sulphide	Deep yellow
Cerric oxide	Brown
Chromium (III) oxide	Green
Cobalt (II) oxide	Deep blue
Copper (II) oxide	Turquoise
Iron (II) oxide	Turquoise
Iron (III) oxide	Pale yellow green
Iron sulphide	Brown
Magnesium (II) oxide	Colourless
Magnesium (III) oxide	Purple
Selenium oxide	Ruby red
Titanium oxide	Violet
Uranium	Fluorescent yellow green
Vanadium	Yellow green

Figure 4.2c.1   Colours of soda lime silicate glass

Glass has a wide range of characteristics that have seen it used extensively in everyday life. These include:

Transparency: One of the unique characteristics of glass is its ability to allow light to be transmitted with minimal scattering allowing a clear view through it, or to be patterned or frosted in such a way that light can enter a room but a clear view is masked. This feature of variable opacity/transparency leads to a wide variety of uses both functional and aesthetic.

Chemically inert: The lack of reactivity with most chemicals makes glass an ideal material for storage (Figure 4.2c.2).

Non-toxic: the lack of reactivity shown by glass and the absence of toxic breakdown products has led to the extensive use for food storage.

Biocompatibility: relates to the compatibility of a material for the continued health of a biological environment with which it comes into contact.

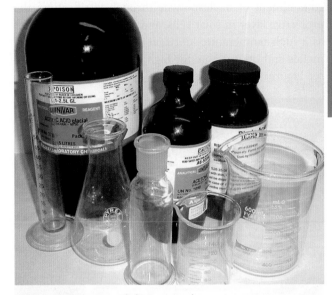

Figure 4.2c.2   Inert laboratory glass

Hardness: Glass resists scratching under normal conditions of handling and cleaning leading to long service, with minimal degradation.

Brittle: The main drawback with glass is that it can be brittle and inflexible. On fracture, annealed glass may break into numerous sharp shards that can pose a danger. Developments such as laminated glass and toughened glass reduce this risk.

Aesthetic appeal: When moulten, glass is extremely plastic, allowing it to be formed, drawn, blown and joined into any imaginable shape. Because of its ability to be coloured, glass has always found favour as a material for artistic expression in addition to its functional use.

Electrical insulator: Glass is an excellent electrical insulator (or dielectric material) and because of this has found extensive use as an insulator on high voltage overhead electrical transmission lines.

Cheap: The high volume production, abundant raw materials and ability to recycle glass (known as cullet), makes glass a relatively cheap material to produce.

Applications of glass

As indicated previously, the stability, inertness and transparency of glass sees its widespread use in windows, food and chemical containers, lighting, and lenses; however glass finds a far more extensive range of applications. These include the use in moulding as fibre glass, the containment of nuclear waste through vitrification, the protective layer in solar cells, and in the form of powder as a high temperature lubricant in the hot extrusion of metals and optical fibre for high speed communications, see Figure 4.2c.3.

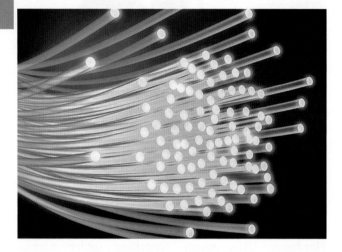

Figure 4.2c.3   Optical fibre

Changes to the composition of glass can result in significant changes in its characteristics. One of the characteristics that is modified by composition is the coefficient of thermal expansion. As mentioned previously ordinary soda glass is very brittle. This glass has a coefficient of thermal expansion of approximately $9\times10^{-6}\text{K}^{-1}$. If exposed to a sudden temperature change, as may occur if boiling water were introduced into a cold glass bowl, the sudden thermal expansion can be sufficient to result in fracture.

If a small amount of boron oxide B_2O_3 is added to the composition, a glass known as borosilicate glass is produced. This glass has a coefficient of thermal expansion of less than half that of silica glass, at approximately $4\times10^{-6}\,\text{K}^{-1}$. The borosilicate glass produced by Corning® and known commercially as Pyrex®, contains approximately 12.6% B_2O_3. Because of its low coefficient of thermal expansion, high thermal shock resistance and chemical resistance, borosilicate glass has found use in applications as diverse as home cookware, laboratory equipment and the mirrors of large telescopes. More recently Corning® has developed a flexible borosilicate glass called Willow™ Glass for use as a substrate in LED displays. Corning® have also developed a scratch resistant glass, as thin as 0.3mm for the cover glass of LED televisions, mobile phone and laptop screens. This glass marketed as Gorilla® glass is

strengthened by ion-exchange in which smaller sodium (Na) atoms are replaced with larger potassium (K) atoms as the glass is submerged in a moulten potassium salt bath held at 400–600°C. When the glass is withdrawn from the salt bath and cools it is in a state of compression.

Lead glass also known as lead crystal contains between 24% and 30% lead oxide (PbO), while glass with additions of PbO below 18% is known simply as crystal glass. The lead addition imparts a high refractive index giving a sparkling, bright, relatively soft surface that can be further enhanced by faceting and has led to great popularity in decorative glassware. At one time used in drinking glasses and to hold drinks, health concerns regarding the leaching of lead into the liquid, have significantly reduced this use. Lead glass finds extensive use in electrical equipment due to excellent insulating properties. The lead glasses will not, however, withstand high temperatures or sudden changes in temperature, (Figure 4.2c.4).

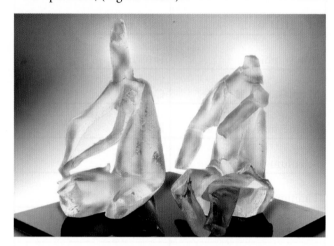

Figure 4.2c.4   Polished lead crystal glass

Lead glass with PbO additions above 65%, are used as radiation shielding because lead absorbs gamma rays. Shielding glass is sold in terms of lead equivalent thickness, that is, 12 mm of lead shielding glass may have a lead equivalent thickness of 2 mm.

Recovery and disposal of glass

Recycled glass, known as cullet, is used to make new glass. When glass products in the form of bottles and jars are collected for recycling they are taken to a processing plant were they are separated into groups of green, brown and clear glass before being crushed into fine pieces as shown in Figure 4.2c.5. In this form, the glass cullet can be charged into a furnace for remelting and the manufacture of new glass containers.

Using cullet has many environmental benefits, it preserves the countryside by reducing quarrying, and because cullet melts more easily, it saves energy and reduces emissions.

Figure 4.2c.5   Glass cullet

Almost any proportion of cullet can be added to a batch of glass, provided it is in the right condition, i.e. free from impurities, especially metals and other ceramics. Green glass is now commonly made from batches containing 95% cullet.

4.2d–PLASTICS

ESSENTIAL IDEA

Materials are classified into six basic groups based on their different properties.

© IBO 2012

NATURE OF DESIGN

Most plastics are produced from petrochemicals. Motivated by the finiteness of oil reserves and threat of global warming, bioplastics are being developed. These plastics degrade upon exposure to sunlight, water or dampness, bacteria, enzymes, wind erosion and in some cases pest or insect attack, but in most cases this does not lead to full breakdown of the plastic. When selecting materials designers must consider the moral, ethical and environmnetal implications of their decisions.

© IBO 2012

AIM

Early plastics used from 1600 BCE through to 1900 CE were rubber based. Prompted by the need for new materials following the first world war, the invention of Bakelite and polyethylene in the first half of the 20th century sparked a massive growth of plastic materials and as we identify the need for new materials with particular properties, the development of new plastics continues.

© IBO 2012

One of the earliest man-made plastics was that produced by the British metallurgist Alexander Parkes, and exhibited at the Great International Exhibition of London in 1862, as Parkesine. Patented in 1856, Parkesine was a mixture of cellulose and nitric acid (forming nitrocellulose also known as pyroxylin) combined with a solvent consisting of chloroform and a plasticiser of castor oil. It was advertised that Parkesine could be cast, stamped or moulded under heat and pressure into products reported to be as hard as horn while being as flexible as leather. Because it used castor oil, Parkesine was exhibited in the vegetable products section of the exhibition and was the recipient of the bronze medal in this section for 'ingenuity of invention'. The high cost of raw materials, however, prevented the production of Parkesine in quantity at low cost and his business failed.

In 1869, while experimenting with nitrocellulose, and following information in one of Parkes' patents regarding the addition of a small amount of camphor to increase plasticity, the American inventor John Hyatt found the clue to making the first true thermoplastic, which he called celluloid. Initially used to make dental plates, it soon found use as a replacement for ivory and in fashion articles such as men's cuffs and collars, and later cinematic film, despite being flammable and subject to bursting into flames if exposed to heat.

The first synthetic plastic to be produced from a mineral oil rather than a vegetable oil was discovered in 1907 by the American inventor Dr Leo Baekeland and was known as bakelite. Baekeland used the aromatic organic compound phenol (C_6H_5OH), derived from coal tar (a by-product of producing coke from coal) which he mixed with formaldehyde in a sealed autoclave. When heated under pressure in the autoclave an amber coloured liquid resin was produced. When this resin was heated in a mould under pressure a solid was formed that would not remelt on reheating. Bakelite was the first thermosetting plastic and its properties such as hardness, dimensional stability, resistance to acids, and its thermal and electrical insulating properties found widespread use.

Today plastics are typically manufactured from the hydrocarbons ethylene (C_2H_4) and propylene (C_3H_6) obtained from crude oil or natural gas. This process involves passing crude oil through a distillation process at an oil refinery where it is separated into various hydrocarbon mixtures. This process is called fractionation. One of these fractions is naphtha. By passing naphtha through a steam 'cracking' process, ethylene is produced which can subsequently be processed into propylene. Phenol is also produced from petroleum today rather than coal tar.

It has been estimated that up to 8% of world oil and gas production is used in the production of plastics, either as feed stock or fuel.

As a response to the anticipated difficulty in obtaining future crude oil supplies, industry is again turning to vegetable products for the raw materials of plastic production. An added advantage of these plastics is that they can be produced in a biodegradable form although this is not a necessary consequence of the change in feed stock. Figure 4.2d.1 shows an example of biodegradable plastic already on the market. The raw materials for

these new age plastics include vegetable oil, corn starch, cellulose, sugar.

The biodegradable plastics gradually degrade due to exposure to ultra violet light, water and bacterial action.

Figure 4.2d.1   Biodegradable plastic eating utensils

Structure of thermoplastics

A polymer, as we experience it, is a combination of many millions of polymer molecules joined together by both physical entanglement and intermolecular forces of attraction. These intermolecular bonds are not, however, achieved by a primary bond such as the covalent bond used to construct the molecules themselves, but rather by way of a weaker secondary type of bond (Figure 4.2d.2). Two of these intermolecular bonds are the hydrogen bond and van der Waals force.

Both of these bonds result from asymmetry in the electron clouds that can result in the molecule forming an electric dipole, in which one pole is positive and the other negative. The intermolecular attraction of these poles is the weak secondary bond formed between polymer molecules.

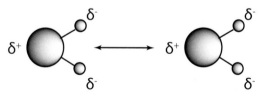

Figure 4.2d.2   Model of the electrical dipole associated with a water molecule and resulting secondary bond attraction between molecules

Thermoplastic material consists of carbon atoms arranged in a single chain from which there may be many branches. Each chain is joined to its neighbour by van der Waal forces, which weaken on heating, allowing the material to become fluid.

The large degree of physical entanglement between the molecules can be visualised as a tangled mass as illustrated in Figure 4.2d.3.

The properties of the thermoplastics are determined by structural features such as the degree of branching present and the length of individual chains, typically measured in terms of molecular weight. These factors determine the degree of crystallinity (regions with orderly chain packing) and density of the polymer, which in turn influence factors such as tensile strength, impact resistance, hardness and melting temperature.

The thermoplastics are available in a number of grades that typically involve blends of chains of differing density and molecular weight such that they are defined in terms of a molecular weight distribution (MWD). The MWD determines the ease with which the polymer can be processed such that, as the MWD becomes broader, the polymer becomes easier to process. The melt flow index (MFI) is used as a measure of processability. This test involves the pushing of a measured amount of polymer through an orifice at a specified temperature and weighing the amount extruded over a 10 minute period. The higher the MFI, measured in g/10min, the easier is the processability. Because of the presence of a distribution of densities and molecular weights, properties such as MFI and melting temperature are often expressed as a range.

Those polymers with an unbranched chain structure similar to that illustrated in Figure 4.5.3 (left) can form with relatively close alignment, leading to higher density and stronger secondary bonds. In contrast, the alignment of branched chains also illustrated in Figure 4.5.3 (right) is restricted, leading to lower densities and correspondingly lower secondary bond strength with consequential effects on tensile strength and melting point.

Due to their linear structure, thermoplastics can be drawn into fibres (nylon is an example). Typically, the characteristics of thermoplastics can be summarised as:

- ductile

- easily fabricated

- easily drawn into fibres

- can be injected into a mould

- can be remelted and remoulded.

Common thermoplastics are Polyvinyl chloride (PVC), Nylon, Perspex, Polytetrafluoroethylene (PTFE). These

materials become plastic at elevated temperatures, allowing formation by a number of processes.

Figure 4.2d.3   Representation of the tangle of linear molecules comprising a thermoplastic.

When thermoplastics are heated, the weak bonds between chains are broken, allowing the molecular chains to move past each other. In this state the thermoplastic can be plastically formed into a new shape. On cooling, the weak bonds between chains are re-established and the material stays in the new shape to which it was formed.

Because thermoplastics allow numerous cycles of heating and reforming into various shapes without deterioration these plastics are well suited to recycling.

Structure of thermosetting plastics

Thermosetting materials (also known as thermosets) are heated to a plastic state under pressure. Under these conditions of elevated temperature and pressure they are said to set, forming three-dimensional structures linked by covalent bonds. The thermosets therefore form a single large 3-D network rather than the mass of molecular chains linked by secondary bonds, as is the case for the thermoplastics, as illustrated in Figure 4.2d.4.

Figure 4.2d.4   Representation of the tangle of linear molecules of a thermoset showing a single 3D structure

The thermosets are generally formed as part of a two part process in which linear chains are first formed followed by a second step in which these chains are connected (or cross-linked) to neighbours by primary bonds, forming a three dimensional structure. Because the cross-link bonds formed between the chains are strong primary bonds, the chains cannot slide past each other and are not easily broken. This rigid three dimensional structure leads to these materials exhibiting high strength but low ductility.

Thermoset materials cannot be reheated to a plastic state for reforming. On further heating the primary carbon bonds are broken, rather than the secondary bonds between the chains being weakened, and the material decomposes. Common thermosets are: bakelite (phenol formaldehyde), melamine and diallyl phthalate. Typical characteristics of thermosets can be summarised as:

- rigid

- cannot be remelted and remoulded

- higher strength than thermoplastics.

Recovery and disposal of plastics

Plastic in its myriad forms has become one of the most extensively used materials today offering a wide array of properties for most applications including low unit cost, lightness, corrosion resistance, thermal and electrical insulation, flexibility or rigidity and production by way of processes ranging from blow moulding to machining.

Apart from structural uses of plastics in applications such as piping and plumbing fittings, structural panels and electrical wire insulation, plastics are used extensively for consumer products such containers for; cleaning products, toiletries and food stuffs. It is from the consumer goods part of the market that large amounts of refuse are created such as empty containers and packaging. This domestic waste material is collected and, if not separated for recycling, often finds its way into landfills. Because plastic does not readily undergo the normal processes of biodegradation, plastic in landfills can take up a large volume reducing the effective life of the landfill. More problematic is the waste plastic that finds its way into waterways, posing a danger to wildlife. Figure 4.2d.5 shows the remains of an albatross and its stomach contents of plastic.

Figure 4.2d.5   Remains of an albatross containing ingested flotsam, by Chris Jordan, US Fish and Wildlife Service, Wikimedia Commons

In order to reduce the impact on landfills, waterways, wildlife and the environment in general, recycling of plastic is increasingly being encouraged. One problem with such programs in the past has been the wide variety of plastics in use and the difficulty of easily and quickly identifying them. To this end, each of the major polymer groups in use have been given a numerical designation from 1 to 6, see Figure 4.2d.6 This identification is moulded into the surface of the plastic during manufacture and allows the easy separation of plastic consumer waste into groups for recycling.

Figure 4.2d.6   Plastic recycling identification codes

Although theoretically recyclable, PVC from domestic sources can pose problems for recyclers due to the large number of fillers that can be used, which may contaminate recycled plastic. Incineration is also of concern due to the potential for the release of toxic by-products such as dioxins. Because of these concerns and the extra expense incurred by sorting PVC products, many collection agencies continue to send PVC to landfills. New technologies are also under development that are hoped will allow waste plastic to be recycled into oil.

INTERNATIONAL MINDEDNESS

The raw material for plastics (mainly oil) is extracted in a country, exported to other countries where conversion to plastics takes place and these are re-exported at considerable added value.

© IBO 2012

As mentioned previously in section 4.2a, extraction often takes place locally with added value occurring in another country. While many developing countries have oil reserves within their land and maritime borders, and have constructed refineries for the initial processing of their oil, the industrial infrastructure required to further process the refinery products is often not available.

Because of this, the refinery products are often exported to more industrialised countries for transformation into plastics.

4.2e–TEXTILES

ESSENTIAL IDEA

Materials are classified into six basic groups based on their different properties.

© IBO 2012

NATURE OF DESIGN

The continuing evolution of the textiles industry provides a wide spread of applications from high-performance technical textiles to the more traditional clothing market. More recent developments in this industry require designers to combine traditional textile science and new technologies leading to exciting applications in smart textiles, sportswear, aerospace and other potential areas.

© IBO 2012

AIM

There are many ethical considerations attached to the production of natural fibres. The strongest natural silk known to man is harvested from silk spiders and notoriously difficult to obtain, and labour intensive. In an effort to produce higher yields, scientists have altered the genome of goats so that they produce the same silk proteins in their milk.

© IBO 2012

Some spiders have the unique ability to spin webs of silk fibre, secreted through several spinneret glands located on the spider's abdomen. Consisting of an amorphous polymer and chains of two simple proteins this biopolymer fibre has exceptional mechanical properties.

Commercial farming of spiders for silk has been attempted and failed due to the territorial, aggressively predatory and cannibalistic nature of the spiders. If kept in close proximity the spiders attack, kill and eat one another.

Spider silk is considered to be the strongest of all fibres, naturally occurring and synthetic. Rated at five times the strength of steel and twice as strong as Kevlar®, spider silk is also highly elastic, waterproof, resistant to bacterial breakdown and around 10 times tougher than cellulose and collagen.

Genetically engineered goats have been developed to excrete milk containing spider silk proteins. These transgenic animals are created through the insertion of a gene from one animal into another's genome. While spiders and goats are very different creatures they share similar systems i.e. protein production and storage organs such as silk and mammary glands.

Spider genes spliced into goat DNA are activated in mammary gland tissues to the point where the genetically modified goats produce milk containing silk proteins ready to be extracted and spun into thread. Processing involves alignment of the protein chains by forcing them through a narrow die before stretching. This technique imitates the spider's natural processes creating a zigzag pattern in the protein chains. After processing, just one gram of silk generates up to 9 km of thread. Fibre produced in this fashion is termed BioSteel®.

The artificial production of spider silk continues to improve but many hurdles have prevented scientists from replicating the physical properties of the natural fibre. Current efforts to produce spider silk have resulted in a product of inferior strength with a much larger diameter than its natural counterpart. Scientists have yet to bridge the technology gap to make this material viable.

Raw materials for textiles

Textiles are manufactured from fibres, the origin of which can be subdivided into two basic divisions either from natural (organic) or synthetic (man-made) sources.

- Natural (organic) fibres have either a plant or animal origin such as cotton, linen, wool and silk.

- Synthetic (man-made) fibres have been created by chemical processes. Many are polymer-based originating from oil and coal, while some are manufactured from glass, metal ceramic and carbon.

A common factor of both natural and synthetic fibres is that they are made of long chain molecules aligned with the long axis of the fibre.

Properties of natural fibres

Because natural fibres are grown, their quality and length will depend on environmental conditions and maturity at the time of harvesting. Most natural fibres are short, with the exception of silk which can have fibre length of up to 1 km.

Natural fibres often have the ability to absorb moisture which allows the removal of perspiration from the surface of the skin. This property leads to them creating 'breathable' fabrics. Their affinity for moisture also aids in the colour dying process. Typical properties include:

- flammable

- easy to dye

- poor resilience

- attacked by mildew

- dimensionally stable

- good conductor of electricity

- good absorbency (fibres are hydrophilic).

Wool: is an animal fibre and is typically obtained from sheep although some comes from alpaca, and from cashmere and angora goats. The fibres consist of overlapping scales of keratin that grow from follicles in the skin of the animal. An image of a sheep's wool fibre of approximately 5 μm diameter is shown in Figure 4.2e.1. It is the scaly surface of the fibres that can give wool the 'scratchy' feel when worn next to the skin. This effect is overcome when fine fibres are grown and is the reason why ultra-fine wool (10-18 μm diameter) from Merino sheep is valued for clothes.

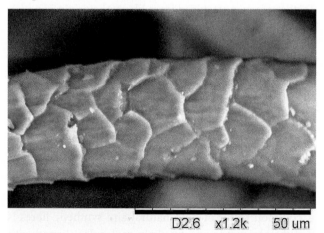

Figure 4.2e.1   *SEM image of a sheep's wool fibre illustrating the overlapping scales along the surface*

Wool fibres can vary from 25 mm to 200 mm long with growth determined by the animal DNA and environmental conditions during growth. Wool exhibits the lowest tensile strength and stiffness of the natural fibres but the highest

elongation. Wool absorbs dyes readily, is flame resistant tending to smoulder and char rather than burn and provides good insulation against heat and cold. Coarser fibres tend to have a greater lustre than fine.

Wool finds extensive use in the apparel industry due to its good draping qualities and comfort arising from its elasticity and water absorption. Coarser fibres find use in carpets.

Properties of wool fibre

Specific Gravity:	1.32 g/cm^3
Moisture regain:	13-18%
Tensile Strength:	125-200 MPa
Elongation at break:	25-40% (dry)
	25-50% (wet)
Stiffness:	3-4 GPa (dry)
Tenacity:	1.0-1.7 gm/denier (dry)
	0.8-1.6 gm/denier (wet)

Cotton: is a vegetable fibre originating from the cotton plant and has been manufactured since 3000BCE. The cotton fibres form in the cotton boll portion of the plant and consist of cellulose.

The cross-section of cotton fibre is tubular, laid down in helical layers. Before drying the centre of the fibre, the 'lumen', is filled with a liquid containing the cell nucleus and protoplasm. On drying the lumen collapses producing the twists and convolutions distinctive of cotton fibre, as can be seen from Figure 4.2e.2.

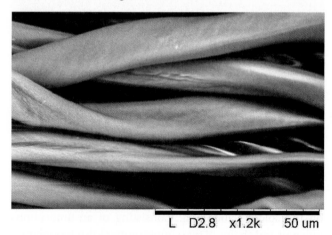

Figure 4.2e.2   *SEM image of cotton fibres exhibiting a flat oval shape with lumen convolutions*

Cotton is one of the most widely used textile fibres in use today, being second only to polyester. The cotton fibres are relatively short at 12 mm to 60 mm. Lustre is poor although fabric drape is good. Cotton is stronger when wet than when dry. Cotton treated to withstand shrinkage is known as 'mercerised' cotton after the Scotsman John

CORE

Mercer who developed a process for treating the fibres with caustic soda and stretching them to improve their appearance.

Properties of cotton fibre

Specific Gravity:	1.5 g/cm^3
Moisture regain:	7-11%
Strength:	400 MPa
Elongation at break:	5.6-9.6% (dry)
	3.0- 7.0% (wet)
Stiffness:	30 GPa
Tenacity:	2.1-4.9 gm/denier (dry)
	2.1-6.4 gm/denier (wet)

Linen: originates from the flax plant. The fibres are generally cylindrical in shape with distinctive nodes occurring at regular intervals along there length, similar in appearance to bamboo. The fibres can vary from 300 mm to 500 mm in length.

Figure 4.2e.3   SEM image of linen fibres exhibiting a cylindrical shape with distinctive nodes

Linen fibres are strong, and lustrous and exhibit good absorbency. Linen is one of the stiffest of the natural fibres however, resulting in poor drape properties. The fibres also have very low resilience leading to them breaking if exposed to repeat bending. Linen fibres find extensive use in bed sheets, curtains, table cloths and handkerchiefs. When used for apparel they are often blended with other fibres such as polyester and cotton.

Properties of linen fibre

Specific gravity:	1.50 g/cm^3
Moisture regain:	12%
Strength:	500-900 MPa
Elongation at break:	1.6% (dry)
	3.0% (wet)
Stiffness:	50-70 GPa
Tenacity:	5.6-6.6 gm/denier (dry)

Silk: is a natural protein fibre composed of fibroin produced from the cocoon of the silk worm and is therefore classified as an animal fibre. It is believed to have originated in China around 2500 BCE.

While some cocoons are selected to complete the natural cycle with the emergence of a silkworm moth, in order to obtain eggs to continue production, the majority of the cocoons are steamed, killing the inhabitant. This is performed to avoid damage to the thread that would accompany the developed chrysalis emerging from the cocoon. Following steaming, the cocoons are then placed in bowls of hot water to soften and loosen the thread before the fibre from several cocoons is drawn together to form the yarn. The fibres (shown in Figure 4.2e.4) exhibit a triangular cross-section with rounded edges and a smooth, appearance. This prism-like structure contributes to the lustrous shimmer for which the fabric is noted.

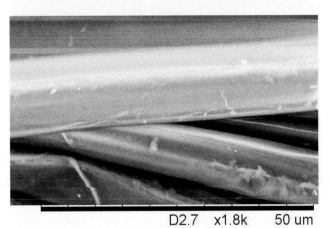

Figure 4.2e.4   SEM image of silk fibres exhibiting a triangular cross-section

Silk fibres are very fine and flexible and are the longest of the natural fibres reaching over a kilometre in length while also being one of the strongest natural fibres. Silk resists wrinkling and has excellent drape and resists mildew although it may be attacked by moths. The fibres are not inflammable and are not affected by moisture. One of the main problems with silk is that it will create a static charge during wear. Silk finds extensive use in female fashion garments and lingerie as well as furnishings and bedsheets.

Properties of silk fibre

Specific Gravity:	1.25 g/cm^3
Moisture regain:	11%
Tensile Strength:	500-900 MPa
Elongation at break:	23-30% (dry)
Stiffness:	5-17 GPa
Tenacity:	3.0-5.2 gm/denier (dry)

Viscose rayon: also known as Evan, Sarille and Tenasco, rayon is a man-made fibre manufactured from a natural source (cellulose) rather than a synthetic source. It is a regenerated cellulose product, with properties similar to cotton. Rayon was first produced commercially in 1905 and was initially known as artificial silk before being called rayon in 1924.

The cellulose for rayon is manufactured from wood pulp or bamboo, that is dissolved in caustic soda to form a soda cellulose called xanthate. The xanthate is then mechanically processed before being exposed to gaseous carbon disulphide (CS_2). A subsequent drying operation is undertaken in hot air to reduce the moisture content to 13%. The fibres exhibit a circular serrated or corrugated appearance as illustrated in Figure 4.2e.5.

L D2.4 x1.2k 50 um

Figure 4.2e.5   SEM image of viscous rayon fibres

The fibres have fair to excellent strength and a high lustre unless affected by pigments. Rayon can be produced in a range of strength and elasticity levels from low to high, however it is weakened when wet and has low dimensional stability and abrasion resistance.

Rayon exhibits good drape, excellent breathability and is easily blended, however it will burn rapidly unless treated. Viscose rayon finds extensive use in apparel particularly when blended with other fibres. It also finds use in home furnishings as bedsheets, curtains and tablecloths.

Properties of rayon fibre

Specific gravity:	1.52 g/cm^3
Moisture regain:	13-15%
Tensile Strength:	545 MPa
Elongation at break:	9-26% (dry)
Stiffness:	2.85 GPa
Tenacity:	1.5-5.7 gm/denier (dry)
	1.9-4.3 gm/denier (wet)
Melting Point	176-204°C

Properties of synthetic fibres

Because synthetic fibres originate from an industrial chemical process in which a polymer is forced through a small orifice known as a spinneret. The fibres so produced are long continuous lengths and are generally much smoother than natural fibres. The properties of the synthetic fibres are determined by their chemical composition and molecular structure.

Most synthetic fibres are thermoplastic and will soften and contract when exposed to heat. While this can pose some problems it carries the advantages of allowing embossing and the production of permanent pleats. Most notably perhaps, the synthetic fibres have a low affinity for moisture creating less 'breathable' fabrics. Typical characteristics of synthetic fibres include:

- resist mildew

- difficult to dye

- good resilience

- thermoplasticity

- dimensionally unstable

- low absorbency (fibres are hydrophobic).

Nylon: is a polyamide. The fibres are smooth and translucent with a uniform circular shape, as can be seen from Figure 4.2e.6. The fibres exhibit a high natural lustre which can be controlled in processing. Strength and elasticity are high. Drape properties can be varied depending on fibre diameter.

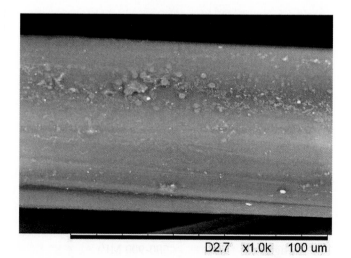

D2.7 x1.0k 100 um

Figure 4.2e.6   SEM image of a nylon fibre exhibiting a smooth uniform circular shape

The low absorbency of nylon however leads to it feeling clammy in humid weather and its relatively low melting temperature can lead to melting on exposure to heat, resulting in the need to iron at low temperatures. Although it will not support combustion, the melted fabric will cling to the body causing severe burns.

Nylon is used extensively on its own in male and female clothing, raincoats, shower curtains, women's lingerie and night gowns, as well as being blended with other fibres to improve strength and stability of the fabric.

Properties of nylon fibre

Specific gravity:	1.14 g/cm^3
Moisture regain:	4.0-4.5%
Tensile Strength:	400-870 MPa
Elongation at break:	20-25% (dry)
	20-32% (wet)
Stiffness:	2-5 GPa
Tenacity:	3.0-7.2 gm/denier (dry)
	2.6-6.1 gm/denier (dry)
Melting Point	212°C (nylon 6)
	250°C (nylon 66)

Polyester: is a generic term for a family of thermoplastics known under a number of names such as polyethylene terephthalate (PET), Dacron and Mylar. Polyester entered industrial production in 1947 and is the most widely used fibre in the world. Polyester fibres are smooth and translucent with a uniform circular shape, as can be seen from Figure 4.2e.7. Lustre can be bright or dull. Polyester fibres exhibit high dimensional stability, good to excellent strength with elasticity greater than cotton or rayon; however the fabric provides poor drape properties. It burns slowly.

Figure 4.2e.7   SEM image of a polyester fibre exhibiting a smooth uniform circular shape

Polyester is used extensively in clothing either on its own or as a blended fabric, it is also found in many household and commercial situations as carpet, curtains and upholstery.

Properties of polyester fibre

Specific gravity:	1.38 g/cm^3
Moisture regain:	0.2-0.8%
Tensile strength:	450-850MPa
Elongation at break:	12-67% (dry)
	15-25% (wet)
Stiffness:	90 GPa
Tenacity:	2.2-6.6 gm/denier (dry)
	2.2-6.6 gm/denier (wet)
Melting Point	249-288°C (PET)

Blending: typically involves the twisting together of a mixture of natural and synthetic fibres to form a yarn. The benefits of blending include:

- reduced costs

- improved processing

- adding of bulk and warmth

- resistance to wrinkling

- multi-colour fabrics

- improved physical properties and dimensional stability

Typical blended textiles include the following.

Wool/polyester –men's suits.
Cotton/nylon/elastane – socks.
Nylon/polyester- women's jackets.
Cotton/lycra – used in stretch jeans.
Polyester/cotton – used in crease resistant shirts.

An example of a blended fabric is shown in Figure 4.2e.8.

Figure 4.2e.8   SEM image of a blended fabric shirt of 50% linen, polyester and cotton

Conversion of fibres to yarn

At the beginning of the process of converting fibres into yarn, the strands are present as a tangle of loose fibres. Natural fibres, with the exception of silk, will also be present in various lengths reflecting their maturity of growth. Natural fibres require some cleaning or refining before any processing can take place. Some mixing may also be required to homogenise the batch. Machinery is employed to draw out individual fibres and tease them into alignment. A small amount of twist is then introduced to provide sufficient strength for handling. Further twisting increases strength by wrapping fibres around each other and the process repeated, all the while lengthening the yarn. The yarn formed is called a 'single', ie. a single strand of yarn.

Conversion of yarns into fabrics

A fabric consists of the interlacing of yarn by way of weaving, knitting or braiding to produce a continuous sheet that has both a significant length and breadth.

Knitting

Knitting is the art and process of forming fabrics by looping a single thread, either by hand with slender wires or by means of a machine provided with hooked needles. Knitting is carried on without making knots; but rather through the formation of interlocking loops, see Figure 4.2e.9. Because of the interlocking nature of the yarn in knitted fabrics, the destruction of one loop threatens the destruction of the whole web, unless the meshes are reunited. Two distinct variations of knitting occur; warp and weft knitting.

Figure 4.2e.9   SEM image of a knitted fabric

Warp knitting, is always undertaken by machine and involves a series of zig-zag stitches in parallel columns (Wales) along the length of the fabric as shown in Figure 4.2e.10.

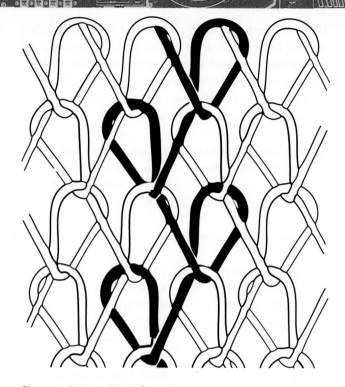

Figure 4.2e.10   Warp knitting

Weft knitting may be undertaken by hand or machine and uses one continuous yarn to form 'Courses' across the fabric as shown in Figure 4.2e.11.

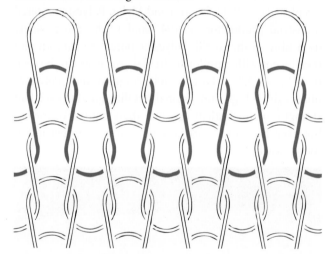

Figure 4.2e.11   Weft knitting

The principle of knitting is quite distinct from that of weaving. In the weaving of cloth, the yarns of one system cross those of another system at right angles, thus producing a solid, firm texture. The great elasticity of any kind of texture produced by knitting is a result of its interlocking loop construction and is the chief feature that distinguishes it from woven cloth.

The advantages of knitting include the following.

- Fabric can stretch.

- Low stress on the yarn.

- 3–D structures created.

- Higher production rate than weaving.

- Large number of stitch types available.

Weaving

Weaving is undertaken on a machine called a loom. Every woven piece of cloth is made up of two distinct systems of threads, known as the warp and filling (weft), which are interlaced with each other to form a fabric. The warp threads run lengthways of the piece of cloth, and the filling runs across from side to side. The manner in which the warp and filling threads interlace with each other is known as the 'weave'. Today this process is fully automated for mass production.

The interlacing of the warp and weft can be accomplished in a number of ways. If a simple pattern of alternately passing the weft over and under the warp is used a simple weave pattern is produced, as illustrated by Figure 4.2e.12.

A twill weave pattern is produced by alternately passing under two and over one (Figure 4.2e.13b) while a sateen weave is obtained by passing (or 'floating') four warp strands over the weft stands before passing under a weft strand (Figure 4.2e.13c). Because of the long distance that the yarn 'floats' a smooth satin finish is achieved. By using a warp yarn of different thickness to the weft, ribs may be produced in the fabric.

Figure 4.2e.12   Woven fabric

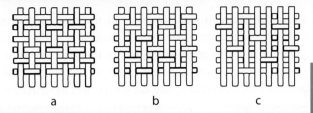

Figure 4.2e.13   Weaving styles

Lace-making

Lace is an openwork, stitched fabric, patterned with holes, see Figure 4.2e.14. Originally made from linen, silk, silver or even gold thread, lace-work is now most commonly made from cotton.

Lace may be made by hand with a needle, bobbins or machine and is created by looping, plaiting one thread with another, independent of any backing material. When the work is constructed with a needle it is known as 'needlepoint lace'. When bobbins, pins, and a pillow or cushion are used; this is called 'pillow lace'. Machinery may be used when limitations of both point and pillow lace preclude the production of patterns.

Synthetic threads are often used for machine-manufactured lace and, due to their high strength-to-weight characteristics, intricately patterned sheer laces can be produced. Relatively cheaper synthetic threads create a ready market for these lace designs.

Figure 4.2e.14   Lace sample

Felting

Felt has traditionally been made from animal fibres such as sheep's wool, rabbit or beaver fur although today felt may also be made from man-made fibres such as viscose rayon.

The felting process is dependent in part upon kinks in the fibres, but mainly upon irregularities in the surface that allow the fibres to lock together. In the case of animal fibres, these are the scales which cover the surface, see Figure 4.2e.15. In good felting wools, the scales are more perfect and numerous, while inferior wools generally possess fewer serrations, and are less perfect in structure.

D2.6   x1.2k   50 um

Figure 4.2e.15 SEM image of a rabbit wool fibre illustrating the overlapping scales along the surface

Mohair obtained from the Angora goat, for instance, is not used to make felt because the scales are too fine, see Figure 4.2e.16. By comparison, Angora wool from an Angora rabbit felts readily.

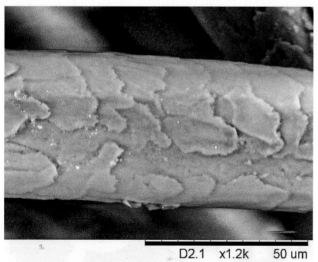

D2.1   x1.2k   50 um

Figure 4.2e.16   SEM image of a mohair fibre from an Angora goat showing the fine scales along the surface

Felt made from wool is produced by progressively depositing layers of cleaned and combed fibres into a large tray. Consecutive layers are deposited at 90 degrees to each other. Hot soapy water poured over the fibres assists with lubrication and reduces friction, allowing fibres to move and become entangled in the scales on the fibre surface, see Figure 4.2e.17.

The combination of heat, pressure, water, lubrication and friction bond the fibres to form a cloth. As an alternative

needle felting is a dry process involving combining fibres using specially barbed felting needles. Felting techniques are centuries old with archaeological digs recovering remnants of felted tents and other products.

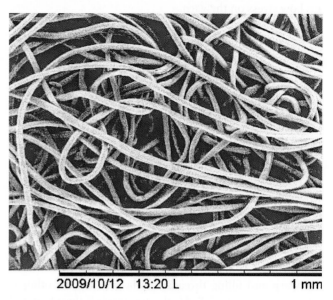

2009/10/12   13:20 L   1 mm

Figure 4.2e.17   SEM image of felt

Recovery and disposal of textiles

The development of new textiles and related technologies needs to consider sustainability issues such as use, recycling and disposal. In the design phase the development of reusable or multi use items instead of single use products can extend product life and usefulness. Extracting the maximum benefit from materials resources makes social, economic and environmental sense. The triple bottom line mantra of, "people, profit, planet" applies directly here.

Wastage from textiles may be categorized as either pre- or post-consumer. Pre-consumer textile waste consists of those materials generated as by-products of production processes. Recycling of waste and by-products can yield large volumes of material suitable for use in the soft furnishing, automotive, construction and paper industries. Post-consumer waste refers to clothing or household textiles reused or recycled instead of being disposed. Reuse of fabrics and garments may take the form of eco-fashion, re-tasking or redistribution (through second hand outlets and charities).

Recycling involves the reprocessing of used clothing, fibrous material, fabric scraps and waste from the manufacturing process. Besides natural fibres such as wool, cotton, silk and linen, popular synthetic fabrics such as polyamides, polyesters and acrylics can all be recycled. Once collected, cleaned and sorted, recyclable textiles may be processed; mechanically where fibres are separated before re-spinning into yarn or chemically through repolymerizing fibres to again spin into yarn.

Knitted or woven woolens are 'pulled' into a fibrous state for reuse in applications such as: insulation, padding or raw material for felting. Cotton can be re-tasked as rag, compost or form a constituent of high-quality paper. Garment, buttons, zippers and hardware may be recovered for reuse. Waste reduction, reuse and recycling results in:

- lowering purchase prices

- reducing use of virgin materials

- reducing disposal costs and landfill

- generating less air and water pollution

- keeping materials out of the waste stream

- preserving the 'embodied energy' used in manufacturing.

Solid wastes can be reduced by up to 95% if all methods of recycling and reuse are exploited.

INTERNATIONAL MINDEDNESS

The economics and politics of the production and sale of clothing by multinationals can be a major ethical issue for consumers and the workforce.

© IBO 2012

The globalisation and the interconnectedness of international economies continue to impact on textile industries. Historically the industry has been constrained by various agreements and quotas, protecting manufacturers by limiting or restricting imports from developing nations. Increased liberalization of trade was originally thought to solely benefit developing countries, as production rates increased. However, as multi-national industries have established their own manufacturing plants in developing nations, improved communications and transport infrastructure have made it viable for companies to have a location based on the role required within the company as whole.

While textiles industries and clothing manufacturing sub-sectors are closely linked, there are variations to their infrastructure and requirements. Garment assembly mostly involves lower levels of technology and can be labour-intensive. This generates considerable local employment, however, the financial benefits tend to be

with the manufacturers selling their product in affluent global markets at the expense of the workers. The majority of garment assembly workers in developing nations are women and children who work long hours in poor conditions for small financial return. In developing nations where labour is both cheap and abundant these activities are still commercially viable. Local environmental legislation that may not be as stringent as developed nations also allows practices to continue that would be outlawed elsewhere.

Textile industries however tend to be more capital-intensive and require a skilled or semi-skilled workforce. The siting of textiles factories needs to address, price, infrastructure, speed and quality issues, with the final determining factor being distribution.

Companies have now created international, sophisticated, highly-connected, 'value chains'. This transportation network connects distributors, major brand manufacturers and retailers to small scale, low-wage subcontractors (often in developing countries). The process of garment assembly remains labour intensive due to the:

- varied nature of fabrics

- rapid changes in fashions

- constant demand for new product

- complexity of assembly processes.

THEORY OF KNOWLEDGE

Designers use natural and man-made products. Do some areas of knowledge see an intrinsic difference between these?

© IBO 2012

Before embarking on this question a student should examine what is meant by the word 'intrinsic'. A standard definition would be a property belonging to a thing by its very nature. That is, it is independent of how much or how little there may be of that thing or the form in which it might be found.

The question is therefore whether there is something that differentiates a natural product from a man-made product by its very nature.

From a scientific point of view there is no intrinsic difference between natural or man-made chemicals; that is the chemical in and of itself cannot be distinguished with regard to its origin. Vitamin C from fruit is exactly the same as Vitamin C that has been synthesised in a laboratory. However, many would argue that vitamin C obtained by eating an organically grown orange is better than eating an orange in which synthetic insecticides were used in its production, and this would be better than reconstituted orange juice, which in turn would be better than a vitamin C pill.

There appears to be in these distinctions a human evaluation of the product and production process, but are products intrinsically different? If the value or attribute comes from outside of that product or thing it would actually be an extrinsic value.

The natural world itself does not appear to assign any particular intrinsic value to anything, as the extinction of countless organisms over the millennia would seem to attest. The question of intrinsic value is an attribute conferred by mankind and is therefore subject to change. However the question relates to whether different areas of (human) knowledge see intrinsic differences between natural and man-made products.

Certainly from a religious point of view one would expect that an intrinsic difference would be argued to exist independent of whether such a difference was recognised by man or not.

The student should examine other areas of knowledge such as environmentalism, the biological sciences, mining and engineering, to examine whether difference in perspectives exist.

4.2f–COMPOSITES

ESSENTIAL IDEA

Materials are classified into six basic groups based on their different properties.

© IBO 2012

NATURE OF DESIGN

Composites are an important material in an intensely competitive global market. New materials and technologies are being produced frequently for the design and rapid manufacture of high quality composite products. Composites are replacing more traditional materials as they can be created with properties specifically designed for the intended application. Carbon fibre has played an important part in weight reduction for vehicles and aircraft.

© IBO 2012

AIM

As designers develop new products, they should always be aware of the materials available. In an effort to increase productivity and lose weight, carbon fibre parts are often glued together. The use of an epoxy adhesive rather than traditional fastening methods allows manufacturers to create complex shapes quickly and easily. These materials and methods are being transferred to consumer products.

© IBO 2012

A composite represents a class of material whose properties derive from the combination of two or more materials that are bonded together such that each of the constituent materials contributes to an improvement in mechanical, physical, chemical or electrical properties.

Bone and wood represent examples of composites in nature. Bone is an example of a ceramic matrix composite consisting of the ceramic Hydroxyapatite (calcium phosphate) and the natural polymer collagen, contained within a gel like matrix of protein. In bone, the collagen is present as long fibres, which provide a strong flexible structure in much the same way that individual fibres can be formed into a rope. Small crystals of hydroxyapatite attached to the surface of the collagen fibres provide stiffness. In addition, the collagen fibres are arranged in concentric layers around a central blood vessel, with each layer of collagen contra laid, that is, arranged in opposite directions, as illustrated in Figure 4.2f.1. The structure formed has many similarities with that found in wood. Bone consequently exhibits the characteristics of strength and stiffness while retaining some flexibility.

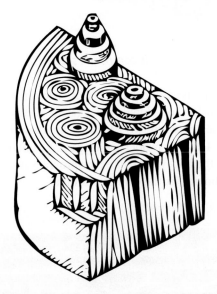

Figure 4.2f.1   Schematic representation of the composite structure of bone, image by R. McNeill Alexander (1994), Bones:the unity of form and function. Nevraumont Publishing Co., NY.

One of the earliest man-made composite materials was straw reinforced bricks. At a much later time, cement, gravel, and steel bars were combined to form reinforced concrete. Development of thin fibres and thermosetting polymers led to the creation of fibre-reinforced materials such as glass reinforced polymers (GRP). Much more recent examples are carbon-polymer and metal-matrix composites. Increasingly, composites are being employed to provide improved properties, increase efficiency, reduce costs and provide additional functionality.

Form: fibres/sheet/particles and matrix

The incorporation of the materials into a composite can occur in a number of ways but generally speaking there are three basic categories of composite.

- Laminar.

- Fibre-reinforced.

- Particle reinforced.

Laminar: Laminar materials consist of two or more layers of material bonded together usually with an adhesive to form a new composite material with improved properties.

The most commonly recognised laminar material is plywood, but many other materials are produced through lamination. Plywood is most often manufactured from an uneven number of 'plys' and finds applications where high-quality, high-strength, large-sheet material is required. It is resistant to cracking, breaking, shrinkage, twisting and warping. It finds uses both indoors and outdoors and may also be used as an engineering material for architecture or light weight stressed-skin applications such as those required in marine and aviation environments. Figure 4.2f.2 shows a chair by Danish designer Greta Jalk manufactured using laminated and bent plywood.

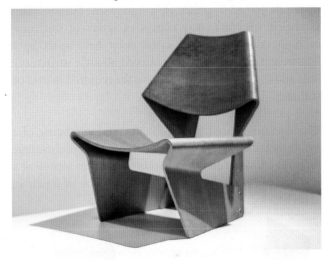

Figure 4.2f.2   Grete Jalk plywood chair, image by tomislav medak [CC-BY-2.0 (http://creativecommons.org/licenses/by/2.0)], via Wikimedia Commons

Laminated glass (introduced to car windscreens in 1927) consists of a sandwich of two layers of glass and a polymer interlayer of Polyvinyl butyral (PVB) joined under heat and pressure in a furnace called an autoclave Figure 4.2f.3. If manufactured using annealed glass, laminated glass can be cut. When broken, the PVB interlayer holds the pieces of glass together avoiding the release of otherwise dangerous shards of glass. The fracture of laminated glass produces a characteristic pattern of radial and concentric cracks often described as a spider-web pattern, represented in Figure 4.2f.4.

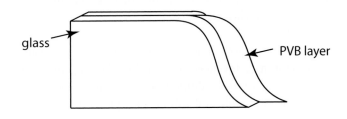

glass

PVB layer

Figure 4.2f.3   Construction of laminated glass

131

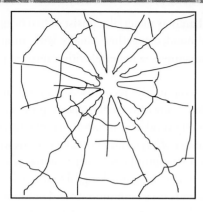

Figure 4.2f.4 Spider web fracture pattern typical of laminated glass

Figure 4.2f.6   Ceramic composite sandwich

Laminar composites may also be laminates of different materials joined together in a 'sandwich' fashion. This sandwich structure, may consist of layers of thin uni- or bidirectional fibres or metal sheet held apart by a lightweight core (foam or honeycomb-style structure). This allows the designer to achieve the required inertia or stiffness.

Plain bearings, used in crankshafts, and consisting of a 'white metal' surface layer bonded to a copper intermediate layer on a low carbon steel backing plate also represent a laminar composite. Figure 4.2f.5 shows one of a pair of plain bearings

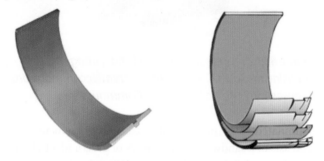

Figure 4.2f.5   Plain bearing laminar composite

Figure 4.2f.6 shows a ceramic composite sandwich developed by NASA composed of a ceramic foam core between two ceramic composite face sheets.

This structural concept provides high strength and stiffness at low density — 1.06 g/cm^3. Choice of fibres and weave structures allows for variable coefficients of thermal expansion and elasticity.

The integrated structures possible with this composite could eliminate the need for non-load-bearing thermal protection systems in addition to structural components, thus reducing weight and cost for aerospace missions.

The ubiquitous cardboard box is also a laminar composite as it consists of fluted corrugated sheets of paper sandwiched between two flat paper linerboards as shown in Figure 4.2f.7. Its properties are gained from its structure in which the honeycomb like core provides strength while the linerboards fix the core in position.

Figure 4.2f.7   Piled sheets of corrugated cardboard

Laminar textiles can also be produced by the lamination process. Textile laminates can be built up using what are known as 'prepregs' which consist of a textile that has been pre-impregnated with resin. These prepregs can then be stacked in any orientation to each other to build up a composite with the desired combination of properties.

An example of a laminar textile is the sailcloth shown in Figure 4.2f.8 that consists of layers of carbon fibre sandwiched between a polymer film and taffeta. Sails made from this laminate find use in racing yachts due to their properties of low stretch, strength and durability.

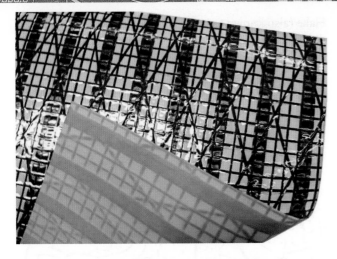

Figure 4.2f.8   Sailcloth laminate of film-carbon fibre bands-Technora® strands-Taffeta backing

Another example of the formation of a laminar composite like structure is the practice of diffusing elements into the surface of a metal to change its chemistry and mechanical properties. Processes such as case carburising and nitriding aim to diffuse carbon and nitrogen respectively into the surface of steel to change the surface properties. An example of case carburising is provided in Figure 4.2f.9 in which a hardened case has been created on a gear tooth. Through such a process a high carbon surface layer with increased hardness and wear resistance is obtained while a tough low carbon core is maintained.

Figure 4.2f.9   Carburised gear tooth

Weld hard-facing would constitute another common example of a laminar composite in which a high alloy wear resistant material is deposited by welding to a lower alloy metal substrate. Other processes used to bond two or more dissimilar metal layers together include:

- explosive welding

- diffusion bonding

- roll forming

- centrifugal casting.

Fibre-reinforced composites: are composed of fibres embedded in a matrix. The matrix material, in powder or liquid form, is combined with reinforcing fibres in a mould and the combination subjected to heat and pressure until fusion occurs.

Different materials can serve as the matrix including metals, ceramics and plastics but it is the bond obtained between the fibre and the matrix that provides the strength of the composite.

In this respect, the aspect ratio (ratio of length to diameter) of the fibres plays an important part, with fibres of high aspect ratio creating a stronger composite.

Fibres are excellent in tension although individual fibres cannot support compressive forces. In an effort to have fibres more readily accept compressive loads they are 'glued together' within a matrix (usually an epoxy resin). In this structure the fibres work together to accept compressive loads without moving apart and yet retain their excellent tensile properties. As a general rule, strength increases as the volume of fibres increases, up to approximately 80%. Above this level of fibre reinforcement, the matrix cannot be guaranteed to fully encase all the fibres.

Fibres within composites may differ in length and arrangement. They are commonly divided into five fibre arrangement types as shown in Figure 4.2f.10: a) continuous unidirectional, b) continuous orthogonal layers, c) continuous multiple fibres, d) discontinuous unidirectional, e) discontinuous random orientation.

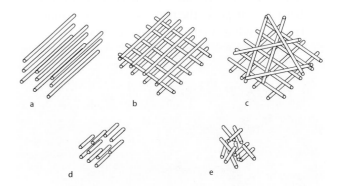

Figure 4.2f.10   Fibre arrangement types

Since the early 1980s the aerospace industry has made increasing use of fibre-reinforced polymer composite parts in aircraft construction. In general terms, advanced composites have found increasing application in commercial aircraft structures as a result of the strength, stiffness, fatigue-resistant, corrosion-resistant and weight benefits they afford. Safety and reliability are high priorities for integrating composite components into commercial aircraft structures. In developing the A380 passenger aircraft, Airbus Industries designed an aircraft to carry 555 passengers, using up to 40 tonnes of composite parts as a means of reducing weight and operating costs. The twin-deck A380 model even uses advanced carbon fibre composites in the construction of new wing sections.

Sports equipment has made extensive use of fibre reinforced plastics to increase strength and stiffness while reducing weight. Figure 4.2f.11 shows a section through a tennis racket that was reinforced with both glass and carbon fibres.

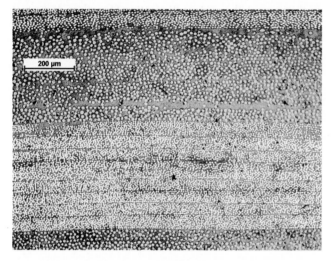

Figure 4.2f.11   Section through a tennis racket reinforced with glass fibre and carbon fibre

Concrete composites have also been produced using short discrete fibres and are known as fibre reinforced concrete (FRC), see Figure 4.2f.11. These composites incorporate the fibres randomly throughout the concrete to increase its structural integrity. The fibre used can vary from steel to glass, depending on the properties desired.

Figure 4.2f.12   An example of fibre reinforced concrete (FRC) using sisal fibre as the reinforcement

Flake (also known as grey) cast iron consists of randomly dispersed flakes of graphite in a metal matrix of iron, see Figure 4.2f.13. The graphite flakes are not strictly fibres, but interconnected flakes similar in nature to flat discs, and which appear fibre like when viewed in a two dimensional section.

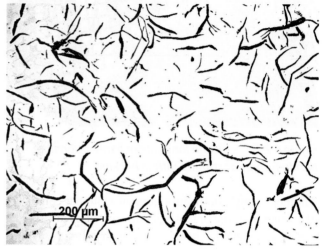

Figure 4.2f.13   Microstructure of flake graphite iron

Particle reinforced composites: typically consist of a relatively soft matrix in which hard particles of roughly uniform dimensions are embedded. As illustrated in Figure 4.2f.14, these particles may be symmetrical or asymmetrical in shape. The particle reinforced composites generally exhibit isotropic properties, that is, their physical and mechanical properties such as stiffness, strength, conductivity etc., are the same in all directions.

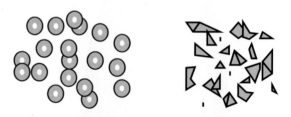

Figure 4.2f.14   Particle reinforced composites

An example of a composite of this sort is tungsten carbide tooling which typically consists of hard, irregularly shaped particles of tungsten carbide (WC) in a soft cobalt matrix shown in Figure 4.2f.15. This composite is produced using a powder metallurgy process in which a fine powder containing the constituent components is formed under heat and pressure to a near net shape product. This composite represents a cemented carbide and belongs to a material group known as cermets from ceramic (cer) and metallic (met).

TM-1000_0300   2009/11/24   15:25 L   20 um

Figure 4.2f.15   Microstructure of a tungsten carbide insert

Figure 4.2f.17   Carbon fibre fabric – plain weave pattern

Spheroidal graphite (SG) cast iron (also known as Ductile or Nodular Iron) can also be considered a composite material with soft spheroidal particles of graphite dispersed within a metallic matrix, see Figure 4.2f.16. In this instance, the graphite is formed naturally as the molten iron cools and solidifies. In this structure the graphite provides some dampening and crack arresting properties by blunting an advancing crack.

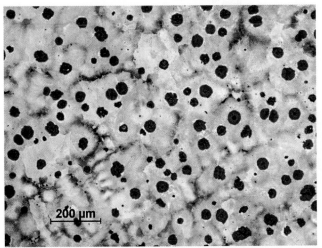

200 µm

Figure 4.2f.16   Microstructure of spheroidal graphite cast iron

Process: weaving, moulding, pultrusion and lamination

Textiles along with glass and carbon fibres are commonly used to create woven pre-forms that are later bonded with resin. An example of woven carbon fibre is provided in Figure 4.2f.17. By using the weaving process, large quantities of flexible matting can be produced that can be cut to size and positioned to follow the contours of a mould in order to create complicated shapes.

Moulding

Lay-up

Lay-up involves the creation of a composite of textiles encased in a resin typically consisting of a styrenated unsaturated polyester. This process can be undertaken as a fully manual process known as 'hand lay-up or semi-automated as 'spray lay-up'.

Hand lay-up involves the laying of woven mats of a textile such as fibre glass, carbon fibre , Kevlar®, etc. into a mould that has been pre-coated with a cold curing resin using a paint brush or roller. Once in place, the mats are coated with another layer of resin so that the textile mat is both impregnated by, and encased in, the resin as shown in Figure 4.2f.18.

In the spray-up process the textile fibres are cut up and mixed with the resin before being sprayed together into the mould by a semi-automated spray system, as illustrated in Figure 4.2f.19.

135

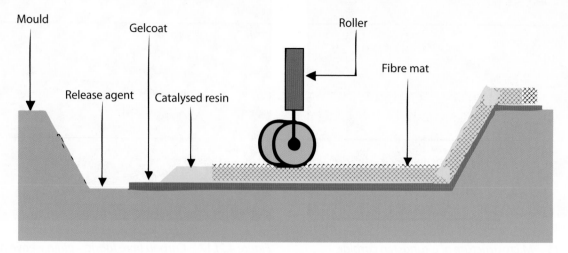

Figure 4.2f.18   Hand lay-up process

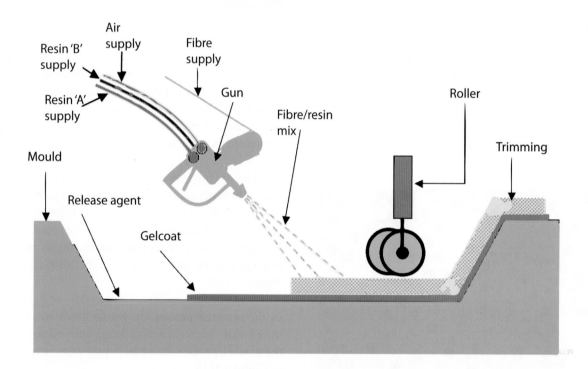

Figure 4.2f.19   Spray lay-up process

Resin transfer moulding (RTM)

RTM involves the use of fibre preforms that are positioned within a closed mould before a liquid resin is pumped (or transferred) into the mould under pressure. Following curing of the resin, the composite is removed and the mould prepared with another preform. The bismaleimide (BMI) thermosetting composites used in the F22 raptor and F35 Joint Strike Fighter are manufactured using the RTM process.

Pultrusion

Pultrusion is similar to extrusion with the exception that the material to be formed is pulled through a shaped dye rather than being pushed. The name is a contraction of pull and extrusion. Mats of glass, polymer or carbon fibre stored on reels are pulled through a thermosetting resin impregnation bath and then guided through preformer dies to align the fibres and remove excess resin. In the final stage of production the preform is pulled through heated dies to cure the resin. The cured fibre reinforced composite exiting the heated die in a continuous length is then cut to length.

This process produces long continuous lengths of constant cross-section with high stiffness and flexural strength. It is often used in the production of supports for optical fibre cables.

Lamination

Lamination is the process in which multiple layers of material are combined using, adhesives, heat and or pressure to form a new laminar composite material with improved properties.

Composition and structure of composites:

Concrete

Concrete consists of a cement matrix composed of sand, water and cement into which is mixed aggregate consisting of small stones of various sizes. Concrete therefore represents a particle reinforced composite, see Figure 4.2f.20.

The stone particles provide strength and reduce the cost, while the relatively weak (and expensive) cement acts as a binder or matrix. By using aggregate of various sizes, better packing is obtained with fewer voids in the cement matrix.

Composites of this type may be polished to produce an aesthetically pleasing surface on driveways, around swimming pools and outdoor entertainment areas.

Figure 4.2f.20   Concrete in which aggregate is mixed in a cement matrix of sand water and cement

Concrete composites known as fibre reinforced concrete (FRC) have also been produced using short discrete fibres as shown previously in Figure 4.2f.12.

Engineered wood, includes those products that are man-made such as plywood, particle board, glued laminated timber (Glulam), and Laminated veneer lumber (LVL).

Plywood

Plywood consists of thin wood sheets or veneers 2 to 3mm thick laminated together to create a timber with improved properties.

Wood is an 'orthotropic material' having different properties in three mutually perpendicular directions, with the strongest of these being parallel to the grain.

By placing alternate sheets at 90° to each other and then gluing with a phenolic resin before pressing the assembly together until the glue sets, a strong versatile isotropic material is created. Types of laminated timber include plywood, blockboard, and laminboard. An example of plywood is shown in Figure 4.2f.21. These products should not be confused with Laminated Board, which consists of a photographic image of timber, resin sealed and bonded to a core of high-density particleboard, followed by a backing board.

Advantages

- cheaper than solid timbers

- any thickness can be created

- stronger and more resistant to warping.

- decorative veneers can be applied to the surface

- laminates free of gross imperfections can be created.

Disadvantages

- cannot be made thinner

- if other than standard thicknesses are required, extra sheets need to be glued in place

- glue lines at panel edges are subject to moisture ingress and the loss of interlaminate glue and must be protected.

Figure 4.2f.21   Plywood sheets

137

Particleboard

Particleboard is manufactured by gluing small flakes, chips or pieces of timber together under pressure, see Figure 4.2f.22. Chipboard is perhaps the best known example. Vulnerable to water, it may also be treated to be moisture resistant and covered in a plastic veneer to produce more serviceable surfaces for use in kitchens, bookcases, desktops etc.

Figure 4.2f.22   Particle board sheets

Fibreglass

Fibreglass is a composite consisting of a thermoplastic or thermosetting polymer matrix with embedded glass fibres. The glass is typically E-glass (indicating its excellent electrical insulating properties), and represents a calcium-alumino-borosilicate. E-glass accounts for over 90% of the fibreglass market. The glass fibres are manufactured using the pultrusion process to a diameter of 5-25 microns (a micron is 10^{-6}m). These fibres may be supplied in a number of forms such as chopped fibre mats or as woven mats of various patterns, as shown in Figure 4.2f.23.

Figure 4.2f.23   E-glass textile in biaxial and bidirectional forms

Fibreglass entered mass production in the mid 1930s and found use during World War II in radar domes.

As indicated below, E-glass is very strong and stiff when individual fibres are placed in tension. The glass fibres are however weak in shear, so a weave is chosen with fibre orientation best suited to loading conditions, with the polymer matrix acting to constrain the fibres in the desired orientation.

Properties of E-glass

Specific Gravity:	1.25 g/cm^3
Moisture regain:	0%
Tensile Strength:	1500-3000 MPa
Elongation at break:	3-4% (Dry)
Stiffness:	73 GPa
Tenacity:	6.3-6.9 gm/denier (Dry)

Today fibre glass still finds widespread use in storage tanks, canoes and kayaks, protective helmets and equipment panels.

Kevlar®

Kevlar® is the registered brand name of an aromatic polyamide polymer fibre patented by Stephanie Kwolek in 1966, while working as a research chemist for DuPont. Kevlar® entered commercial production in 1971. Kevlar® incorporates a backbone of benzene rings in which the monomers connect in the trans conformation where the phenol groups form on opposite sides of the amide bond producing long straight chains. The molecular structure of the Kevlar® monomer is shown in Figure 4.2f.24. The molecules interact with each other through aromatic stacking in addition to van der Waals forces. This structure produces a fibre with a combination of high strength and stiffness.

Figure 4.2f.24   Representation of the molecular structure of the Kevlar monomer

The yarn is typically golden in appearance although treatment for UV resistance produces a black yarn. A low power magnification of Kevlar® is shown in Figure 4.2f.25.

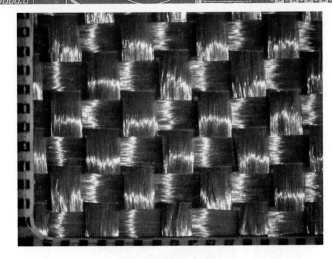

Figure 4.2f.25   Kevlar fibre in a regular weave (Scale in millimetres)

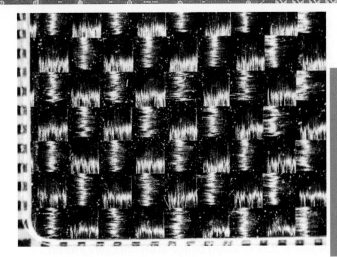

Figure 4.2f.26   Carbon fibre in a regular weave (Scale in millimetres)

Kevlar® fibres are resistant to organic solvents and fire and are difficult to cut with all but the sharpest shears. Its operational temperature range is –196° to +177°C.

Specific Gravity:	1.44 g/cm^3
Moisture regain:	4-8%
Tensile Strength:	2760-3150MPa
Elongation at break:	3-4% (Dry)
Stiffness:	60-90 GPa
Tenacity:	4 gm/denier (Dry)
Melting Point:	560°C

The fibres can be woven into textiles and used in applications such as sailcloth, gloves, ropes or sheathing for fibre optic cables. When combined with other materials such as epoxy, polyester or carbon fibre, Kevlar® finds use in such applications as boat hulls, sporting goods, and body armour.

Carbon-reinforced plastic: Carbon fibre reinforced plastic (CFRP) offers a higher strength and lighter weight alternative to glass fibre reinforced plastics. It is replacing glass fibres where the additional cost can be justified, with the exception of those applications where the insulative properties of glass are important. Although strong in tension, carbon fibres are very weak in shear and can be cut easily. Once embedded in a plastic matrix, however, CFRP is strong in all directions.

Carbon fibre was originally produced by heating asphalt and pulling fibre through a die. Today carbon fibre is produced by heating rayon fibre in an inert atmosphere to drive off all atoms other than carbon. The carbon fibres are then wound onto bobbins from which woven sheets may be produced as shown in Figure 4.2f.26. These mats may be laid in a mould and covered or painted with a polymer.

Properties of carbon fibre

Specific Gravity:	1.8 g/cm^3
Tensile Strength:	2 300–3 700 MPa
Elongation at break:	1.5-2.2 (Dry)
Stiffness:	220–480 GPa

Glued Laminated Timber (Glulam): consists of individual lengths of timber glued together such that their grains all run in the same direction. It is a stress rated engineered wood product in which the wood laminations, or 'lams,' typically 50mm or less in thickness are bonded together with strong, waterproof adhesives as shown in Figure 4.2f.27.

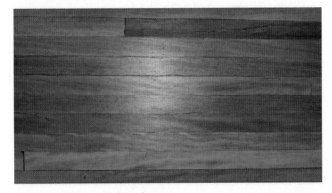

Figure 4.2f.27   Glulam beam

Glulam has greater strength and stiffness than comparably sized lumber. Kilogram for kilogram, it's stronger than steel. That means glulam beams can span long distances with minimal need for intermediate supports. This may be seen in Figure 4.2f.28 of a wooden bridge in Montmorency forest, crossing the Montmorency River, Quebec, Canada.

Figure 4.2f.28 Wooden bridge in Montmorency forest crossing Montmorecy River, Quebec, Canada. Made with 12 glulam arches. [Creative Commons: Cephas - own work]

Glulam eliminates the natural performance variations that characterise solid sawn lumber. Glulam beams are engineered wood products manufactured to meet specific performance characteristics.

Laminated Veneer Lumber (LVL)

LVL is a structural laminate composed of a number of layers of timber veneer (each typically 3.2mm thick) glued together such they all share a common grain direction, aligned with the member length.

This arrangement takes advantage of timber's strength and stiffness associated with the longitudinal direction (parallel with the grain).

LVL is therefore an orthotropic material similar to solid timber. However, because defects such as knots can be removed from the veneers, the LVL product is stronger than an equivalent product made from solid timber.

The product is typically a beam or billet form having a high aspect ratio, in that the length is significantly longer than the width and thickness. LVL lengths are commercially available up to 12m, although this presents concerns, primarily associated with transportation of longer lengths.

Advantages:

* shapes can be cut

* can be formed into curves and arches

* can be produced in almost any length.

Parallel Strand Lumber (PSL)

PSL consists of long strands of clipped wood veneer glued together under pressure with the grains of the veneers all running in the same direction to form a high strength structural section such as a beam.

An example of PSL product marketed by Weyerhaeuser as Parallam®, is shown in Figure 4.2f.29.

Figure 4.2f.29   View of a Parallam® beam being secured in place. [Image courtesy of Weyerhaeuser]

PSL products are finding increasing use in the timber framing industry as beams and columns due not only to their advantages of high strength and uniformity but also their aesthetic appearance. A close up view of the surface of a Parallam® beam showing the oriented nature of the clipped veneer strands is provided in Figure 4.2f.30.

Figure 4.2f.30   View of a Parallam® beam being secured in place. [Image courtesy of Weyerhaeuser]

INTERNATIONAL MINDEDNESS

Many composite materials are expensive to produce and their dissemination globally is limited.

© IBO 2012

While a large number of composites are relatively cheap to produce such as the timber composites and those involving the lay-up of fibre glass, there are a number of composites that require specialised processing equipment to produce the constituent fibres as well as requirements for equipment such as vacuum chambers and large autoclaves.

Ceramic matrix composites using SiC fibre reinforcement, for example, have very high resistance to heat and have been used in some specialised ballistic applications. The cost and availability of the fibres is such however that they are of limited attractiveness to most parts of the world. Similarly bismaleimide (BMI) thermosetting composites have found use where its advantages of light weight, strength and elevated temperature performance outweigh the significantly higher cost compared with alternatives. One such use of BMI has been in the F22 Raptor and F35 Joint Strike Fighter.

Expensive composites, as might be expected, find use in those applications requiring extraordinary properties that cannot be met by cheaper alternatives. These composites are typically produced for specialised roles associated with the aerospace industries and military.

Such materials apart from requiring specialised equipment can be difficult to repair and inspect for damage.

4.3–SCALES OF PRODUCTION

ESSENTIAL IDEA

The scale of production depends on the number of products required.

© IBO 2012

NATURE OF DESIGN

Decisions on scale of production are influenced by the volume or quantities required, types of materials used to make the products and the type of product being manufactured. There are also considerations of staffing, resources and finance.

© IBO 2012

AIM

The growing phenomenon of mass customisation brings consumers into the design process, allowing them to make choices that make a product unique, to make it their own. Companies have developed 'design stations' in their retail stores where consumers can create virtual 3D models, 'try them out' using digital technology and place their order.

© IBO 2012

One-off, batch and mass-production

One-off production

One-off production is sometimes called 'bespoke' or custom-made and involves the creation of products to the buyer's specification. This form of manufacturing was once the province of individual craftsmen. The most common form of this production has been the manufacture of tailored clothing and stands in contrast to mass produced 'off-the-rack' clothing. Such techniques have also often been applied to the manufacture of structural elements of unique public buildings such as Opera Houses and Cathedrals. The rise of modern computer controlled manufacturing, however, means that increasingly, one-off production techniques can be applied to private homes.

Batch production

Batch production fits between craft production and mass production. In batch production a limited quantity of the product or 'batch' is produced. Many batches may be produced in succession but flexibility exists in between batches to make modifications to the product or change the product batch completely. An example of batch production occurs in bakeries.

Batch production is a technique often used by smaller enterprises that do not have the resources to proceed to full-scale mass production or need the cash flow to maintain viability. Batch production can allow quicker responses to individual clients and the marketplace.

Mass production

In contrast to batch production, mass production tends to involve the large scale production of a product over an extended period of time. Because of this, the unit costs are lower than might otherwise be the case although at the expense of flexibility. The efficiencies associated with mass production come from large volume production runs with little or no variation. The high capital investment makes changing product an expensive exercise. Mass production is particularly suited to food, household appliances, automobiles and consumer goods such as mobile phones where a large market exists. Figure 4.3.1 shows a production line for the mass production of PET bottles.

Figure 4.3.1   Mass production of PET bottles, image by Krones AG CC-BY-SA-3.0]

Today mass production relies heavily on mechanisation and automation of many stages of production, often including the use of robots.

INTERNATIONAL MINDEDNESS

Mass customization enables global products to become individual items.

© IBO 2012

Mass customisation employs flexible manufacturing systems, (often computer driven), to bring the efficiencies of mass production to short job runs even down to single orders. The advantages include low costs and fast production times. In some ways it is considered to be the opposite of mass production where large numbers of identical products are produced.

Mass customisation places the individual consumer in control. Rather than companies responding to market expectations, individuals tender their requests directly to the manufacturer. Coupled with online technologies, manufacturers can meet consumer demands from computers in their homes where they can review products that are modified at the click of a mouse.

A clear example of mass customisation coupled with online communication is Nike's ID program. Consumers can log-on to the Nike website and customize the style, colour and any text additions of footwear while reviewing these changes on screen. The completed design can be purchased online and despatched to the consumer directly from the factory.

Further reading

Barlow, J. (1999). *From Craft Production to Mass Customisation?* Customer-focused approaches to house building.

4.4–MANUFACTURING PROCESSES

ESSENTIAL IDEA

Different manufacturing processes have been developed to innovate existing, and create new products.

© IBO 2012

NATURE OF DESIGN

Designers sometimes engineer products in such a way that they are easy to manufacture. Design for Manufacturability (DfM) exists in almost all engineering disciplines, but differs greatly depending on the manufacturing technologies used. This practice not only focuses on the design of a product's components, but also on quality control and assurance.

© IBO 2012

AIM

Advancements in 3D printing have resulted in the ability to have a 3D printer at home. Consumers can download plans for products from the internet and print these products themselves.

© IBO 2012

Additive techniques:

Additive manufacturing processes build physical models by fusing, sintering or polymerizing separate pieces of material together. Modern additive manufacturing is often referred to as: rapid prototyping, solid free form fabrication, layered manufacturing or direct digital manufacturing. It consists of a range of processes used to produce solid components through the deposition and fusing of consecutive layers of material.

Initially, designers create a CAD model which is then converted into an STL (STereo Lithography) file. This format was originally developed for stereo lithographic manufacturing. The process converts surfaces into polygons with their geometries recorded as mathematical coordinates.

In some situations, IGES, (Initial Graphic Exchange Specifications), formatting of the data may also be appropriate. The advantage of rapid prototyping lies in its ability to quickly and cost-effectively produce any shape that can be modelled in a CAD program. Once started, the build operation requires no operator input.

The production of physical models is done through the slicing of the formatted 3–D CAD models into multiple layers ready to be sequentially rebuilt without the use of any tooling or complex tool paths. This significantly reduces the amount of time to produce a prototype or fully functioning model. While there are at least 20 different commercial additive manufacturing processes they all fall into just four major groups.

- Lamination.
- Photopolymers.
- Deposition (fibre and inkjet).
- Powders (layered and sprayed).

Use of these technologies significantly reduces the lead-time required to bring a design to market.

Paper-based rapid prototyping, involves the use of paper to create a prototype using 3–D additive printing techniques. Because it uses paper as the raw material, it is much quicker and cheaper than other forms of 3–D additive printing. In this process, rather than distributing powder over the surface and fusing the material with heat, sheets of paper are bonded with an adhesive to progressively build up a 3–D prototype.

A number of paper-based rapid prototyping techniques are available, two of which are outlined below.

Selective deposition lamination (SDL) was invented in 2003 by Fintan and Conor MacCormack. Their company Mcor Technologies markets a 3–D printer that uses standard A4/legal sheets of paper to create a 3–D model.

In the SDL process the standard STL format 3–D digital data file is processed using a control software called SliceIT, which divides the computer model into slices the thickness of a sheet of paper. An A4/legal sheet of

143

paper is initially attached to the build plate as the model foundation, and a water based adhesive selectively deposited over the surface, such that a denser deposit is placed in those areas that will become part of the model and a lower density of adhesive supplied elsewhere. A tungsten carbide blade then cuts the model outline into the top sheet before the next application of adhesive and sheet of paper is introduced. By repeating this process a laminated model is progressively built.

On completion, the surrounding waste portions of paper are removed to expose the 3–D model.

Laminated object manufacturing (LOM) is an older form of paper based rapid prototyping than SDL, and involves the fusing or bonding of paper sheets using heat to melt a layer of plastic on the bottom of the paper. This is then cut with a blade or laser, as illustrated earlier in Figure 3.5.2. Kraft paper backed with a polyethylene-based, heat sensitive adhesive is often used as the modelling material. This product is both cost-effective and environmentally friendly.

Once the layer has been cut, the table moves down and the paper supply is advanced ready for the next layer of the model to be added.

Paper models are regularly sealed to prevent damage from moisture and to improve their overall strength.

Stereolithography (SLA) was developed in 1984 by Chuck Hall of 3–D Systems Corp. SLA uses a liquid resin that is cured by ultraviolet light. The prototype is formed on a movable platform situated within a container of resin. Starting at an elevated position with only a thin layer of resin present, a laser beam of UV light is directed at the surface. Once the desired area has cured, the platform lowers sufficiently to allow resin to cover the cured resin on the platform and the cycle repeats, gradually adding to the model layer by layer, as illustrated earlier in Figure 3.5.1. Because a liquid is used, the developing model would be unsupported if support structures were not produced concurrently and which require removal after completion.

When the model is completed, the platform is raised out of the resin container and the model removed.

Selective laser sintering is a 3–D manufacturing process in which a CO_2 laser is selectively focused onto a section of a moveable table covered with a heat-fusible powder. The power of the laser is set to bind the powder without it melting (sintering). Repetitive scans of the table with the laser build up the model in layers.

As each layer scan is completed, a new layer of powder is deposited over the top and pressed flat with a roller. The act of compressing the powder allows the model to be constructed without supporting structures. Models may even be manufactured with moving parts.

Once complete, the model is dusted off with excess powder recycled. SLS powders can be manufactured from: thermoplastics, polystyrene, sand, wax, ceramics, steel and even stainless steel, as illustrated earlier in Figure 3.5.4.

Wasting/subtractive techniques

Subtractive prototyping is a relatively new term used to cover operations using traditional manufacturing tools such as; drills, lathes, routers and milling machines. The term has been introduced as a contrast to the newer additive technologies that have arisen.

Starting with a block or blank, subtractive manufacturing continues to remove material until the part is finished. These machines and processes may also be automated.

The major advantages of subtractive technologies are:

- high degrees of accuracy

- very smooth surface finishes

- suitable for a wide range of materials

- smaller per part costs when mass produced

- larger dimensions and greater range of materials than additive prototyping methods.

Subtractive or machining processes strike some difficulties with varying thickness sections, deep slots, square corners and features such as undercuts. As parts become more complex, so too do tool paths. The number of tool changes also increases. Although issues such as these are resolvable, they require great skill, creativity and problem-solving abilities. From designing tool paths and machining strategies to operating and monitoring the process, machining is the work of experienced craftsmen.

Cutting, encompasses a wide variety of operations used to reduce a material usually in sheet form into smaller or differently shaped products. The selection of the appropriate method depends on a number of considerations, such as material hardness and thickness, accuracy required, production speed and material type (wood, plastic, metal, ceramic, etc.).

Cutting processes include:

- mechanical cutting: hacksaw, bandsaw, circular saw

- abrasive cutting: cut-off wheel, water-jet

- thermal processes: oxy-acetylene, plasma, laser, hot wire

- electrical discharge: wire cutting.

Abrasive water-jet cutting involves the direction of a thin stream of water, mixed with fine abrasive particles, through a nozzle at ultra-high pressures. Pressures of 280 to 690 MPa and water velocities of between 400m/s and 600m/s are used. Water cutting can be used to cut a wide variety of materials including metals, plastics, leather, stone, paper and rubber.

Oxy-acetylene cutting is a process in which acetylene and oxygen supplied from separate pressurised containers are supplied via rubber hoses to a cutting torch were the gases are mixed to produce a flame that burns at about 3 500°C (6 330°F). Oxy-acetylene cutting finds extensive use in the cutting of steel due to its portability and versatility. Figure 4.4.1 shows the equipment secured to a trolley allowing movement to wherever it is needed.

Figure 4.4.1   Oxy-acetylene equipment

A flashback arrestor is usually installed on both lines at the connection to the torch and the gas supply. The flashback arrestor prevents shockwaves passing along the hoses to the gas cylinder where an explosive decomposition might otherwise occur. The flame of the cutting torch is used to preheat the workpiece. Once the starting position for cutting has been heated to a cherry red colour the oxygen blast trigger on the top of the torch is depressed and an increased flow of oxygen is produced changing the flame from neutral to oxidising. In this condition, the steel surface is oxidised and, since the melting temperature of iron oxide is only about half that of the steel, liquid iron oxide forms and is blown away by the flame, allowing

continued oxidation and cutting. Figure 4.4.2 shows manual oxy-acetylene cutting of a 25 mm steel plate.

Figure 4.4.2   Manual control oxy-acetylene cuttiing

Advantages associated with oxy-acetylene cutting include portability of equipment, large pieces can be cut in place and the ability to cut curved and thick sections. It is also faster than mechanical cutting methods with a lower initial capital equipment cost when compared with mechanical tools. Disadvantages of oxy-acetylene cutting include the creation of a heat affected zone and the limited number of materials that may be cut. Metals such as aluminium and stainless steel, which form tenacious oxides that prevent further oxidation are unsuitable for cutting using this method.

Plasma cutting involves the ionization of a high velocity gas stream to form a plasma of high temperature (~25 000°C) and high kinetic energy. The gas employed may be either an inert gas or, more commonly today, compressed air. The material to be cut needs to be electrically conductive meaning it is restricted to metal cutting applications. The temperature of the plasma melts the metal, with the molten material being blown away by the plasma stream.

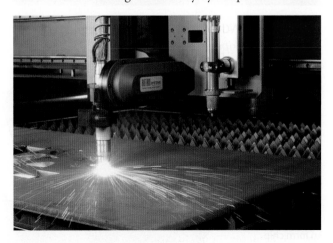

Figure 4.4.3   CNC plasma cutting 25mm steel plate, Image by Steve Brown, Wikipedia CC-BY-SA-3.0

Laser cutting uses a high power laser directed towards the flat sheet surfaces to be cut. A high quality surface finish is generated as the laser vaporises the sheet material. Laser cutters may also be used on piping or structural shapes. Through the adjustment of power levels, laser cutters may also be used for; 2–D cutting, welding, boring and engraving. A variety of laser cutters are employed dependent on their application. Examples include:

- CO_2 – boring and engraving

- Nd – high energy, low repetitious cutting

- Nd-YAG –very high power engraving or boring.

When repetitive, complex or long production runs are required, a computer may be employed to direct the laser, as shown in Figure 4.4.4. Laser cutting offers the advantages of fine, accurate cutting with smooth surfaces and lower energy requirements than plasma cutting. Kerf widths as narrow as 0.10mm are possible resulting in a lower heat affected zone. Metal thicknesses are however limited in all but the newer higher energy units of 6 000 watts.

Figure 4.4.4   CNC Laser cutting steel sheet, image by Mercurybds, Wikipedia CC-BY-SA-3.0

Machining

Machining is a subtraction process in which a cutting tool moves across a work piece to remove material from the surface, as illustrated in Figure 4.4.5.

The cutting tool was, at one time, high speed steel ground to produce a cutting edge. Today the cutting tool typically consists of a tungsten carbide or ceramic insert that is mechanically fixed to the tool holder. The cutting tip is shaped such that the tip has a slicing action through the workpiece and the material being removed (known as the swarf) is turned back on itself and fractures. It is important that the swarf is removed cleanly away from the cutting tip into a waiting scrap pan in order to avoid damage to the workpiece and cutting tool. This is particularly the case in CNC machining operations, where stoppages to clean away entangled swarf would significantly reduce efficiency.

Machined surfaces may be produced to very fine tolerances. Skilled workers are required to operate machines or technicians to monitor automated processes. In both cases expensive capital equipment is required.

Turning

The process of turning is a machining operation performed on a Lathe in which material is clamped securely between a head stock and tail stock and rotated (turned) at high speed as a cutting tool, fixed in a movable tool post, is moved along the surface, see Figure 4.4.6.

Turning operations are ideally suited to the production of symmetrical shapes and have traditionally been performed under the manual control of a machinist, although today repetitive operations are often automated through computer numerical control (CNC) systems.

Figure 4.4.7 shows a ceramic insert cutting tip secured to a tool post.

Figure 4.4.5   Machining, Wikipedia CC-BY-SA-3.0

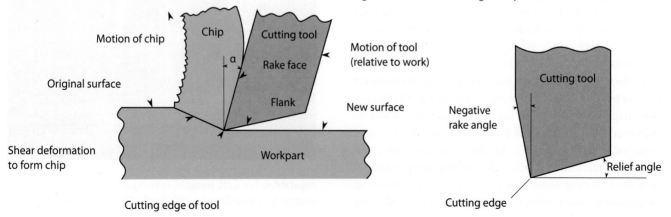

Figure 4.4.6   Turning operation

Figure 4.4.7   Cutting tool used in turning

Milling

The process of milling is a machining operation using a rotating cutter head, around which a number of cutting inserts are fixed, that remove material from a workpiece secured to a bed. The cutting bed moves the workpiece through the cutting area allowing the rotating cutter head to remove material from the surface as shown in Figure 4.4.8.

Figure 4.4.8   Figure 4.4.9 Milling operation

Abrading

Abrading involves the physical wearing away of surfaces by means of rubbing, friction or erosion. The harder the material, the more resistant it is to abrasion. Processes employed depend on the material to be abraded. Abrasives may be:

- rigid tools such as files and abrasive wheels

- suspended in a liquid e.g. water jet cutting

- carried by a jet of compressed air as in sand, steel shot or iron grit blasting.

Abrading may be used to remove material, shape an article, smooth or add texture to a surface. Materials suitable for abrasion include: ceramics, concrete, glass, polymers, metals and composites. In Figure 4.4.9 a process of abrasion of a steel work piece using a grinder can be seen.

Figure 4.4.9   Abrasion of a steel surface with a grinder.

Shaping techniques

Moulding

There are a number of shaping techniques that involve moulding to create a product, including the following.

- Injection moulding.

- Blow moulding.

- Rotational moulding.

Injection moulding involves the injection under pressure of molten thermoplastic into a closed die mould consisting of at least two metal platens into the surface of which is machined a shape to be cast. The dies are typically machined from hardened tool steel to provide wear resistant surfaces.

Parts from small to moderate size (up to ~16 kg) can be made. Intricate parts with fine detail and thin walls can be produced, although hollow objects cannot be produced, unless assembled into such items as illustrated by the model plane produced by injection moulding shown in Figure 4.4.10.

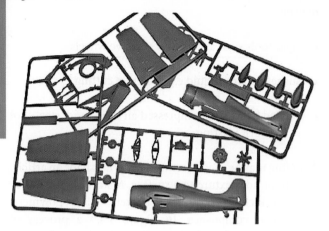

Figure 4.4.10   Model aeroplane manufactured by injection moulding

The injection moulding process uses a mechanism composed of two basic parts, consisting of the injection unit and the clamping unit as shown in Figure 4.4.11.

Figure 4.4.11   Injection moulding process

The injection unit consists of the polymer processing section where polymer granules are heated to a molten state ready for injection, while the clamping unit comprises a permanent mould consisting of two platens, one of which is fixed and the other moveable.

Products are created one after another in an automated cycle in which polymer granules loaded into the feed hopper are fed under gravity into the barrel containing a screw system. Heaters on the outer surface of the barrel melt the polymer as it is carried by the screw towards the end, where a non-return valve allows molten material to build-up increasing hydraulic back-pressure against the screw. Sensors monitor this pressure and when sufficient molten material has accumulated, rotation of the screw is stopped and the hydraulic cylinder and ram move the screw forward and the accumulated molten polymer is pushed through the nozzle and into the sprue, injecting the polymer into the die. The molten polymer passes along a runner system machined into the platen surface before passing into the product. The runner system is therefore located at the die parting line.

The mould remains closed until the polymer has cooled sufficiently, following which the movable platen is retracted, and the part formed is ejected. Although the initial capital cost of machinery and dies is high - surface finishes are excellent, intricate detail can be achieved and large production runs lower costs per unit.

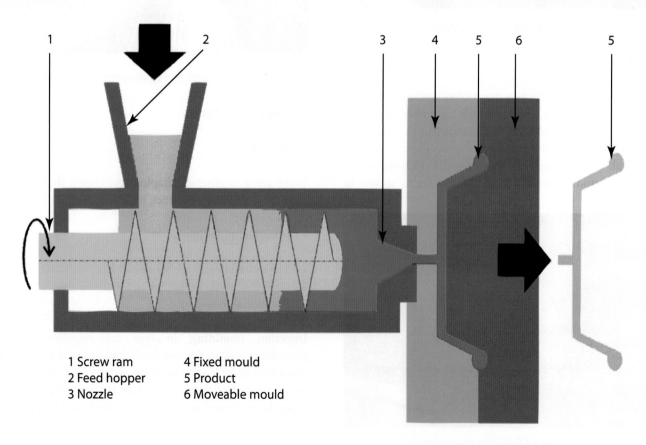

1 Screw ram   4 Fixed mould
2 Feed hopper   5 Product
3 Nozzle   6 Moveable mould

Resin transfer moulding (RTM) is similar to the injection moulding process described above, with the exception that RTM is used to produce a composite material. In this process, a reinforcing mat such as fibreglass is placed in the mould chamber and takes up the contours of the closed mould. Resin is then injected (transferred) into the mould under vacuum. Once the resin has cured the mould is opened and the part ejected.

Blow moulding is used where a large hollow object such as a bottle is required. The process involves the confinement of a semi-molten hollow plastic tube (parison) within a mould such that one end of the tube is closed and the other open. While the plastic tube is still at a temperature above its glass transition temperature, (softening temperature), compressed air is blown into the open end of the tube, expanding it until it conforms to the shape of the mould. Three variants of blow moulding are used known as:

- extrusion blow moulding

- injection blow moulding

- stretch blow moulding.

Extrusion blow moulding is illustrated in Figure 4.4.12 and involves the extrusion of molten plastic through a die to form a tube of plastic. The extruded tube passes between the two halves of an open blow mould in an inverted orientation. The mould is closed, pinching off the tube at the mould base to create the parison. Compressed air is then forced through the bottle top, expanding the plastic against the mould wall. When the plastic has cooled sufficiently, the mould is opened and the bottle removed.

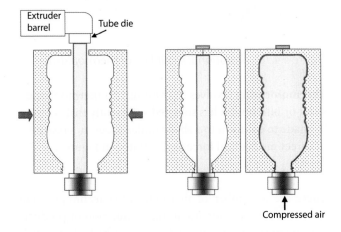

Figure 4.4.12   Extrusion blow moulding

Advantages of extrusion blow moulding include low capital costs, low tooling costs, high production rate and the viability of small production runs.

Disadvantages:

- high scrap rate

- poor surface finish

- limited wall thickness control

- scrap needs to be trimmed from container.

Injection blow moulding is a two stage process and is illustrated in Figure 4.4.13. The first process stage involves the initial injection of molten plastic into a mould containing a parison core. When solidified, the mould is opened and the core with the surrounding parison attached is transferred to the blow mould while still hot, ready for the second process stage. The blow mould is closed around the core and parison and compressed air blown into the core. The core then acts as a blowing rod, forcing the plastic parison out against the mould wall. When cooled the blow mould opens and the product is ejected ready for the next cycle.

The injection moulding process is also known as transfer blow moulding and is the slowest of the blow moulding processes but can be used to produce complex shapes and is often used in the production of small plastic medicine bottles.

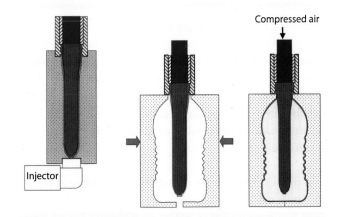

Figure 4.4.13   Injection blow moulding

The advantages associated with injection blow moulding include high production rates, little or no scrap to be trimmed and superior transparency compared with extrusion blow moulding. Injection moulding of the parison also allows more control of shape and size.

Disadvantages associated with injection blow moulding include the fact that two moulds are needed and high initial capital costs.

Stretch blow moulding is illustrated in Figure 4.4.14 and involves the positioning of a parison body into a mould where the parison body is heated to the glass transition temperature. Once this temperature is reached, a blowing rod is inserted through the top and compressed air is blown through the end of the rod stretching the parison longitudinally while air is also ejected from the surface of the blowing tube, pushing the parison radially toward the sides of the watercooled mould where it cools. The stretching operation aligns the molecular chains, increasing the strength of the walls while also improving solvent resistance and transparency.

Widely used for PET, PE and PVC bottles. The high wall-strength produced allows the containment of pressures associated with carbonated drinks.

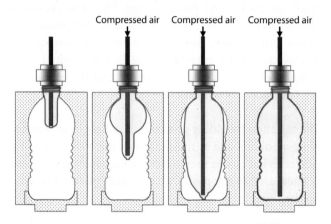

Figure 4.4.14   Stretch blow forming

Advantages associated with stretch blow forming include low scrap, low labour costs, good surface finish, high production rates and the variety of parison blanks available 'off-the-shelf.' Disadvantages associated with stretch blow forming include the need to carefully control the process due to the thin walls.

The mould chamber for stretch blow moulding is shown in Figure 4.4.15.

Figure 4.4.15   Stretch blow moulding chamber, image by AG Krones

Rotational moulding also known as rotomoulding is used to produce hollow plastic products and involves the rotation or spinning of the mould in two axes to allow centrifugal forces to press the molten plastic against the inner surface of the mould as shown in Figure 4.4.16.

The process involves four basic stages.

• Fill mould chamber with the required amount of the thermoplastic plastic powder.

• Heat mould chamber until the plastic is molten.

• Spin the mould chamber to evenly distribute the molten plastic within the mould.

• Cool the chamber to solidify the plastic.

The mould rotation is then stopped, the product removed and the process repeated. Typically, this process is employed in the manufacture of seamless water tanks.

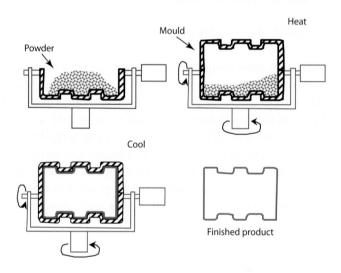

Figure 4.4.16   Rotational moulding of thermoplastic

Thermoforming involves the heating of a thermoplastic sheet or film until it has softened sufficiently that it can be made to conform to a shape under vacuum, pressure or direct mechanical force as illustrated in Figure 4.4.17

There are a number of thermoforming techniques and the process finds wide use in the production of products varying in size from cups and trays to vehicle dash panels and plastic pallets.

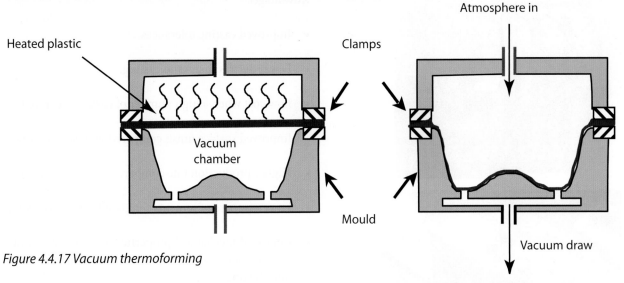

Figure 4.4.17 Vacuum thermoforming

The advantages of thermoforming include short lead times, low tooling costs, low forming pressures, injection moulded quality, high production rates and the availablity of cheap wooden patterns. Disadvantages include poor dimensional accuracy and the inability to form holes and threads.

Casting

Casting involves the transformation of materials into a liquid form before pouring (casting) them into a mould or pre-prepared cavity for solidification or setting. It is one of the oldest processing techniques known to man and many variations exist depending on the material to be cast, the number of items to be produced, the complexity and surface finish required.

These considerations will determine the equipment required to transform the material to be cast into a liquid and the type of mould to be used.

Metals, food (jelly, chocolate) plastics (resins) composites (metal matrix composites) and ceramics (glass and concrete) are all suitable materials to be cast. Neither timber nor textiles lend themselves to this approach. The advantages of casting include:

- Complex and hollow shapes with smooth section changes are possible.

- Applicable to small or large product runs.

- Large or small products are possible.

- Since castings are produced on a batch basis, their chemistry can be generally made to order.

There are a number of commonly used casting methods employed such as die casting, sand casting and precision casting (lost wax casting).

Two forms of die-casting are performed and are named after the method by which molten metal enters the die:

- gravity die-casting

- pressure die-casting.

Both forms of die-casting use a permanent mould consisting of two platens, with the product shape and runner system machined into the surface. The die-casting mould is typically machined from tool steel for wear resistance and strength. Metals suitable for die-casting are those with good fluidity and low melting points such as lead, tin, magnesium, zinc, aluminium and their alloys.

In gravity die-casting (sometimes called permanent mould casting), metal is poured from a ladle into the sprue and the molten metal fills the mould under gravity. Because of the relative simplicity of the process, after the cost of the dies has been taken into account, gravity die-casting is relatively inexpensive. Automation can of course be included when high volume production is required. The casting of lead 'sinkers' once performed by many anglers at home is an example of gravity die-casting.

Figure 4.4.18 shows 'tin' soldiers, approx. 65 mm high, being cast in antique moulds from the early 20th century. The two mould halves are clamped together, and the molten metal alloy of tin and lead, (approx. 300°C) is poured by hand from a ladle into the mould. Once the metal has solidified, the mould is opened. Sprues, (pouring channels) and extraneous flash seen in the bottom image are eventually removed during the fettling process.

Figure 4.4.18   Gravity casting, image by Janke [CC-BY-SA-2.5 (www.creativecommons. org/licenses/by-sa/2.5)], via Wikimedia Commons

Advantages:

- Improved casting tolerances.

- Fewer defects than sand casting.

- Low cost when a high number of castings required.

- Improved surface finish compared with sand casting.

- Higher production rate compared with sand casting.

- Lower space requirements compared with sand casting.

- Improved mechanical properties resulting from faster cooling rate and smaller grain size compared with sand casting.

Disadvantages:

- Design changes costly.

- Casting weight and size limited.

- High initial die costs although cheaper than pressure die casting.

- Limited range of metals can be cast compared with sand casting in order to avoid early deterioration of the mould surface.

Articles produced by gravity die casting include exhaust manifolds and train brake discs.

Not withstanding the limitations listed above, a special category of permanent mould casting is responsible for the majority of steel production.

In the conventional practice for the mass production of steel for subsequent rolling, molten metal ingots are cast or 'teemed' through a nozzle at the bottom of a large 'ladle' into large permanent moulds made of grey cast iron, see Figure 4.4.19. In this instance the moulds are of a simple shape and are suitable for purpose in the as-cast condition, that is, no machining or heat treatment is required. The high thermal conductivity of the iron mould allows rapid extraction of heat from the steel surface while contraction of the steel ingot and the tapered mould wall allow later separation of the ingot and mould.

Once the steel has sufficiently cooled within the mould the moulds are 'stripped' from the ingots and the ingots placed into gas fired 'soaking pits' until hot enough for rolling. The mould is then allowed to cool before being reused. Over a period of time, exposure to the thermal cycles described results in the cracking of the inner surface of the ingot mould. Moulds are routinely examined and those badly cracked are replaced to avoid metal penetration that might hinder the 'stripping' operation.

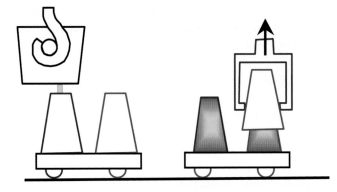

Figure 4.4.19   Schematic representation of the ingot casting process

This process has largely been replaced by continuous casting techniques for the mass production of standard steel grades, shown in Figure 4.4.20. In continuous casting, molten steel is poured from a ladle into an intermediate container known as a tundish. The tundish serves as the place where slag and impurities are removed from the melt and from there it enters an open ended water-cooled reciprocating copper mould.

Steel exits from the bottom of the mould in a continuous strand with a solid shell and still molten core. Water sprays continue to cool the strand, while rollers direct it along a particular path for cutting, transportation and further processing.

As long as the tundish is supplied with sufficient metal to continue casting into the mould, casting can continue uninterrupted. Therefore, as the main ladle is emptied, a new ladle is usually waiting to take its place to continue the sequence.

In modern steelmaking, the continuous casting process may also be integrated with metal rolling. This secondary rolling operation is a forming process that changes the shape of the metal it processes.

Continuous casting is very economical in that the rolling mill can be fed directly from the continuously cast metal casting strand.

The rate of the rolling operation is carefully synchronised with the speed of the continuous metal casting, effectively combining the two operations as one.

Continuous casting offers a number of advantages over the traditional ingot route:

- Faster production.

- Improved surface finish.

- Reduced space requirements.

- Reduction in scrap metal losses.

- Reduction in energy requirements.

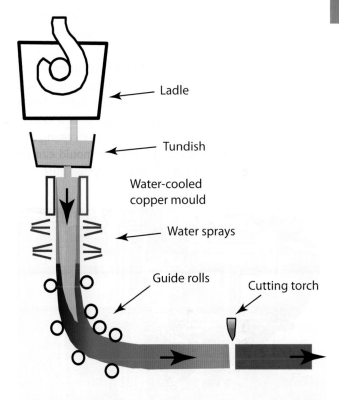

Figure 4.4.20 Schematic representation of the continuous casting process

Pressure die-casting involves machinery consisting of a fixed die platen and a hydraulically activated movable platen as shown in Figure 4.4.21.

Die-casting has an enormous range of applications. A lot of manufacturing industries rely on one of the many variations of pressure die-casting that include hot-chamber and cold-chamber die-casting.

Industries employing this type of technology range from the automotive through to aerospace and appliance manufacturing.

Figure 4.4.21 Die-casting machine and dies, image by Swoolverton (own work) CC-BY-3.0], via Wikimedia

A modern die-casting machine is shown in Figure 4.4.22 in which molten metal from a melting furnace is sucked under vacuum into an injection chamber before being injected at high velocity under pressure into a water-cooled die. Pressure is maintained until the casting has solidified and cooled sufficiently that the mould can be opened and the cast part ejected using injection pins. The die is then closed ready for the next cycle.

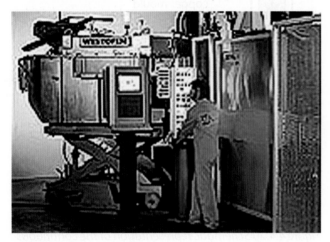

Figure 4.4.22 Die-casting machine and operator, image by METT Pty Ltd

High production rates are possible with this process, producing parts of near net shape and excellent surface finish. As molten metal enters the die any air trapped within the cavity will be entrained in the molten metal and result in the formation of compressed bubbles within the casting. If such bubbles are present, heat treatment is not recommended as expansion of the entrapped air can lead to cracking. In those instances where heat treatment is desired, special provisions must be included to remove the air.

Two techniques for air removal involve either the use of a vacuum to evacuate air prior to metal injection, or the provision of several small channels leading from the die

cavity to the outside known as vents. The vents allow the displacement of air from the die as metal enters.

Unlike other casting processes die-casting does not incorporate a metal reservoir such as a riser to feed the cooling and contracting metal. Metal shrinkage is controlled by the injection pressure and appropriate design of the metal flow.

Advantages:

- Low unit costs.

- Good surface finish.

- High volume production.

- Excellent surface finish (typically 1–2.5 Ra).

- High dimensional accuracy typically within 0.1 mm.

Disadvantages:

- Size limitation.

- Tooling costs high.

- Changes to die difficult.

- Not all alloys can be die cast.

- Parting line restrictions limit shapes possible.

High-pressure die-casting is used extensively for products such as automotive trim, handles, iron sole plates, disc drive chassis, musical instruments, rotors for electrical motors, kitchen faucets, steering wheels.

Sand casting: involves the production of a temporary mould produced, as the name implies, from sand. A mixture of sand and various binding agents are poured into a box containing a half pattern of the casting. Following the setting of the moulding sand, the pattern is removed and the cavity surface is painted with a refractory slurry.

The final mould is subsequently constructed by joining the individual parts, see Figure 4.4.23. The top half of the mould is known as the 'cope' while the bottom half is the 'drag'. Intricate and hollow shapes are created by the incorporation of appropriately formed internal shapes, also made of sand, known as 'cores'.

Provision is made during the moulding process for metal entry into the mould and the 'feeding' of the casting during solidification.

Figure 4.4.23 shows molten metal being cast from a small ladle into the sprue of a sand mould. In this figure a number of weights can be seen on top of the mould, positioned to ensure that hydrostatic pressure does not result in the cope lifting.

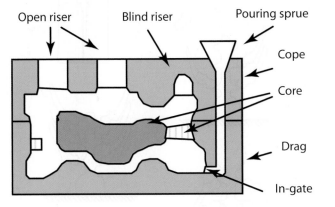

Figure 4.4.23   Schematic representation of a sand mould

Castings solidify first at those positions where heat removal is greatest. These positions generally correspond with areas where the molten metal comes into contact with the mould wall. Solidification therefore usually proceeds from the outer surface toward the casting's interior.

Figure 4.4.24   Sand casting

As the casting solidifies, it contracts and the molten centre 'feeds' the growing front of solidifying metal. If extra molten metal is not supplied, the last part of the cavity to solidify will have insufficient metal to be completely solid and a 'shrinkage' cavity will result. To avoid this situation reservoirs of molten metal are often provided by the incorporation of 'risers' into the mould. Risers are designed to be the last part of the casting to solidify and act to feed molten metal into the casting. If correctly designed, any shrinkage is contained completely within the risers, which are removed during the 'fettling' or clean-up stage.

Heat from the casting gradually degrades the binding agent and the mould crumbles allowing easy removal or 'knock-out' of the casting.

Because these castings are relatively large, the grain-size can also be large leading to lower strength. Grain-size is controlled by adjusting casting temperature and solidification rate and with the addition of grain-refining elements.

Precision casting, also known as investment casting and lost wax casting, is a foundry process in which high precision items are produced. While the process is one of the oldest known to man, it is used today as then for its dimensional accuracy and fine surface finish along with its ability to create castings of great complexity.

In the lost wax casting process shown in Figure 4.4.26, a permanent mould or die, often made of metal, is used to produce an expendable wax pattern. The pattern may then be incorporated into an assembly with similar patterns, and attached to a wax feeding system. The whole assembly is subsequently dipped into a ceramic slurry to build up a coating. Fine sand is then added to form a strong shell and the assembly allowed to dry. The dry assembly is then placed in a mould flask and surrounded by a coarser sand/slurry mixture and dried. This courser sand/slurry backing is technically known as the 'investment'. After setting, the mould is gently heated to melt the wax pattern leaving a smooth mould cavity behind. In the final stage of production, metal is cast into the mould to form the required part.

Controlled breakdown of the sand/binder mixture from exposure to the temperature of the solidifying metal allows the solidified casting to be easily removed from the mould for fettling. During the fettling operation the casting is separated from the metal feeder system of sprue, runners and in-gates.

Advantages:

- Near net shape.

- Freedom of design.

- No joint lines present.

- Allowance for pattern removal not required.

- Production of thin sections and sharp detail.

- High dimensional tolerances and surface finish possible.

- No limit to cast metal composition, subject to restrictions of melting fluidity and soundness.

Disadvantages:

- Labour intensive.

- Casting size limited.

- High initial die costs.

- Thick sections not generally cast.

- Die design changes may be costly.

Lost wax casting represents a sub-set of sand casting and, based on archaeological evidence, has its origins in Mesopotamia around 3000–4000 BCE. It appears that the process was in use in most civilisations of the ancient world, mostly for artistic purposes, from jewellery to statuary both large and small. The bronze statue of Perseus holding the head of Medusa produced by Benvenuto Cellini in 1554, and the aluminium statue of Eros in London's Piccadilly Circus cast by Alfred Gilbert in 1893 (Figure 4.4.25), are famous examples of the process.

While the lost wax process continued to be used in artistic circles because of the intricate detail, excellent surface finish and near net shape characteristics it offers, the mainstream engineering use of the process did not begin until the Second World War. At that time, capacity restraints in machining led to the use of the lost wax process because of its ability to produce components that did not require machining. Following the war, the development of the jet engine created an increasing demand for the process in the production of high precision castings of refractory metals used for components such as gas turbine blades.

Today, the lost wax process also finds use in the production of hip and knee prosthetics, dental implants, valves and auto parts along with traditional roles in the production of items such as jewellery, and instrument keys. Figure 4.4.26 shows the lost wax process as used to produce hip replacements.

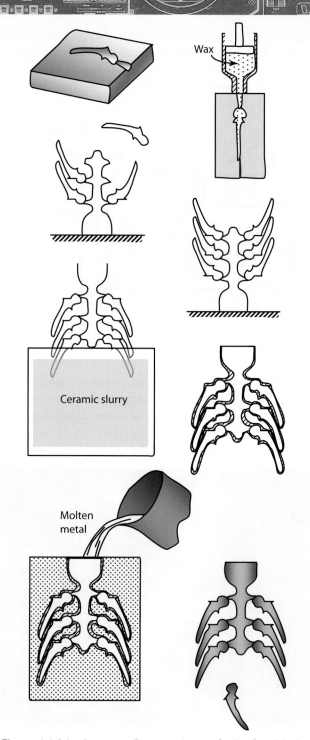

Figure 4.4.26   *Lost wax Ppocess, image by Beeley, P.R. & Smart, R.F. (1995)*

Laminating represents a permanent bonding process in which improved properties can be obtained as discussed previously in section 4.2f.

Knitting, as previously noted, is a manufacturing process in which a single thread is looped to form an interlocking construction that produces a flexible fabric. While textiles for the apparel and home decoration industries have been the traditional materials and markets supplied by the knitting process, a wide variety of materials and applications are today produced by knitting to

Figure 4.4.25   Statue–Eros in Piccadilly Circus London

take advantage of the resilience and flexibility that can be obtained. Commonly knitted materials outside of traditional textiles include polymers and many metals including: stainless steel, steel – both black and galvanised, aluminium, monel, tantalum, platinum, gold and copper. Metal wires suitable for knitting are generally in the range 0.11mm to 0.35mm diameter. Examples of some of the applications making use of the features of both the metal and the knitting process are listed below.

- Oil and air filters.

- Mufflers and silencers.

- Heat transfer and insulation.

- No-cut stainless steel gloves.

- Cryogenic seals and gaskets.

- Metal alloy compression springs.

- Platinum-rhodium alloy gauze for use as a catalyst.

An example of knitted polymer shade cloth is presented in Figure 4.4.27.

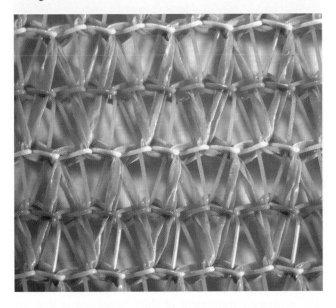

Figure 4.4.27   *Knitted polymer shade cloth*

Weaving is the process of passing fibres or threads of material under and over each other, (most often at right angles, called warp and weft) in an interlacing fashion. Weaving appears in Egyptian writings and biblical references and some think that forms of weaving existed in the Palaeolithic era.

Similar to knitting, weaving has traditionally been associated with the textile industry, however today a much broader range of materials are woven. These include:

- metals–steel, gold, silver, platinum, copper, titanium, aluminium (woven wire jewellery, screens, fence panels, sieves, catalyst gauze)

- ceramics (fibreglass mat), plastics (outdoor furniture, mats, safety barriers)

- composites (woven fabrics within resin matrices)

- timber (furniture, privacy screens and shades).

An example of a fly screen woven from polymer coated steel wire is shown in Figure 4.4.28.

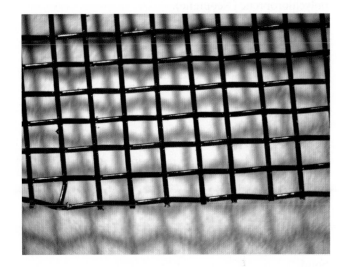

Figure 4.4.28   *Woven polymer coated metal wire fly screen*

Permanent joining techniques

Permanent joining techniques are those that, once formed, cannot easily be separated without damage. Because of this, such items are not easily repaired or modified tending instead to be discarded in favour of a new item exhibiting the functions and capacities desired. Permanent joining techniques include the use of adhesives, and fusion welding.

Adhering, or the joining of two surfaces by adhesion is generally considered to be attained through the interaction of van der Waals forces or polar forces. The process typically involves the introduction of a thin layer of liquid polymer (the adhesive) between the surfaces to be joined. The adhesive undergoes polymerisation in-situ. Adhesives, depending on their bonding action, may allow for the separation of parts with little or no damage to the original surfaces. They are commonly used to join thin or dissimilar materials and don't employ heat, which may cause distortion or damage. Some adhesives, composed of metallic flakes, are even electrically conductive, cure at room temperature and cause no damage to heat sensitive componentry.

Common adhesives include the following.

Polyvinyl Acetate (PVA)–a water-based adhesive suitable for bonding porous materials such as wood, paper or cloth.

Epoxy Resin – Can be used to join most materials and is available in one or two-part systems consisting of a resin and hardener.

Contact adhesive–applied to both surfaces to be bonded to form a strong bond. Commonly consists of polychloroprene (Neoprene).

Cascamite–a powdered adhesive based on urea-formaldehyde that is mixed with water before use. Forms a strong waterproof joint when cured.

Tensol cement–used for bonding a wide range of thermoplastics such as acrylic.

Cyanoacrylate (superglue)–represents a special type of acrylic resin. Fast curing through a reaction with moisture. Joints must be close fitting.

Polyurethane glue–available in one or two-part systems. Fast curing. Often used with primers. Forms a flexible bond.

Anaerobic acrylic–cure when air is excluded often used as thread locking compounds.

Toughened acrylic–fast curing high strength adhesive usually as a two-part system.

Fusing, or welding is a permanent process in which disassembly requires breaking of the welded items by breaking the join and most probably the product itself. Manufacturers require specialised equipment, skilled tradesmen and a specially prepared environment for welding.

Fusing typically involves the heating of the surfaces to be joined until melting and intermixing at the joint occurs to form a metallurgical bond. This heat may be provided by a variety of methods including gas, friction, electric-resistance or electric arc.

Additional metal may be introduced to the joint using either a consumable electrode, as in manual metal arc welding (MMAW), or by a separate filler wire that is fed into the heat source as in gas welding or tungsten inert gas (TIG) welding.

Other heat sources for specialized applications include laser and electron beam welding. In order to maintain a clean surface and reduce the chances of oxides forming during fusion welding, a protective slag or inert gas shield is generally provided. The joint formed is usually as strong as the parent material and is probably the most widely used method of fabrication in use today.

A macro-etched cross section through a butt weld joining two plates is shown in Figure 4.4.29. The weld has been polished and etched to show the weld metal, heat affected zones (HAZ's) and parent metal. This weld was performed from one side with the aid of a backing bar at root.

Figure 4.4.29   Section through a butt weld joining two plates, formed by multiple weld runs

Soldering and brazing are similar operations and involve the joining of two or more parts by melting a filler metal with a heat source. The molten filler metal flows into the joint and, on solidifying, holds the parts together. The heat source for soldering is usually a hot 'iron' while brazing is accomplished with the aid of an oxyacetylene torch.

The primary difference between the processes is the temperature at which the filler metal solidifies. Soldering uses filler metals with a solidification temperatures <500°C (e.g. Pb, Sn, Sb etc.) while brazing uses alloys with solidification temperatures >500°C (e.g. Cu, Ni etc.).

The primary requirement of these processes is that the surfaces to be joined are free of oxides, so that the filler metal can 'wet' the surface. Fluxes designed to remove oxides from the surface are used to provide a clean joint.

Temporary joining techniques

Fastening or joining materials mechanically through the use of screws, rivets, bolts, pins, clips, nails, press-studs and snaps are considered temporary joining techniques.

Blind rivets (also known as break-stem rivets and pop rivets) are typically used for the joining of sheet metal and consist of a solid stem or mandrel terminating in a button-like head. A short tubular body or shaft with a flanged end is positioned on the stem just below the head, as may be seen in Figure 4.4.30. This joining method is not intended for structural applications.

Figure 4.4.30   Pop rivets

Installation is achieved by inserting the tubular body into a prepared hole in the sheet metal being joined so that the head of the mandrel protrudes from the other side. A setting tool is then positioned over the mandrel stem such that the flanged head of the shaft is held against the sheet metal surface.

With the aid of the setting tool, the mandrel is pulled back through the tubular shaft. As this takes place, the button head of the mandrel compresses and deforms the end of the tubular body between itself and the sheet metal surface. Compression continues until the tensile strength of the mandrel is exceeded and it fractures, leaving behind a completed joint. An example of a blind rivet installation is presented in Figure 4.4.31 were blind rivets have been used to secure a cabinet hinge.

Figure 4.4.31   Pop-rivets securing a hinge in a sheet metal cabinet

Advantages of pop rivets include the fact that no heat is involved and only a single operator is required. They may also be installed from one side and securing does not require high level of skill.

Disadvantages are that surfaces have to be perforated with a drill and that rivets can only be used on relatively thin material.

Screws and nails both rely on physical interaction with the material being joined. Nails remain in place by the pressure of the surrounding fibres. Removal requires frictional contact forces to be overcome. Screws derive their fixation strength from a mechanical bond in which pull-out requires the shearing of material contained between the threads. As a screw is driven into an assembly, the joint is placed in compression when the head of the screw meets the surface.

Bolts act to hold two or more parts of an assembly together by applying a clamping force between the bolt head and nut. As the nut is tightened the bolt is placed in tension and the joint assembly in compression. Bolts are available in a variety of materials, strength levels and head designs to match the situation. A typical hexagonal head bolt is shown in Figure 4.4.32.

Figure 4.4.32   Hexagonal head bolt

INTERNATIONAL MINDEDNESS

More expensive modern processes tend to take place in technologically advanced regions/countries.

© IBO 2012

Expensive modern processes rely for their continued operation on a highly skilled workforce and a sophisticated service sector to ensure the continued availability of parts supply and maintenance. These services tend to only be available in technologically advanced regions/countries.

4.5–PRODUCTION SYSTEMS

ESSENTIAL IDEA

The development of increasingly sophisticated production systems is transforming the way products are made.

© IBO 2012

NATURE OF DESIGN

As a business grows in size and produces more units of output, then it will aim to experience falling average costs of production - economies of scale. The business is becoming more efficient in its use of inputs to produce a given level of output. Designers should incorporate internal and external economies of scale when considering different production methods and systems for manufacture.

© IBO 2012

AIM

The design of a production system requires a complete understanding of a product, its function and the quality of finish. Each system can be unique and specific to the product it is creating, often requiring the designer to adapt their design to be manufactured using certain methods.

© IBO 2012

Craft production

Craft production, or one-off production involves the production of single, unique, individual products. Craft production general involves manual skills where the skill of the artisan determines the quality of one-off unique pieces. While frequently slow, this method was often locally based and allowed clients to converse directly with the manufacturer to produce customized items. Because craftsmen manufacture a project from start to finish they may be required to have a variety of skills.

One-off production is often used for prototype development and testing before moving to larger scales of production. Today, master craftsmen produce individually designed pieces tailored to client requests. These pieces exhibit both high quality and cost. Examples of this approach include: haute couture fashion, jewellery and customized furniture.

In developing countries one off production is still viable due to the low cost of labour and lack of distribution infrastructure. Locally based artisans meet the needs of local clients with appropriate technologies and available materials.

Mechanised production, involves the introduction of machinery into a process with the intent of automating the process to some degree. In its simplest form it replaces hand-crafting operations with machine based tooling. As a general rule, mechanization has allowed for the production of cheaper products, faster, and of an improved quality.

Automated production, involves the replacement of human labour with mechanical, electronic or computer controlled machinery processes and systems that operate automatically or independently.

Such control has its origins in the work of Joseph Marie Jacquard (1752-1834) a French inventor who developed a system of punched cards (Figure 4.5.1) that controlled the operation of a loom for the weaving of textiles with complex patterns.

Figure 4.5.1   Jacquard loom cards

Jacquard's work was said to have influenced Charles Babbage (1791-1871), the English mathematician, mechanical engineer and inventor who is credited with laying much of the foundation for the computer.

Numerical control systems were developed in the 1940s and 1950s to meet the demands of mass production, uniformity and consistent part quality. This advance allowed for the automatic control of machines to perform repetitive operations continuously, to exacting standards and to operate in environments otherwise harsh or hazardous to humans.

The term 'numerical control' or 'control through numbers' refers to the automation of machining operations using programmed commands as opposed to mechanical input such as hand-wheels, levers or cams. These commands, stored using a variety of media; taking the form of punched cards, magnetic tape and punched tape, are converted into output signals that directly control machine operations such as: spindle rotation, tool type, tool movement, and cutting fluid flow.

Numerical control (NC) machines are not connected to a computer and receive their instructions from punched cards or tape. These punched cards, made of paper, are fragile and have a limited life expectancy. The card reading technology (hard wired to the machine) can also be unreliable. NC controlled machines have no mechanism to provide feedback to the operator such as display monitors or graphic user interfaces.

Today automation generally indicates computer control. Automation offers significant advantages by taking over complex, repetitive operations in dangerous or dirty environments. In this manner they may relieve some tedium and reduce the need for physical strength from workers. Workers may also be required to have higher-level skills and training. Automation also brings with it faster production times, reduced costs, finer tolerances, automated mass customization and near-perfect repeatability. Faster production rates also give manufacturers the opportunity to change production runs more often, allowing for a diversity of product types.

Along with these advantages some disadvantages arise including reductions in the workforce, higher levels of stress as the complexity of work increases and production rates rise.

Assembly line production, is an industrial process used in mass production. It involves the movement of the product to be manufactured from station to station, often using conveyor belts or other transportation systems.

The product moves past workers, tooling and machinery stations until the product is complete.

Often referred to as 'reductionism', assembly line workers were typically involved in work reduced to simple, repetitive tasks that have no association with the production of a final product. While mechanised assembly lines can remove much of the physical burden placed on workers, the workers are often deskilled compared with the craftsmen of previous times. As mechanisation increased many of the tasks simply became machine tending.

While Henry Ford was not the first to use the assembly line, he is credited with refining the controlled movement of standardized parts and revolutionizing mass production. Labelled as 'Fordism', this allowed the mass production of vehicles of a consistent quality. Consumers at this point, however, had their purchase options limited as defined by Ford's legendary quote, "My customers can also get any colour, as long as it's black." Figure 4.5.2 shows workers on a Ford assembly line in 1930.

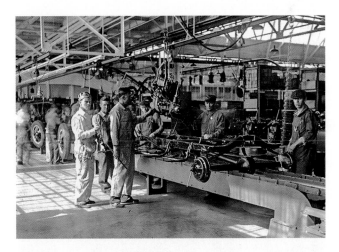

Figure 4.5.2   Ford assembly line (1930)

Mass customisation, employs flexible manufacturing systems, (often computer driven), to bring the efficiencies of mass production to short job runs even down to single orders. The advantages include low costs and fast production times. In some ways it is considered to be the opposite of mass production where large numbers of identical products are produced.

Mass customization places the individual consumer in control. Rather than companies responding to market expectations, individuals tender their requests directly to the manufacturer. Coupled with online technologies, manufacturers can meet consumer demands from computers in their homes where they can review products that are modified at the click of a mouse.

A clear example of mass customisation coupled with online communication is Nike's ID program. Consumers can logon to the Nike website and customise the style, colour and any text additions to footwear while reviewing these changes on screen. The completed design can be purchased online and despatched to the consumer directly from the factory.

Computer numeric control (CNC)

In CNC systems, an operator generates a computer file that can be directly loaded into the CNC machine for manufacturing. In some cases, the computer file may be a drawing. The computer program then extracts the information required for manufacturing. CNC machining systems use a computer or machine control unit that calculates optimal settings and issues commands accordingly. These commands are issued in the form of numeric data to motors that position slides, select tools, adjust spindle speeds, manipulate tool paths and control coolant.

Multi-tool CNC machines are used where the outcome requires more than one cutting process. For example, a CNC lathe is able to drill, ream, thread, cut and part-off components. Figure 4.5.3 shows a CNC router assembly.

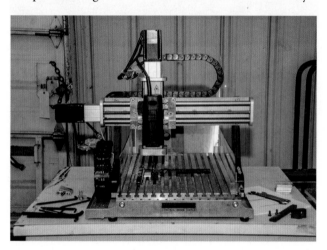

Figure 4.5.3   CNC router, image by Jon 'ShakataGaNai' Davis CC-BY-SA-3.0 unported (www.creativecommons. org/licenses/by-sa/3.0/) via Wikimedia Commons

A programming language known as G code is used to impart instructions to CNC machines. G codes instruct machines to perform a particular function or move in a specified way. The information supplied by these codes relates to tool feed rates, spindle speeds depth and direction of cut etc. Examples of some common G codes are recorded below. Note, these codes may vary between software packages and individual CNC machines. These codes are provided as a guide only.

G00 Rapid positioning
G04 Dwell
G21 Programming in mm
G28 Return to home position
G33 Thread cutting.

Such systems are now appearing outside of industrial workshops. The CEREC (short for chairside economical restoration of esthetic ceramics or CEramic REConstruction) is a benchtop milling machine used in dental surgeries to create individualised ceramic restorations (Figure 4.5.4).

Figure 4.5.4   CEREC miller

Using an intraoral camera the dentist makes a digital image of the region requiring an insert or crown and a CAD/CAM image is created and sent to the CEREC miller, in which a silicate ceramic block, colour matched to the patient's tooth, is waiting to be milled. The ceramic blocks used in this process (Figure 4.5.5) are adhesively fixed to a platform allowing them to be clamped within the milling chamber.

Figure 4.5.5   Ceramic blocks used by the CEREC miller to create dental inserts and crowns

A view inside the milling chamber is shown in Figure 4.5.6 in which the two burrs used to mill the ceramic block can be seen attached to their respective motor units. The burrs move back and forth in concert to machine the insert from the block, completing their work within 6 to 15 minutes.

Figure 4.5.6   View inside the CEREC milling chamber

Production system selection criteria

The selection of a production system involves a wide number of interconnected considerations such as: materials, process flow, employee training, manufacturing efficiency, health and safety, process control and flexibility, waste and emissions controls, etc., in order to create an effective, efficient and robust production system. The use of Design for Manufacture DfM guidelines in the early stages of production system design is often adopted as a means of achieving these goals.

Design for manufacture (DfM)

Design for manufacture is an important tool in reducing production costs through considerations of efficiencies of design, manufacturing and assembly. DfM is a process of refining the product by optimizing its design to improve rates of production and/or quality and can be a dominating constraint on a design brief.

DfM can be conveniently split into several sub-groupings:

Design for materials: is a mechanism by which designers select materials with the aim of reducing toxic substances, hazardous waste, polluting emissions and the quantity of materials required. Wherever possible single component materials are specified for moulding and recyclable materials are specified and marked for later identification. Similar specifications are then also applied to packaging.

Design for process: involves reductions in process related issues such as, the amount of energy consumed, waste generated, emissions produced and the reduction of the number of parts requiring additional operations such as plating, painting, printing, labelling, riveting and welding.

Design for assembly: is an approach used by designers to analyse components and sub-assemblies with the goal of reducing costs through the reduction in the number of parts and maximizing the efficiency of assembly processes. Consideration of tools to be used along with a rationalisation of the variety and number of tools required during assembly may also be important.

Design for disassembly: is a process that facilitates ease of repair, reuse, remanufacturing or recycling of a product. It has become increasingly popular with manufacturers as they strive to maintain profitability while meeting the legislated requirements of Directive 2002/96/EC on Waste Electrical and Electronic Equipment (WEEE) and Directive 2002/95/EC Reduction of Hazardous Substances (RoHS) of the European Parliament. Manufacturers also see benefits associated with the potential to reduce production costs. To be effective, disassembly of a product into its component parts, in preparation for recycling can only be achieved if it is considered early in the design process through the application of appropriate guidelines that include the following.

- Material selection–use recyclable materials and limited variety where possible.

- Fastening techniques–minimise use of adhesives and wherever possible use thermoplastic adhesives. Use semi-permanent connections such as screws, bolts and snap fittings when possible. Avoid permanent connection techniques such as welding, brazing and soldering.

- Design and specification of components, assemblies and sub-assemblies. Whenever possible reduce the number of component parts. Modular design allows sub-assemblies to be combined in a variety of ways and facilitates removal and replacement.

This framework not only facilitates product disassembly but also assists with repair, recycling, salvage and reuse, thus, reducing the need for virgin resources. Standardisation of fasteners throughout the product means similar tools and skills sets are required for disassembly and maintenance. Similarly, the location of regularly replaced components, such that they are easily accessed, facilitates repair and maintenance.

Adapting designs for DfM

Adaptation of designs for DfM will involve a review of the design to standardise components wherever possible

163

and substitute custom made parts, such as fasteners, for commercially available, lower cost parts. This reduces the need to maintain a wide range of parts and tools.

The next stage of design adaptation is to review the design for opportunities to simplify and stream-line the product by reducing the number of components involved and adopting a modular approach to construction.

Designs should also be such that connections should only be compatible when such a connection is desirable, in order to avoid parts being connected back to front or upside down.

INTERNATIONAL MINDEDNESS

The geographical distribution of different modes of production is an economic and political issue.

© IBO 2012

The location of industries was at one time dependent largely on geographic factors such as the location of raw materials, power and transport sources such as rivers, distance from markets and the ready availability of cheap sources of labour.

The development of modern means of communication, power and transport along with the globalisation of markets allowed manufacturing industries in particular to locate based on measures of competitive advantage specific to their industry.

The textile and clothing industries for example have increasingly transferred their production facilities from higher labour cost developed countries, to developing countries, where labour costs are significantly lower and government regulations with regard to tax and environmental regulation are often more favourable. In this instance, modern transportation means that the geographical distance from markets is a minor consideration. Similarly, modern communications and the ready availability of a highly educated work force has meant that many countries have outsourced Information Technology functions and call centre operations in lower labour cost countries such as India.

By contrast, developed countries have an advantage in a generally more highly developed infrastructure and availability of highly skilled workforce. This is reflected in the location of research and development intensive industries such as biotechnology, pharmaceuticals, electronics, aeronautics and finance.

Other industries owe their continued operations within an economy to heavy government tariffs and subsidisation of production. This is seen in many developed economies such as the USA, Europe, China and Japan where industries such as agriculture and automobile manufacture are often protected from free market trade due to domestic political concerns regarding the loss of tradition, workforce unemployment and national security.

THEORY OF KNOWLEDGE

The geographical distribution of different modes of production is an economic and political issue.

© IBO 2012

Thoughts of a craftsman operating in isolation with simple tools to fashion a product from conception through to finished product, reflective of a pre-industrial revolution world, has a flavour of traditional knowledge about it, but is not necessarily central to the question posed. The first part of the question involves the meaning of craftsmanship and whether it has been affected by dependency on automation. We can define a craftsman as someone who is skilled in the manipulation of materials. This does not imply that such manipulation was performed with their bare hands. Tools (including machinery) have always been used by craftsmen and indeed many tools were developed by craftsmen to allow certain tasks to be performed more accurately and precisely. However when we talk about craftsmanship we generally mean something related to the quality of the work produced whether it is a Chippendale chair, Fabergé egg or a Steinway piano, hence the common saying "It is a poor craftsman who blames his tools". The traditional craftsman produced product varied from one article to the next, an attribute that is actually valued in many objects today as it reflects the time and care of a craftsman involved in the production.

A humorous scene from the musical *Fiddler on the Roof* occurs when the tailor Motel proclaims on finally obtaining a sewing machine:

"From now on my clothes will be perfect.
Made by machine!
No more handmade clothes!"

Modern manufacturing using automation and robots seeks to eliminate variability as much as possible. To achieve this, production is often divided between a number of work stations, each of which performs a relatively limited number of operations on the material before it is passed to the next stage. Each machine is typically overseen by an operator who monitors operations.

This organisation undoubtedly allows the efficient mass production of products at a level matching or exceeding that of a skilled craftsman of a previous age, provided material parameters do not change. If conditions change, however, it is the operator's understanding of the material and the capabilities of the machinery that allows them to make the required changes and maintain quality. Students should consider whether this intervention rises to the level of craftsmanship.

The second part of the question dealing with whether technology has affected traditional ways of knowing can be seen in large part as one of degree. What was the traditional way of knowing? In many cases it involved an apprentice working and learning skills under the watchful eye of a master craftsman. The student might explore the supplementation of this model of knowing with the rise of theory based learning about the attributes of materials, formal qualifications available through technical colleges, and the availability of computers and the internet.

Further reading

Mckay, B., and Mckay, K. (2013). *Measure twice, cut once: Applying the ethos of the craftsman to our everyday lives.* [Available online at http://www.artofmanliness. com/2013/07/03/measure-twice-cut-once-applying-the-ethos-of-the-craftsman-to-our-everyday-lives/]

Invasion of the super piano.
[Available online at http://www.piano-lessons.net/news_item.php?id=114]

Oretega, A. (2014). *Ray Garzia a new look for shoes with a traditional craftsmanship.* Fashionbi Insights. [Available online at http://fashionbi.com/newspaper/ray-garzia-a-new-look-for-shoes-with-a-traditional-craftsmanship]

Koyano, S. (1979). *Technology of traditional industry and the role of craftsmen.* The United Nations University, HSDRJE-1/UNUP-84. [Available online at http://d-arch. ide.go.jp/je_archive/english/society/wp_je_unu1.html]

ACMP (2009). *That carbon fibre cello.* The Chamber Music Network Newsletter.
[Available online at http://www.luisandclark.com/wordpress/wp-content/uploads/2009/09/ACMP-winter-newsletter.pdf]

4.6–ROBOTS IN AUTOMATED PRODUCTION

CORE

ESSENTIAL IDEA

The development of increasingly sophisticated robotic manufacturing systems is transforming the way products are made.

© IBO 2012

NATURE OF DESIGN

Designers should consider the benefits of increased efficiency and consistency when using robots in production and be able to explore the latest advances in technology to ensure the optimum manufacturing process is used. However, a good designer will also understand their responsibility to consider the moral and ethical issues surrounding increased use of automation, and the historical impact of lost jobs.

© IBO 2012

AIM

The introduction of robots to an assembly line has had a major impact on the labour force, often making skilled workers redundant in favour of a technician who can maintain and equip a large number of robots.

© IBO 2012

Primary characteristics of robots: work envelope and load capacity

The International Standards Organisation, (ISO), standard ISO 8373:1994 defined an industrial robot as, 'an automatically controlled, reprogrammable, multipurpose, manipulator programmable in three or more axes, which may be either fixed in place or mobile for use in industrial automation applications.'

The revision of this standard in 2012 required recognition of a broader range of robots in the marketplace so that ISO 8373:2012 defined a robot as an 'actuated mechanism programmable in two or more axes with a degree of autonomy, moving within its environment, to perform intended tasks'.

The new definition recognises that robots are now fulfilling a wider range of activities that can include both industrial and non-industrial roles including the following.

- Industrial robots.

- Service robots.

- Personal care robots.

- Medical robots.

Figure 4.6.1 shows a generic example of an industrial fixed robotic arm. Typically, industrial robots are comprised of four basic components:

- power source – electrical, hydraulic or pneumatic

- tooling – fixed, multiple or interchangeable tools

- mechanical unit – structural arm, sensors, joints, actuators

- control system – computer or microprocessor driven controller.

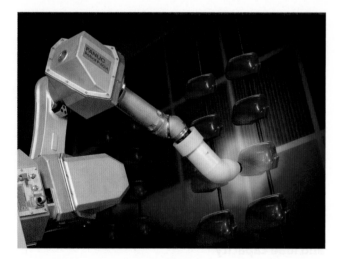

Figure 4.6.1   Typical robot arm, image by "P-50iA" by RoboGuru, own work. Licensed under Creative Commons Attribution-Share Alike 3.0 via Wikimedia Commons

Robots are not the answer to all of a manufacturer's problems. There are many tasks that may never be assigned to robots, although the range of applications continues to grow. At present, the role of industrial robots can be divided into three basic categories:

- quality control and inventory

- fabrication or assembly operations

- materials handling and transportation.

Quality control robots use sensors to inspect products for defects. These robots may be stationed throughout the assembly line and may be independent or programmed as part of a multi-tasking robot operation.

Improved management of robotic systems is achieved using flexible manufacturing or Computer Integrated Manufacturing (CIM) systems, where computers monitor and control the entire process of manufacturing from scheduling each step of production to keeping track of parts inventories, tool use and warehousing.

Materials handling robots transport materials, components and finished product throughout a plant. They may be used for complex palletising of products in a warehouse, retrieving multiple components ready for the assembly line or moving sub-assemblies between stations. Automated warehouses are an example of this application as shown in Figure 4.6.2.

Figure 4.6.2   Robotic materials handling and transport image by Mukeshhrs, own work. Licensed under Public domain via Wikimedia Commons

Fabrication or assembly robots work in a variety of ways i.e. single robot - single-task, multi robot - single task or single robot - multi task situations. Single task robots perform one operation such as spot welding. In multi-robot situations a team of robots may work together to place components and hold them in place while other robots drill, weld or rivet. Multi task robots may perform a variety of operations within the one cell using interchangeable heads or multiple arms.

Single-task robots

Single-task robots perform specific operations. These robots are often limited in their ability to move e.g. left or right, up or down. Most commonly known as servo robots these machines use servomechanisms to control arms and grippers. This technology provides robot arms with greater flexibility i.e. 5 to 7 directions. These robots may weld joints, hold assemblies or paint parts repeatedly without variation, with a high degree of precision. This type of robot is particularly successful at relieving human operators of boring, repetitive or dangerous tasks. Single-task robots may also be employed in multi-robot situations to achieve the desired outcome within an operational cell.

Multi-task robots

Through their complexity, multi-task robots provide a greater degree of flexibility. Making use of priority controlled, pre-emptive scheduling or even artificial intelligence. Multi-tasking robots can handle both complex and parallel operations, employing independent secondary axes and using a variety of tools. Pre-programmed tool changes on one of the axes increase the robot's versatility yet still allows the continued independent operation of the other axis.

Teams of robots

Robots work in co-operative teams where multiple functions are required. These include moving, locating, holding and fixing processes. These processes must be efficiently coordinated and programmed to ensure effective, accurate, repeatable and collision-free operations. Assembly operations such as those associated with automobiles require robot systems not only to manoeuvre parts into place but also to hold components precisely while they are being secured. In these situations, multiple robots may be required to strategically weld assemblies held in place by another robot. A clear example of this could be a car door panel. The door assembly must be quickly and accurately aligned with, and held against, the body shell while another robot welds the hinges in place. Once the routine is established and programmed, the robots can continue to repeatedly perform this function.

Machine to machine (M2M): represents technologies that allow the communication of devices over wireless and wired connections without the necessity for human intervention.

A common example of M2M communication is in mobile devices that automatically look for updates to apps and upload them to the device.

Web-based applications can connect vehicle sensors wirelessly to internet services that allow customers to track their vehicles, warn occupants of the need to check vehicle systems such as oil level or tyre pressure and alert them to changing traffic conditions.

Perhaps the most ubiquitous applications of M2M technology are the Automatic Teller Machine (ATM) and Electronic Funds Transfer at Point of Sale (EFTPOS) card readers that allow millions of small financial transactions to be made by connecting to bank accounts to check availability of funds before deciding on acceptance of a transaction (Figure 4.6.3).

Figure 4.6.3   EFTPOS card reader

INTERNATIONAL MINDEDNESS

The use of robots in automated production can depend on the local cost of manual labour.

© IBO 2012

The decision to automate production is almost always based on the need to lower the cost of production. However, the reduction in labour obtained by introducing such systems needs to be balanced against the initial capital cost of the machines, in addition to ongoing human involvement in programming and maintenance which can be quite high. Decisions will therefore depend on the cost of labour and the production volumes projected.

Where long production runs and repetitive operations are involved, automation is often adopted even in low labour cost countries. When short production runs are involved however, the costs of reprogramming and the adaptation of automated systems can be prohibitive compared with the cost associated with manual labour.

THEORY OF KNOWLEDGE

Technology in the form of robots currently serve man. Is man's place secure – will the nature of man change due to technological enhancement – will he be superseded altogether by technological developments?

© IBO 2012

There are at least three parts to this question and the student will need to deal with each of them to some degree. Firstly, in considering whether the nature of man will change due to technological enhancement one needs to establish what is the nature of man? What are the attributes that we would recognise as belonging to man? This is not a trivial question and has occupied many philosophers since the ancient Greeks along with theologians, psychologists and political scientists.

Aristotle for example considered human nature to be associated with reasoning and rational thought as well as desires and passions.

The second consideration, based on the first, is whether human nature is immutable or is it subject to change as the question implies? Values and civilisations may change but can human nature? How might technological enhancements change human nature, and if change in human nature occurs is it not still human nature?

Thirdly, is the question whether through technological enhancement of man or robots, mankind will be superseded? The student could explore this theme through any number of science fiction themes involving self-conscious machines and the almost ubiquitous 'Three Laws of Robotics' proposed by Isaac Asimov.

Technological enhancement of man may one day allow all of the organs of the body to be replaced with synthetic substitutes of greater robustness. Artificial organs are under development and it has been proposed that nano-robots may be injected into the blood stream to fight disease and electronic chips may be placed in the brain to enhance memory. At what stage of replacement would we say it was no longer the same person or even a man? Is this a form of the Ship of Theseus Paradox?

Further Reading

Closson, D. (1992). *The Nature of Man* [Available online at: http://www.leaderu.com/orgs/probe/docs/naturman.html

Perlman, L. (Spring 2012). *The truth about human nature.* The New Atlantis, Number 35, pp142-148. [Available online at: http://www.thenewatlantis.com/publications/the-truth-about-human-nature].

Sack, W. (1997). *Artificial human nature.* Design Issues, Vol.13, pp55-64. [Available online at: http://danm.ucsc.edu/~wsack/Writings/wsack-design-issues.pdf]

Rubin, C.T. (Spring 2003). *Artificial Intelligence and Human Nature.* The New Atlantis, Number 1, pp 88-100. [Available online at http://www.thenewatlantis.com/publications/artificial-intelligence-and-human-nature].

Materials testing, evaluation and reporting

The simple engineering report provided by Bureau Veritas on the following pages is typical of a non-destructive materials analysis undertaken by materials engineers (metallurgists). These tests are conducted by engineers to determine if part failure is due to materials concerns, manufacturing or to allow replacement parts to be made if original specifications are not available.

The part, a pinion, is a common component of many engineered products requiring transmission of rotational motion. Some client-specific details have been removed from the report.

The report includes the following:

Date.
Client.
Reason for test.
Tests performed.
Results related to relevant standards.
Comments.
Photographic record.

The original report would also include the name and position of the report author and reviewer.

CASE STUDY:

Materials and design testing

Report: xxxxx

Client: xxxxx

Attn: xxxxx

Order xxxxx

Date: xxxxx

Traditionally a company logo and company details would appear here.

Since the size and colour of the BV logo are strictly policed as are most company logos it is not reproduced to be visible here.

Component: Pinion Material Identification

The tests marked 'X' were carried out to determine the material grade, heat treatment, etc.

X	Chemical Analysis – AES/ EDS		Replication
	Mechanical Testing	X	Hardness Test
	Microexamination		Site Hardness Test

A pinion was received from xxxxxxxx for non-destructive material identification testing. Images of the pinion are provided in Figures 1 and 2. The following identification was present on one end.

62402   13   L = 196,83   TA

A visible heat tint was present on the ends of the pinion and top land of each tooth suggesting selective surface hardening.

Chemical analysis was performed using Atomic Emission Spectrometer (AES) on the end of the pinion and the results presented below in Table 1.

C	Mn	P	S	Si	Ni	Cr	Mo	Al	Cu
0.44	1.20	0.009	>0.12	0.16	0.13	1.31	0.25	0.024	0.21

These results indicate the pinion had been manufactured from a medium carbon free machining low alloy steel similar to 41CrMoS4 (Wk No 1.2331). This material approximates a resulphurised version of AS1444/4140. This material is suitable for induction hardening. A sulphur print was performed on the end of the pinion to confirm the high sulphur result and is shown in Figure 3.

Hardness tests were performed on the end of the pinion, tooth top land and tooth flanks using an Equotip portable hardness tester using an LD+15 impact device with the results presented below.

Flank hardness 267-296 HV (HL_{D+15})

Top land and End hardness 296-322 HV (HL_{D+15})

The results suggest that despite evidence of a heat tint on the end of the pinion and top land of the teeth, that the surface had not been effectively induction hardened.

Comments

A free machining grade would not normally be recommended for gear components and a change in specification to AS1444/4140 is suggested.

Figure 1 General view of the pinion as received

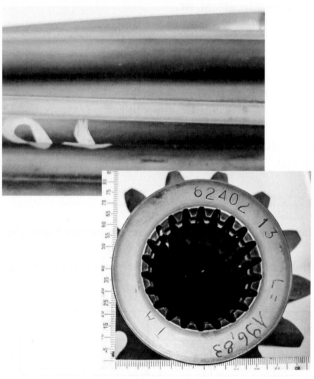

Figure 2 View of heat tint indications along top tooth land and end of pinion

Figure 3 View of sulphur print performed on end of pinion confirming high sulphur content

SAMPLE QUESTIONS

1. Glasses are called amorphous because they:

    A   are transparent
    B   are highly structured
    C   have no crystalline structure
    D   have low coefficients of expansion.

2. Which type of production method would be used for the production of single, unique, individual products.

    A   Craft.
    B   Batch.
    C   Mechanised.
    D   Fully automated.

3. Thermosetting polymers are difficult to recycle because of their:

    A   strength
    B   3–D bonding
    C   linear chains
    D   insulative properties.

4. A material's ability to resist cracking is called:

    A   strength
    B   ductility
    C   toughness
    D   malleability.

5. Explain how alloying may increase the strength of a material.

6. Explain the difference between single robot–single task, multi robot–single task and single robot–multi task situations.

7. Explain the difference between mechanising, automating, and computerising a manufacturing process.

8. Describe how robots help with the process of mass customisation.

9. Discuss the use of thermosoftening polymers from environmental and manufacturing perspectives.

10. Describe why man-made LVL is a popular choice over natural timber in construction.

INNOVATION AND DESIGN

CONTENTS

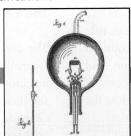

CORE

5.1–INVENTION

ESSENTIAL IDEA

The protection of a novel product that solves a problem is a major factor in commercial design.

© IBO 2012

NATURE OF DESIGN

Invention by lone inventors or in collaborative, creative teams is at the forefront of design. Designers must not only be creative and innovative, but understand the concepts that will make a new product viable. A designer must use imagination and be firmly grounded in factual and procedural knowledge whilst remembering the needs and limitations of the end user.

© IBO 2012

AIM

Inventions are often the result of an individual or group's curiosity about whether something can be done or a problem can be solved. On occasion, inventions are the result of an individual's curiosity about something other than the product finally developed. These inventions include microwave ovens, ink-jet printers and post-it® notes.

© IBO 2012

Drivers for invention

People invent for a variety of reasons including the meeting of basic human needs, self fulfilment, financial gain or by altruism and the wish to make life easier and better for others.

Invention has been critical to the development of modern society. Englishman Thomas Malthus (1766–1834) warned that population growth, if unchecked would exceed the capacity of the earth to provide food, a position again proposed by Paul Ehrlich in his 1968 publication, 'The Population Bomb'. In both cases projections of the date at which such calamities would occur were averted by technological changes that increased food production. These technological changes took place in a range of fields, including but not limited to transportation, food preservation, agriculture and communications technologies. Norbert Wiener (1894–1964) mathematician and philosopher clarifies these thoughts in his statement, "We live only by the grace of invention; not merely by such invention as has already been made, but by our hope of new and as yet nonexisting inventions for the future".

As suggested in the previous paragraph, motivations for improvement have included grand ideals such as betterment of society and even baser instincts such as survival, however, the drivers for invention are complex and often a combination of factors.

Necessity is the oft-quoted mother of invention. Little could be more pressing than the need to feed an ever growing population. The spectre of an increasing population coupled with unreliable food supplies led the political economist Thomas Malthus in 1798 to suggest that population predictions could not be supported by known methods of food production and would lead to a correction by mass starvation. While his prediction proved inaccurate, it was the increasing pace of innovation during the Industrial Revolution that led to a solution to the food supply problem. The introduction of rail transport greatly increased the amount of food that could be distributed in a short period of time plus the ability to rapidly move grain and meat large distances also meant that new areas of land distant from cities and towns could now be linked to markets economically and were therefore now viable locations for food production. As iron and steel production increased, farm implements previously made of wood began to be replaced by mass produced equipment made of sturdier, longer lasting iron and steel. The efficiency of farm production was also greatly improved by the invention of mechanical tools such as the stump jump plough and combine harvester.

Many inventors of the past have been inquisitive explorers, driven by a creative pursuit or personal interest to develop something new. The nature of innovation for many is seen as a personal challenge to be overcome, associated professional standing within a professional community and career advancement along with financial recompense may be powerful drivers. Clearly, the commercial side of the equation is important for independent inventors and the desire to make money from a new invention ranks highly.

Design competitions, both recent and historic have been strong motivators for individuals to create or invent a solution to an identified problem. Some examples follow.

In 1809 Nicolas François Appert developed a system for preserving food in glass bottles in response to a challenge set by Napoleon Bonaparte. A prize of 12,000 francs was on offer to the person who could better preserve food to sustain Napolean's armies in the field.

The influence behind the development of the IBM artificial intelligence '*Deep Blue*' that defeated world chess champion Gary Kasparov in 1996 was a US $100 000 prize.

The X-Prize Foundation advertised a US $10 million cash prize for the first privately owned aircraft to transport three people into space and then repeat the operation within a two week window. The prize was claimed by Burt Rutan when in 2004 his design, SpaceShipOne successfully met the competition criteria.

Figure 5.1.1   X-Prize Foundation winner SpaceShipOne, image by Ian Kluft, (own image), share alike 3.0 unported

A more altruistic approach is apparent from those who desire to create solutions to problems for the public good.

The lone inventor

The concept of the lone inventor was popularised by journalists during the Industrial Revolution when inventors were associated with the development of significant discoveries. Later, others such as Alexander Graham Bell and the telephone, Thomas Edison and the light bulb or gramophone and later the Wright Brothers and flight also had their efforts promoted by the press.

The classic and most often quoted example of the lone inventor was Thomas Edison, who held patents for more than a 1 000 inventions. Recent research challenges the notion of Edison and others toiling individually. David Burkus, (2013) in his book, *The Myths of Creativity*, claims Edison was the public front man for a whole creative team of engineers, machinists, and physicists. While his ability to innovate is not challenged, the perception that he did it alone is subject to debate.

Figure 5.1.2   Thomas Edison C1882 — lone inventor?

In fact others have also documented the notion of the sole inventor as a myth and include the likes of Tesla, Alexander Graham Bell, Samuel Morse, and Eli Whitney as prominent inventors who relied on the work of others.

Mark Lemley of Stanford Law School, when writing on patent law for the Michigan Law Review, (2012) noted "surveys of hundreds of significant new technologies show that almost all of them are invented simultaneously or nearly simultaneously by two or more teams working independently of each other. Invention appears in significant part to be a social, not an individual, phenomenon".

While historically there are still recorded instances of individuals plucking an idea from the ether, most new technology and inventions have been the result of simultaneous or concurrent research conducted by teams often fronted by an individual who has been able to successfully register or patent an idea first. Inventors as a rule build on work preceding their efforts and often new ideas are floated before one or another group adopt the notion for development, modification or refinement. These changes are often based on new technologies, materials or manufacturing processes.

The advantages and disadvantages of being a lone inventor

Lone inventors are able to exert complete control over the development of their work. The nature of their working style may also indicate they are used to working independently and not part of larger teams where they are just one voice among many. They often have significant emotional investment and ownership issues surrounding their efforts and as such may have difficulty working with others who may wish to take design development in other directions.

The nature of collaborative teams, however, working on new ideas brings a whole new dynamic to the nature of innovation. Collaboration not only brings more than one perspective to an idea but new potential by introducing a range of expertise, experience and problem solving techniques. Singh and Fleming, (2009), in their research paper *Lone Inventors as Source of Breakthroughs Myth or Reality?* propose, "team and/or organization affiliation increases the likelihood of creative outcomes".

During the 20th century things have become clearer and the notion of the lone inventor has gradually disappeared with the emergence of multi-national companies and research and development teams. Increasingly, the majority of products today are very complicated. Materials technology, manufacturing processes and testing procedures are now so complex no one person has the knowledge, skills or resources to successfully bring a product to the market. Once an initial concept is proposed, multidisciplinary teams of experts are required to develop and market the successful product. It is these groups that are now mostly credited with major product developments.

Intellectual property (IP)

The World Intellectual Property Organisation defines intellectual property (IP) as anything that, "refers to creations of the mind, such as inventions; literary and artistic works; designs; and symbols, names and images used in commerce". Common types of IP rights include patents, trademarks and copyright.

Benefits of IP

IP is protected by law and as an extension protects the creator or inventor from having their work used by others. This protection assists inventors and investors to recoup expensive research and development costs without fear of unfair competition. In this way, IP encourages and supports creativity and innovation. IP is a balance between the rights of the inventor and needs or wants of the greater market and consumers. Specifically, the benefits associated with granting of IP rights may include the following:

- consideration by investors as a safeguard of an asset for a start-up company or new product venture requiring funding

- protection from competitors and a guarantee that the product is original in its nature

- protection extended beyond the primary design and the income associated with its sale, any income stream pursuant to derivative designs and licensed production thereof

- searchable documentation through patent databases providing access to the latest developments, technologies and processes, (estimates from the European Commission documents archive suggest 80% of current technical knowledge is stored in patent document form).

Strategies for protecting IP: patents; trademarks; design protection; copyright

Patents

In simple terms, patents protect inventions. A patent provides the registered owner with the right to prevent others from copying, manufacturing selling or importing your invention without express permission. Patents protect a range of IP not limited to physical products but extending to manufacturing processes, software, materials developments and even methods of business.

To ensure a successful patent application, the invention must be new and not directly related to or a derivative of an existing patent. As an additional protection only the inventor may apply for a patent ie. you cannot patent another's invention. Design patents are restricted to the appearance of an article as shown in the drawings and illustrations covered by the patent.

In return for the protections offered by the patenting process, the inventor agrees to make all of the technical information associated with the patent publicly available.

The term 'patent pending' indicates that a patent application has been filed. It does not guarantee the issue of a patent license but serves as a warning that a patent may be issued. Patent license contracts may also include safety and or quality assurance clauses.

Most often patents are territorial in that they offer protection only in the country in which the patent has been filed. Searchable databases such as those held by Google (google.com/patents) and esp@cenet offer access to millions of patent documents from around the world. These databases provide companies and individuals with information and may answer questions that may save valuable time and money. Some of these questions are listed below.

- Does a current patent exist in a particular field?

- Is a patent still in force or has it expired?

- What are competitors in a similar field working on?

- Is there information or technology in existence that can assist with research and development?

Copyright

Copyright is a mechanism to protect the rights of artists and authors. Denoted by an encircled letter 'c' the copyright symbol is applied to works of any medium. Copyrighted works cover a large range of materials including: books, movies, television, music, advertisements, radio broadcasts, software, databases, works of art, drawings, maps, photographs, etc.

The length of time a copyright may be enforced depends on the type of work covered. In the UK, literary, theatrical musical or artistic works are protected for the life of the creator plus an additional 70 years from the year of their death.

Trademarks™, Servicemarks™ and Registered Trademarks®

The marking of goods with a maker's identifying mark goes back to ancient times. However, it wasn't until the establishment of medieval craft guilds that rules started appearing governing their use. In the 1800s consumers started to place a market value on a manufacturer's trade marked goods and the courts began to support traders against infringement of their rights to distinguish a product as their own.

Today the trademark symbol denotes an unregistered trademark. It most often appears in superscripted or subscripted form and is regularly used for brand names of products to differentiate one manufacturer from another in the marketplace.

As the name suggests, servicemarks are appended to services such as advertising as opposed to products or packaging. Service marks may even be sounds used in advertising or in the delivery of a service. As with trademarks, servicemarks must be identifiable and suitably unique.

The registration of a trademark provides a company with a range of protections and opportunities. A registered trademark signals to other companies your legal right to exclusively claim the rights to use the unique marking on your goods. Companies with registered trademarks may take legal action against others who use the mark without permission, however, permission to use the mark may be extended to others through the awarding of franchise rights or licenses. The registered trademark symbol is usually superscripted or subscripted and appears in place of the trademark or service mark symbols.

Figure 5.1.3   Patent, trademark and copyright IP symbols

The effectiveness of strategies for protecting IP

In Europe and the United States, patents are granted for a period of twenty years from the earliest filing date on which the patent was granted. While providing the inventor with a measure of protection and an opportunity to recover expensive research and development costs through the commercialisation of the idea, patenting may have the effect of reducing competition and hampering the development of new products and processes.

The high costs associated with patenting may be mitigated to some degree through licensing fees negotiated with competitors. This is particularly relevant in the field of semiconductors where the existing technology is covered by hundreds of patents held by a range of organisations. For some, however, these fees can be a disincentive to innovate based on existing technology and process.

Without patents, inventors would be forced to keep their ideas secret. If the invention did not go to market then the innovation may be lost without being documented and centrally recorded.

The field with the strongest financial return and need for stringent patent protection is that covering pharmaceuticals and biotechnology. Successful drug developments can yield billions of dollars in profits and the newly identified filed of gene therapy is no different. The path to financial success has proven not to be as clear as first envisioned.

In 2013 the US Supreme court ruled in a unanimous decision that, "A naturally occurring DNA segment is a product of nature and not patent eligible merely because it has been isolated." The ruling invalidates all past claims on natural human gene sequences (approx. 4 000) and secures the future of those which have been patented. This ruling is by no means universal as governments around the world struggle to separate the nature of innovation opposed to the isolation of naturally occurring DNA sequences.

Many companies like those in the biotechnology field have tried to 'lock down' specifics relevant to their businesses to the point where applications can be seen as frivolous. In 2001 the United States Court of Appeals for the Federal Circuit upheld an appeal against the previous Examining Attorney's ruling to refuse to grant a service mark application to the Thrifty vehicle rental company whose application asked for registration of "the colour blue". The application was refused on the grounds of being insufficiently concise.

First to market

If innovations are successful in the market then imitators will seek to replicate the experience, and the lodging of a patent for registration telegraphs to competitive businesses that another manufacturer has an innovation they want to protect. Unfortunately, part of the patent protection process requires the innovator to reveal not only the driving concept behind the new development but also the associated designs, technologies and processes associated with its manufacture. While the cost of patent application is relatively cheap, the time involved and

the costs surrounding the maintenance and defence of patent rights can be excessive. It is for these reasons that many innovative companies in both Europe and the USA value market share, lead time, secrecy and superior sales more than the securing of a patent when considering the maximising of profits from new developments.

Shelved technologies

Some patented inventions simply aren't commercially viable, in that the cost associated with bringing them to market would generate a price beyond the means of the target market. Similarly, some developments simply do not have a commercial application or identified market.

Other, successful and commercially viable innovations identified by rival companies in the same field may be 'acquired'. With a new owner, the innovation may now be incorporated into the host companies products or may be shelved to remove competition from the marketplace.

INTERNATIONAL MINDEDNESS

The role of intellectual property and patents in stifling or promoting inventions globally needs to be considered, especially with regard to the inequalities between countries.

© IBO 2012

In 1859 Abraham Lincoln praised the introduction of patent laws for having "..secured to the inventor, for a limited time, the exclusive use of his invention; and thereby added the fuel of interest to the fire of genius, in the discovery and production of new and useful things." He also claimed patents laws to be one of the three most important developments in the history of the world.

In more recent times the patent process, particularly in the US, has been seen as less than satisfactory. In 2010 a patent application in the US took an average 34.6 months to be processed. At the same time there were 1.2 million applications in the system. Testimony from the US Patent Office made to the The House Judiciary Committee heard the US Patent Office "does not have the resources it needs to speedily process meritorious patent applications and to effectively filter out bad patent claims." and "when applications do not get examined in a timely fashion, important innovations are delayed or lost to the public".

The passing of particularly broad patent claims have the effect of limiting future developments or forcing companies to pay expensive licensing fees. These broad patents may act as a barrier to individuals and companies fearful of infringing existing patents, when litigation defending a new idea may be more expensive than any potential profits from future sales. Companies known as non-practicing entities, patent assertion entities or colloquially as "patent trolls" are organisations which capitalise on these broad patents by purchasing poorly performing companies for their strong intellectual property rights. The troll then uses these patents like weapons in litigation to force other companies to settle out of court to avoid the high costs of litigation. In many cases it is faster and easier to settle out of court rather than risk protracted and expensive litigation costs.

In February of 2013 President Obama referred to patents trolls as individuals and companies that, "....don't actually produce anything themselves ... they are essentially trying to leverage and hijack somebody else's idea and see if they can extort some money out of them."

In a comment on the nature of modern patents and litigation, technology billionaire Mark Cuban, (when referring to the jury verdict in favour of Apple and against Samsung), is quoted as saying, "If the IBM PC was created in this patent environment there would be no Apple. They would have sued them out of existence."

Theory of knowledge

What is the role of imagination in invention? Are there limits to what can be imagined?

© IBO 2012

Imagination is the forming of new concepts, ideas, and images in the mind that are created from a combination of previous experiences or inputs drawn from all of our senses. It is this combining and recombining of existing knowledge in a variety of alternative arrangements unconstrained by the laws of nature that produces creative results, never seen or imagined before.

An argument could be made that this is one of those areas that we don't know what we don't know? How can we imagine a limit to imagination if we can't imagine such a limitation?

Before Pasteur and the germ theory, who imagined that there was microscopic life, let alone viruses, that were responsible for disease? Until something has been discovered or theorized (imagined) to be possible - there is a limit - isn't there? That is not to say that some time in the future the limit will not change.

Students may choose to investigate what imagination is and review some of the world's great thinkers before attempting to apply this knowledge to the fields of invention and design.

Jacob Bronowski (1908–1974), a Polish-born intellectual and mathematician who studied and wrote on the sciences, technology, poetry and the relation between creativity in the arts and the sciences, saw imagination as uniquely human and described it as "the ability to make images and to move them about inside one's head in new arrangements." He goes on to say "Of all the distinctions between man and animal, the characteristic gift which makes us human is the power to work with symbolic images: the gift of imagination."

The American author William Arthur Ward (1921–1994) is famously quoted as writing, "if you can imagine it, you can achieve it." The suggestion here is that imagination is not the limiting factor but the ability of the person to either use their imagination or place faith in it.

RW Beardsmore (1944–1977) argues that imagination unlike memory is not simply recollection but is nonetheless bound by past experiences. The following quote by Richard Payne Knight may sum this more eloquently. "We may compose, paint and describe moments and chimeras of every extravagant variety of form; but still, if we analyse them, we shall always find that the component parts, how much so ever they may be distorted or disguised, have been taken from objects or qualities of objects, with which we have previously been acquainted throughout the organs of sensation." Therefore he his arguing that there is a limit, by his definition. Our imagination has to be limited because it cannot include experiences we have yet to have in the future.

Students should consider questions such as:

* What concepts, objects are difficult to imagine?

* What constitutes the unimaginable?

* What does it mean 'to have a limited imagination?'

Exercise

Explore a range of areas of knowledge and history to identify occurrences of imagination in the development of new products, principles or theories. Examples could be the entire genre of science fiction or Newton's imagining of the moon as a ball thrown hard enough to fall in concert with the horizon.

Consider the quote by Einstein (1879–1955), "Imagination is more important than knowledge. For knowledge is limited to all we now know and understand, while imagination embraces the entire world, and all there ever will be to know and understand."

> Sometimes there are unforeseen consequences of inventions. To what extent might lack of knowledge be an excuse for unethical conduct?
>
> © IBO 2012

American sociologist Robert K. Merton advanced the concept of unintended consequences in the 1930s when examining the relationship between deliberate attempts to affect positive social change and their actual outcomes.

Consideration here should be given to the range of possible causes of unintended consequences he and others have proposed, including:

- ignorance (It is impossible to anticipate everything, thereby leading to incomplete analysis)

- errors in analysis or testing, use of poor data

- human factors of self interest, gain, bias, etc.

- complexity of systems and their interaction with ever-changing environments

- the nature of small changes having far reaching effects as described by the 'butterfly effect'.

Generally it is agreed that unintended or unforseen consequences from the development or introduction of inventions and innovations fall into three distinct categories; desirable, undesirable and a contrarian result that is the reverse of what was originally intended, (the paperless office of the '80s promised as result of the computer revolution comes to mind here). History is littered with unintended consequences as a result of innovation.

The microwave oven, designed to speed the process of cooking food actually removed food preparation largely from the home and spawned a whole industry making pre-prepared meals. This led in turn to individuals heating up their own meals as and when required and thus the reduction in influence of the family dining table on society.

The pharmaceutical industry constantly issues new drugs. These drugs undergo years of rigorous testing in laboratories and field trials and yet over time, after general use in the population, many come with warnings and a list of uninteneded side-effects. Some are even removed from the market.

ARPANET was the forerunner of today's internet and was originally developed to allow the U.S. Department of Defence to connect universities and research laboratories in the US to collaboratively work on their projects. It would be impossible to see all of the positive and negative consequences associated with the public use of such a powerful communications devices including:

- identity theft, cyber bullying, internet addictions, loss of efficiency in the workplace, etc.

- social networking, online medical diagnosis, remote control of machinery and services, online shopping, etc.

The international mindedness section in Chapter 5.2 documents case studies where innovations have been transferred from one culture to another with negative effects. Did these actions constitute unethical behaviour?

Doesn't unethical conduct suggest you have knowledge and are choosing to act unethically? In cases where you don't have knowledge of adverse consequences, but believe there might be some, it may be argued it would be unethical to not put measures in place to avoid unwanted consequences.

The student should examine what might constitute a lack of knowledge. The tobacco industry argued for decades that insufficient evidence, and therefore knowledge, of a link between cancer and cigarette smoking existed even though most of the medical community believed such a link had been shown. Was this unethical behaviour? Unethical conduct can never be condoned or excused, the real test is whether any undesirable side effects from the introduction of a new technology or product could or should have been anticipated in the early stages of research and development.

Exercise

Choose a recent invention, system or environment and examine the unintended consequences (or uses) this technology or product revealed over time. Simple examples could include the iPad, the paperless office, Facebook, solar power rebate schemes and their effect on electricity prices and so on.

5.2–INNOVATION

ESSENTIAL IDEA

There are many different types of innovation.

© IBO 2012

NATURE OF DESIGN

Designers will be successful in the marketplace when they solve longstanding problems, improve on existing solutions or find a 'product gap'. The constant evaluation and redevelopment of products is key, with unbiased analysis of consumers and commercial opportunities.

© IBO 2012

AIM

In order for an invention to become an innovation, the idea of the product needs to be effectively communicated. The communication can take many forms and be between many stakeholders.

© IBO 2012

Invention and innovation

Invention is broadly defined as the act of creating something new or the significant improvement of something already in existence. It most often involves creating something that has not existed before. Inventions may take the form of a product, service or system.

Innovation refers to the successful commercialisation of an invention. An invention with no commercial viability would not be classed as an innovation.

There are many theories on the nature of, and mechanisms that bring about, invention and innovation. These theories range from the 'lone genius', to coincidental discovery and cultural maturation. Most consider the role factors such as chance and serendipity may play in the process.

While some of these theories are contradictory and others sit comfortably beside each other, the debate over market demand versus technological opportunism

continues to rage. Since 1934, when Schumpeter claimed entrepreneurial activities were driven by a technological push, the debate has swung both ways. Today's consensus is with the theories of Schmookler, who in 1962 decided user needs or market pull were the most influential drivers of innovation.

More recent research is swinging the pendulum back towards technology push theories where technological breakthroughs with strong intellectual property protection act as the driving force.

Regardless of the style of approach or driving forces, it is generally agreed innovation is the lifeblood of economic growth.

Reasons why few inventions become innovations

The chances of an invention being developed into a market-successful innovation may be influenced by the following factors:

- expectations of demand

- magnitude of user needs

- expectations of profitability

- degree of positivity of market perception

- amount of intellectual property protection afforded by patents.

Investing in innovation is about risk taking. Innovation tends to be more risky from technological, financial and market success standpoints. Market research is also less reliable for innovative products. Design teams and researchers have to rely on gathering as much feedback as possible from prototypes rather than generations of market-successful product developments. Early markets are also volatile and unpredictable places, characterised by high technological and customer uncertainty. Until customers form clear preferences about what constituents a successful, marketable product there is a great deal of variation in design and technologies on offer, not all of which can survive in a competitive marketplace.

Redevelopment of an existing product, (may only involve incremental adjustments to form or features of an existing product), is more common due to the fact that market demand has already been established.

Categories of innovation: sustaining innovation; disruptive innovation; process innovation

Sustaining innovation

Sustaining innovation is simply the application of incremental adjustments to existing products that allow them to sustain sales and continue in the market. These changes often involve improvements in performance and quality by the addition of new features. Sustaining innovation often involves economies of scale or efficiencies that may be gained through the implementation of cost cutting measures. These deliberate, planned and incremental innovations are more predictable from a financial or investment perspective than disruptive innovations. For example, in the category of household ovens, self-cleaning features make the product more environmentally friendly. Beds with independently adjustable firmness cater for individual sleep habits and vehicles with anti-collision sensors and auto parking make cars safer.

Disruptive innovation

Disruptive innovation is a phrase coined by Clayton Christensen and in his own words refers to, " a product or service (that) takes root initially in simple applications at the bottom of a market and then relentlessly moves up market, eventually displacing established competitors".

Disruptive innovations are often radical solutions to problems in competition with existing products. They galvanise customers and markets alike and are so named because they disrupt existing market behaviour. They often enter the market at the lower end yet compete directly with products that have been developed over time and which have moved to an upper price bracket.

Apple's iPhone is a good example of disruptive design. In a market dominated by Sony Ericsson and Nokia, Apple introduced a new device that captured the markets interest overtaking all in sight. It has transformed the way people communicate, buy and listen to music, access internet services and even navigate using a portable device.

Pioneering or new market disruption is more complex and fraught with difficulties. Because the target market may not currently exist, predictions on sales and profits can be hard to calculate with any certainty. This can make acquiring investment partners particularly challenging. The introduction of 3D printers into the consumer market is an example of new market disruption. Cheaper less well featured versions of successful commercial designs are appearing at the low end of the market.

Process innovation

Process innovation refers to developments associated with the process that create or deliver services and products. Process innovations such as those adopted by Henry Ford in 1913 can have enormous effects not only on productivity, quality and economics but also far reaching social change. The moving assembly line developed by Ford to produce motor cars not only allowed him to generate larger numbers of quality vehicles in a shorter period of time but it also reduced the cost of the final product making automobiles available at a price the general public could afford. While Henry Ford was not the first to use the assembly line, he is credited with refining the controlled movement of standardised parts and revolutionising mass production. Labelled as 'Fordism', this allowed the mass production of vehicles of a consistent quality.

Figure 5.2.1   Ford assembly line Long Beach California c1930

Ikea is another company that used innovation by developing, (in the 1950s), manufacturing processes based around flat-packing, ease of delivery and self assembly.

Figure 5.2.2   Ikea flat pack self assembly furniture

Probably the most significant example of process innovation occurred around the time of the Industrial Revolution, (~1759-1850), when whole industries moved from craft production techniques to mechanisation and the development of centralised factories with the ensuing social change.

Innovation strategies for design: architectural innovation; modular innovation; configurational innovation

There are many ways to characterise innovation. This particular method proposed by Henderson and Clark is useful because it combines a number of innovation styles and charts their relationships relative to each other. The chart in Figure 5.2.3 shows innovation plotted along two axes at 90° to each other. The horizontal axis plots the categorisation of innovation based on product or service components while the vertical axis charts the effects of modifying the linkages between components.

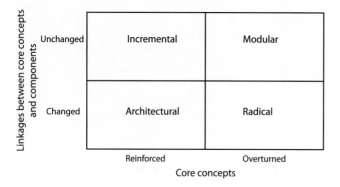

Figure 5.2.3   Innovation framework remodelled from Henderson and Clark, Architectural Innovation, Administrative Science Quarterly, Vol. 35, No. 1, Special Issue: Technology, Organizations, and Innovation. (Mar., 1990), pp. 9-30.

Architectural or configurational innovation

Architectural or configurational innovation works on a systems level, modifying not the individual components of a design but their arrangement, links and interactions to improve performance, usability or functionality. Examining changing fan technologies over time is one example of how incremental and architectural innovation affects the design of a product.

The standard desk fans, shown in Figure 5.2.4, have been a stalwart of the air ventilation industry for decades. Arrangement of blades, motors, guards and controllers is well established and as such little has changed. The

incremental innovation shown has taken place over many decades. It demonstrates superficial refinements of the exterior and the remodelling of an established design with the introduction of more efficient motors and some materials modifications. Essentially, however, the underlying core design concepts, and the links between them, remain the same.

The variations shown point to minor, incremental changes taking place between the 1920s and the 1980s. The core design concepts, systems principles and component linkages largely remain unchanged.

Figure 5.2.4   Incremental innovation— electric fan

Architectural innovation is often triggered by reduction in component size causing new component interactions or re-arrangement of existing components in such a way as to create an innovative response. The reduction in size of electronic components saw portable radios transformed as electronic components became smaller and smaller while the basic principle of the design remained the same.

Figure 5.2.5 shows an example of architectural innovation through the reconfiguration of an existing product by rearranging components in new ways. In this form the basic 'system' stays the same as do the underlying principles that make the product work. The box fan design changes the relationships between the major components and could be considered to be an architectural innovation. With the motor centrally located and the guard serving the additional roles of frame, base and controller mount, the same basic components are arranged in new ways.

Another example of architectural innovation is the development of cloud computing services where software companies make programs available online without the need for users to install them on their computer.

Figure 5.2.5   Architectural innovation—box fan

Radical innovation

Radical innovation overturns the core design concepts of existing designs and brings together both new operational components and also previously unseen architecture or linkages between these components.

In recent times the innovation associated with the Dyson desk fan demonstrates a more radical approach to the problem. In this product development, there are no moving blades or guards evident and air is accelerated in a continuous fashion. Using the principles of inducement and entrainment, the expelled air (driven by nine asymmetrically aligned rotating blades hidden in the base), amounts to 15 times the volume taken into the base.

Figure 5.2.6   Radical innovation—Dyson fan

Successful radical innovations establish new dominant designs that disrupt existing markets attracting existing and new customers to the field.

Modular innovation

The key feature of modular innovation is the introduction of new or substantially different components to a product without changing core design principles affecting the relationship or linkages between component parts. Examples of modular innovation include:

- the advancement from Web 1.0 to Web 2.0 through the technology that introduced interactive content between provider and user as well as user and user

- replacing analog, rotary dialing mechanisms with a keypad

- spring-based balance scales replaced by digital devices.

The impact on design, manufacturing and markets of modular and incremental innovation is less significant than that of architectural and radical innovation.

Innovation strategies for markets: diffusion and suppression

Diffusion

Diffusion is the process of spreading knowledge of the development of an innovation through a consumer or target market over time to enhance the adoption of the product from limited use to widespread penetration and adoption in the market. The key to adoption is perception, that is the consumer must see the innovation as a desirable replacement or substitute for an existing product.

The key tenet of market diffusion theory is that the most influential factor in a consumer's purchasing decision is the previous purchasing choices of other consumers. The communication among consumers through social networking is known as 'the network effect' or more colloquially as the word-of-mouth effect. The digital society has moved from traditional, physical word-of-mouth to social networking. Communication for products and services can spread both rapidly and globally through such systems as Facebook and Twitter. Even corporate websites such as Amazon and Trip Advisor offer consumer reviews of products. Media also plays a role in spreading awareness and information about a product as well as influencing a consumer's decision making process.

According to Rogers, (1962), the stages of innovation diffusion appear as shown by the graph in Figure 5.2.7. Groups of adopters and their relative percentages are identified by the bell curve shaped black line. Market share is indicated by the 'S' shaped grey line ending in market saturation (100%). The 'S' curve shows the initial slow rate of adoption transforming into a steeper more rapid pace of adoption as consumers embrace the new product.

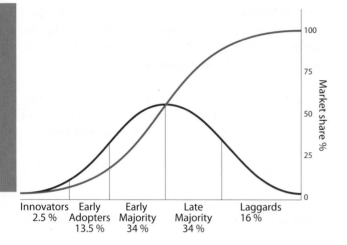

Figure 5.2.7   Rogers —Stages of innovation diffusion

Specifically, the strategies used to influence consumers to make positive buying decisions will depend on the stage of the innovation diffusion cycle.

In the earliest stages of the cycle, product awareness is the key as firms seek to build knowledge about the product and its availability. Product brand identification and quality benchmarks are also established here. Pricing can be variable depending on whether the company is aiming to recover expensive research and development costs or whether a fast market entry strategy to build market and penetration is attempted through aggressive pricing models. Distribution is often concentrated until market acceptance is achieved. Promotion campaigns are targeted to early adopters who assist with market diffusion through social networking.

During the early majority stage of innovation diffusion, strategies shift to product identity encouraging consumers to make a brand preference decision. Pricing tends to be fixed but additional features or services may be added as an incentive. Distribution networks of the product are more widespread and the target audience is widened in marketing campaigns.

Once the product is well established and sales start to taper, product features may be improved and pricing may be discounted. Promotion campaigns focus on product differentiation in the marketplace.

As laggards appear in the market, pricing may be significantly reduced. The product may be discontinued or a new modified/updated version may appear to attract new consumers and target repeat sales to first generation adopters.

Suppression

As documented previously in section 5.1—the effectiveness of strategies for protecting IP - many companies suppress innovation due to the uncertainty surrounding patent infringement and potential litigation. In their 2009 book, *Patent Failure: How Judges, Bureaucrats, and Lawyers Put Innovators at Risk*, law professors Bessen and Meurer showed that in 1999 the global costs of litigation, (outside of the pharmaceutical industry), were US$12 billion while the profits associated with patents in all of the combined fields only amounted to US$4 billion. Clearly the risk associated with patent infringement particularly in grey areas looms large and is a strong incentive for companies to suppress an innovative product.

Litigation may also be used as a delaying tactic against competitors, particularly in the early highly contested phase of introducing new product to the market. Even if patent litigation is not successful, the act of filing a case against a competitor may tie them up in the court system long enough to make their product less viable. Such actions discourage others from entering the field.

On occasions, successful companies may attempt to protect their market share from competitors by lobbying governments to amend legislation making it difficult for a newcomer to enter the market.

INTERNATIONAL MINDEDNESS

Innovations may have positive consequences in some countries/regions and negative ones in others.

© IBO 2012

Culture is a unifying influence on people's behaviour, but it may also create barriers between people. As communications and transportation networks 'shrink' the globe, the introduction of innovation into a variety of communities must consider the ramifications of the 'one size fits all' principle.

The effects of innovation may be less equitable than first envisioned. Process innovation regularly reduces employment opportunities, often replacing labour with capital investment in the form of new technologies. However, when a successful product innovation creates employment, the growth in the workforce may not necessarily take place where the company traditionally bases its operations. Many companies move manufacturing operations offshore for a variety of reasons including wage costs, labour laws and environmental legislation requirements. In this scenario, there may be trans-national winners and losers in the areas of employment and the environment based around the same innovation. In the case of global brands, multinational companies are now able to span the globe with single standardized designs that see profits from local sales distributed to the parent company offshore. This can have a detrimental effect on local employment, manufacturing, research and design and even national economies.

THEORY OF KNOWLEDGE

> Design is always looking to the future and new development. Do other areas of knowledge have universal, timeless truths or are they continually in flux?
>
> © IBO 2012

Whether it be materials developments, new manufacturing processes or the latest aesthetic, the world of design has always been obsessed with the next 'best thing'. The 21st century is characterised as a time marked by the embracing of rapid and constant change and as such all areas of knowledge and human endeavour continue to pursue the 'truth'. Socrates is quoted as saying, 'the only thing we can know is that we know nothing.' Heraclitus of Ephesus (c. 535–c. 475 BCE)), was one of the first to propose that, "radical flux renders it impossible to have knowledge of the sensible world......for there can be no knowledge of that which is in flux."

In all fields of investigation whether it be history, science or psychology, whenever we discover something new we have the opportunity to combine this with what we already know in new ways and thus produce original thought or new knowledge. All areas of knowledge have information that we believe to be true based on our current levels of understanding.

Exercise

Choose one fact from the past and create a timeline of how our knowledge and understanding has changed, e.g. number of planets in the solar system or who invented the telephone.

5.3–STRATEGIES FOR INNOVATION

ESSENTIAL IDEA

> Designers have a range of strategies for innovation.
>
> © IBO 2012

NATURE OF DESIGN

> Companies encourage advancements in technology and services, usually by investing in research and development activities. Even though the R&D may be carried out by a range of different experts from varied fields of research, the development process is often based on common principles and strategies to identify the direction of development. This methodology structures the R&D of new technologies and services.
>
> © IBO 2012

AIM

> Innovation should always occur in context and a deep understanding of the culture as well as the behaviours, needs and wants of the consumer is required.
>
> © IBO 2012

Act of insight

It seems history has few recorded 'acts of insight' or 'eureka' moments. Popular culture would suggest that many innovations are the result of some spark of genius, yet their are few genuinely documented examples. Historic, legendary examples of acts of insight include:

- Greek mathematician Archimedes', (c. 287—c. 212 BCE), 'eureka moment' when bathing he determined a way to establish the density of material using displaced water as an accurate way to measure volume of irregular shapes

- Newton and his epiphany surrounding the nature of gravity while sitting under an apple tree.

Lending credence to this idea of the uncommon nature of acts of insight is the number of inventors discovering new breakthroughs simultaneously yet quite independently. Witness the development of the telephone, electrical batteries and the steam engine to name just a few, all developed from combining existing technologies in new ways.

In more recent times, American engineer Willis Carrier is said to have hit upon the the idea of air-conditioning while watching fog move across a train station platform. He is said to have had a sudden vision of fog being used to cool buildings. Willis patented the idea and became wealthy on the proceeds of his innovation.

Adaptation

Adaptation involves the transferring of successful design solutions or parts thereof to provide new solutions for design problems in entirely different fields.

Biomimicry is an approach to design and innovation that involves transferring successful designs from nature into new design contexts. Development of Japan's Shinkansen bullet train uses solutions found in nature to enhance the efficiency of its design. The nose-cone section of the train, shown in Figure 1.2.4, is modelled on the beak of a Kingfisher bird. The bird's beak is designed to absorb sudden changes in pressure caused from diving into water. A similar situation was observed by Japanese designers when trying to avoid low-level sonic booms caused when their super fast trains exited tunnels.

Figure 5.3.1   Shinkansen bullet train nose-cone, image by Parag.naik [CC-Attribution 3.0 Unported], via Wikimedia Commons

Technology transfer

Technology transfer is the process of transferring scientific knowledge and principles from one field to another area of

application. The process often involves some modification of the technology but the basic operating principles remain the same. As documented previously in section 5.1, the development of the microwave oven occurred through technology transfer on the part of Percy Spencer who was able to successfully convert a radar magnetron into the component driving the principle of modern microwave oven technology.

Analogy

Analogy invokes likeness or similarity. Analogous design therefore involves the transfer of an idea from one situation to another.

Compact fluorescent globes are an example of analogous design. Inspired by the need to reduce energy during the energy crisis of the 1980s designers transferred and modified existing technologies and processes and translated these into a different context within the same field to generate an entirely new product.

Figure 5.3.2   Compact fluorescent globe, image by Giligone [CC-BY-SA-3.0 (http://creativecommons.org/licenses/by-sa/3.0) via Wikimedia Commons

Chance

A number of modern innovations may be traced back to an initial accidental discovery through chance. Well known examples include teflon, velcro, penicillin, laminated safety glass, and polyethylene.

Laminated safety glass was first discovered by French scientist Edouard Benedictus in 1903. When working in his laboratory, a poorly cleaned flask was dropped from a height, only to reveal the damaged glassware to be cracked but not shattered into pieces as expected. The flask contained residue from a previous experiment involving a solution of cellulose nitrate, a type of liquid plastic. Benedictus made the connection between his damaged flask and the newly popular hobby of automobile driving after reading about injuries to drivers caused by shattered glass windscreens. Laminated or triplex glass was not adopted for some time in the automobile industry due to the need for car makers to keep costs down. It wasn't until after WWI, where safety glass found its first successful application in the severe conditions of battle as lenses for gas masks that manufacturers adopted the technology for widespread use in car windscreens.

Penicillin is the most widely used antibiotic in the world yet its discovery was a chance accident. Research biologist Alexander Fleming was working with *staphylococcus* bacteria when he left a petri dish exposed for a number of days, only to find a mould had inhibited the growth of bacteria in his experiment. Florey and Chain later invented a process for isolating the mould later to become known as penicillin which was to prove effective against a range of harmful bacteria. Fleming is quoted as saying: "One sometimes finds what one is not looking for. When I woke up just after dawn on Sept. 28, 1928, I certainly didn't plan to revolutionise all medicine by discovering the world's first antibiotic, or bacteria killer".

Modern antibiotics are tested using methods similar to those employed by Fleming, as shown in Figure 5.3.3.

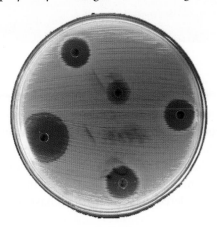

Figure 5.3.3   Staphylococcus aureus - Antibiotics Test plate

Technology push

Technology push is evident when innovative technological breakthroughs occur and companies then search for marketable applications to make them commercially viable. Technology push supporters agree that predicting market needs for products that do not yet exist is near impossible. They do however concede the role market pull has in developing or improving existing products.

The Nike + iPod system is a good example of technology push. Consumers were unaware of their need or want for such a system until this piece of wearable technology became available. Nike has developed monitoring technology linking a portable computing device with a sensor implanted into the sole of its running shoes. One

of the market leaders in this application, data sent from the running shoe sensor provides feedback to the wearer, encourages him/her to sign up for challenges, both virtual and real events and also offers coaching, all through an iPod interface. Developments of the technology allow the athlete to automatically 'tweet' a message through the twitter service and/or post a status update on Facebook. The technology works seamlessly, having been developed and tested over a number of years. Criticism appears to be around the proprietary nature of the sensor technology that only fits Nike shoes.

Figure 5.3.4   Nike sensor and shoe system

Market pull

Market pull is the action of consumers creating a need or market for a product or service that is then targeted by manufacturers when developing new products. The green movement is an example of market pull and is evident in a variety of market sectors including electricity supplies, zero emission vehicles and environmentally friendly cleaning products.

In the specific field of extreme environment transportation, Venturi developed a means of transporting groups of people and equipment safely in regions such as the Antarctic with absolutely no negative impact on the environment. In a less extreme fashion, zero emission consumer vehicles are increasingly popular based on market pull pressures.

Figure 5.3.5   Venturi Antarctica zero emmission vehicle, image by VenturiAutomobiles [CC-BY-SA-3.0 (http://creativecommons.org/licenses/by-sa/3.0)]

Technology push vs market pull

While these terms apply to the creation of an original product concept, these forces are still at play during the entire product lifecycle. As noted previously, the role market pull has in developing or improving existing products is well recognized and technological breakthroughs regularly play a role in product modifications. Most products, however, are a combination of market pull and technology push. Even for an innovative technologically based product to be successful there must be a degree of market readiness or acceptance otherwise the product will be a commercial failure.

Design contexts where each strategy has been applied

Brainstorming is an approach often used in the design world to generate new ideas. While brainstorming is a structured approach to the development of new ideas many inventions come from the result of an individual's interest in something other than the product that is finally realised. This is evidenced in the following examples of the microwave oven, inkjet printers and post-it notes®.

The microwave oven was invented due to the imagination and ingenuity of one individual. The story of Percy Spencer is the stuff of legends. Working for Raytheon during WWII Spencer was responsible for developing a system of improving production of the magnetron, a part critical to the success of radar. Shortly after the war, while still working for Raytheon, Spencer passed by a magnetron and noticed a chocolate bar in his pocket melting. Others had noticed this effect but had ignored it. Spencer tested the effects first on popcorn and then eggs. Spencer's continued experiments with the magnetron and food led to the production of the first working microwave in 1946. This first model was known as the 'radarange' and was the size of a refrigerator, weighed 340 kilograms and required plumbing to cool the magnetron tube. In 1955 the Tappan Stove company produced, (under license from Raytheon), the first domestic microwave for the consumer market. While working on the development of a new computer printer in 1978, Hewlett-Packard engineers observed the action of a coffee percolator. From this they extrapolated the idea of using the power of the boiling ink itself to shoot controlled dots of ink onto paper. While much further development was required in the resistivity of the ink and the nature of the electrodes, the inspirational concept was drawn from a field well outside the area under investigation.

Arthur Fry is the 3M scientist credited with finding an application for a low strength adhesive developed by colleague Spencer Silver in 1968. The success of the post-it®

note is based on a low strength adhesive composed of small spheres that only bond with other materials tangentially and therefore have a low surface area of contact. It wasn't until Fry started using pieces of paper coated with this low strength adhesive to mark places in his hymn book that the first usage of a sticky note occurred. When Fry used the sticky note in the shape of an arrow to mark a passage in a technical report and the sticky note came back annotated, Fry realised the possibilities for a new product. The machinery to manufacture the new product did not exist so Fry set about producing the machinery at home. When samples of his newly manufactured product were sent to executives at 3M they were convinced of the products potential and by 1980 post-it® notes were commercially available to the public.

THEORY OF KNOWLEDGE

Design is continually changing due to its openness to new ideas. Do other areas of knowledge recognise new influences to the same extent?

© IBO 2012

Not only are we constantly creating new knowledge we are also regularly challenging and often turning over information and principles we have previously considered to be facts. While we expect some facts to change such as the population of the earth, speed of computers and the height of the world's tallest building and so on, there are other facts that, for the most part even in recent times, we have considered to be 'known' that have now changed, such as:

- Pluto is no longer a planet but has been downgraded to dwarf planet status

- the four taste senses are now five with the addition of 'umami'

- diamond is no longer considered the hardest substance given that wurtzite boron nitride and lonsdaleite are predicted to be 18 and 58% more resistant to indentation.

The changing nature of information affects all areas of knowledge. As global communications become faster and more ubiquitous alternative cultural perspectives become more readily accessible. Witness the recorded histories of the 'Vietnam War' or the 'American War' written as fact from two very different perspectives. Today's internet news services allow local access to current affairs and events opposed to reports written for outside markets and external consumption, potentially two disparate views of occurrences that will both purport to be true.

In the field of mathematics, the commonly held fact was that a piece of paper cannot be folded more than seven times upon itself and yet in 2005 Britney Gallivan broke the record by folding a piece of paper twelve times. She then went on to write the mathematical proof in terms of a folding limit equation for any given dimension. Today, even this record is being challenged.

This phenomenon is not new. Consider the turmoil affecting academia and the religious world when Copernicus radically claimed that the Sun was stationary at the centre of the universe attempting to overturn centuries of belief in classical astronomy dating back to the days of Aristotle.

The real questions are:

- Why is it important to understand that knowledge is in a constant state of flux?

- What does the knowledge of change mean to our commitment to 'facts'?

- What are the implications for change?

Arbesman, (2012), in his book 'The Half Life of Facts' makes the point, 'Even though I cannot predict what discovery is going to be made or what fact is going to be overturned, there are regularities in how knowledge grows and changes over time.'

Arbesman is an expert in the field of scientometrics. This area studies the state of knowledge and attempts to explain how knowledge changes systematically and in a predictable fashion. In practical terms, knowledge of these processes of change allows practitioners in a range of fields to predict when the reliability of knowledge in their fields may expire.

This question may also be interpreted from the perspective of ways of knowing.

- What is different about design that makes it open to new ideas compared to other ways of knowing?

- Is design more associated with technique, knowledge of materials and aesthetics and functionality?

- Do the arts, science and religion deal with different ways of knowing and knowledge?

Students need to be aware of the distinctions between knowledge and fact and that the terms are not necessarily interchangeable. To further complicate the issue, consideration should be given to the relationships between fact, belief and knowledge

- When there is a disagreement, how can both sides of that disagreement believe they have knowledge even when the facts are in dispute?

Another approach may focus on specifics of the language in the question for example:

- What does it mean to recognise new influences?

Recognition does not necessarily mean acceptance; it could mean rejection and persecution. Types of responses here may include: Darwinian evolution, the Copernican model of a Sun-centered solar system, rejection of an aether and initial rejection of new artistic movements such as expressionism, etc.

Exercise

Think of one 'fact' that has changed over the last 20 years. What were the implications associated with the change from one belief to another?

5.4–STAKEHOLDERS IN INVENTION AND INNOVATION

ESSENTIAL IDEA

There are three key roles in invention and innovation, which can be shared by one or more people.

© IBO 2012

NATURE OF DESIGN

Collaborative generation of knowledge and high efficiency information flow allow for diversity, increased resilience, reliability and stability within an organisation. Through participatory research, stakeholders can make full use of the resulting innovation and invention, by transferring findings relevant to the sector in which they are positioned. A designer's increased awareness through shared industry knowledge enhances profitability and policy.

© IBO 2012

AIM

On occasion, the inventor needs to act as both entrepreneur and product champion. The adoption of these additional roles requires a significant amount of learning to take an idea from the mind, realise it and then diffuse it successfully into the market place.

© IBO 2012

The inventor, product champion and the entrepreneur

Inventors and inventions

Utah State University - intellectual property services define an inventor as an individual who discovers or devises, "a new material (either a new manufactured product or a new composition or matter), a new process, a new use for an existing material, or any improvements of any of these." Due to the complex nature of modern inventions they are often now attributed not to individuals but to research groups or even institutions.

Inventions may include, but are not limited to, new technologies, materials processes or software. In some cases they are simply new combinations of existing knowledge.

Product champions

Most often working with, and even coordinating teams, product champions are passionate about driving particular products to market. They 'champion' the product both within and outside their organization. Product champions have a vision for their passion that, if successful, meets the needs of consumers and the manufacturer. The role of product champions is to have their ideas accepted and then adopted by the public.

Entrepreneurs

An entrepreneur is a person who is willing to financially back a new enterprise calculating the risk of losing money against potential profits.

The inventor as a product champion and/or entrepreneur

Inventors often feel they know their products better than anyone else. They may also fear losing control over the product, its promotion or its eventual market success. For these reasons some inventors continue past the inventor stage and promote and/or control the financial aspects of their product themselves.

Edison blurred the lines between inventor, product champion and entrepreneur.

Writing for the *Atlantic Review* in 1995, Kathleen McAuliffe notes, "the brilliant scientist was also a clever businessman, capable of engineering literally dazzling public-relations stunts." It was this skill he put to use when successfully replacing gas with electricity as the major source of lighting in New York. While Edison's championing of DC power eventually lost out the more practical use of AC power, Edison was able to promote electricity's superiority over gas by developing centralised generation and distribution of electricity that mirrored the existing infrastructure for gas.

In her book *Empires of Light*, author Jill Jonnes comments on the showmanship of Edison, "with one turn of a wheel he put out all the 290 outdoor lights aglow in the snowy streets and pastures. Then, with a turn of the handle, Edison brought those 290 globes back to life" (Jonnes, 2004, p.74).

In this instance Edison was demonstrating the flexibility of electricity to be turned on and off centrally rather than the need for gas lamps to be lit and extinguished separately.

In 1878 Edison used his skills as an inventor, product champion and entrepreneur to convince several astute, high profile financiers including the J.P. Morgan and the Vanderbilt families, to invest in the newly created Edison Electric Light Company of New York.

Edison's record shows him to be not only a good inventor and product champion but also a good businessman who created companies that spanned the globe manufacturing his inventions.

Figure 5. 4.1   Thomas. A. Edison in his laboratory, East Orange, N.J., U.S.A. , image by Library of Congress

Like Edison, Steve Jobs was an inventor, innovator, product champion and entrepreneur. He along with Steve Wozniak was the co-founder of Apple computers.

Jobs surrounded himself with world class designers and engineers but had a very tight grip on the development of all his products. As an innovator Jobs was highly successful at linking existing technology in new ways to develop products of unique simplicity yet highly functional.

Steve Jobs reportedly disliked the term 'showman' that people associated with his product presentations, however there is no doubt about his ability to create a sense of occasion. Jobs's trademark black-turtleneck-and-jeans outfit and his rimless glasses all became part of the performance that was a product unveiling. He used these occasions to enthrall the crowd, educate the public and impress investors. At the time of his death, Steve Jobs had over 340 patents to his name and personal fortune in the billions of dollars. Due to the complex nature of the designs, materials and technologies involved many of his patents often had multiple co-signatories.

A multi-disciplinary approach to innovation

Even in the 1800s when Thomas Edison's Menlo Park laboratory was churning out inventions, there was a recognition of the value of multi-disciplanary teams. Author, historian and research associate Greg Field notes, "One of Edison's greatest overlooked talents was his ability to assemble teams and set up an organisational structure that fostered many people's creativity."

Today, innovation often involves complex principles, processes and materials. So much so that large groups of researchers, technologists and engineers may be required just to bring sufficient knowledge and skills to the endeavour. These multi-disciplinary teams create their own synergies the result of which is often greater than the sum of its parts.

Swedish author Frans Johansson documents what he calls the 'Medici effect,' (named after the 15th century Italian banking family that influenced the development and spread of the Renaissance), in his book *The Medici Effect: Breakthrough Insights at the Intersection of Ideas, Concepts & Cultures*. Johansson sees the interactions and collaboration within multidisciplinary teams as critical to success. The following two quotes express his thoughts on the benefits of multi-disciplinary teams.

"When you step into an intersection of fields, disciplines, or cultures, you can combine existing concepts into a large number of extraordinary new ideas".

"When you bring together diverse teams and perspectives, you have the ability to create an exponential increase in ideas".

The advantages and disadvantages of multi-disciplinary teams

Multi-disciplinary teams by their nature bring together a wide range of backgrounds and expertise to allow for cross-fertilization of ideas. Individuals from a different background than the originator of the idea may question the validity of the proposal from a very different perspective, thus forcing greater scrutiny of ideas from multiple perspectives.

Multi-disciplinary teams nevertheless bring their own set of problems. Unfortunately, not everyone is good at sharing ideas, fearing the potential loss of ownership or control over the idea. Others may be used to working independently and different working styles may not always lead to efficient or effective use of time. Larger groups increase the potential for misunderstanding and miscommunication, while group ownership of ideas may be challenged if teams are constantly formed or reformed. Addition of new members can also change team dynamics and impede communication or sharing of ideas.

THEORY OF KNOWLEDGE

Design favours collective wisdom. Do other areas of knowledge value collaborative thinking?

© IBO 2012

Consideration here should be given to the ever-increasing complexity of knowledge, global economies and the quasi-ubiquitous nature of communication. Some examples are provided below of government level initiatives to foster large scale information sharing and transfer.

Governments around the world are continuing to reshape their focus towards more knowledge-intensive approaches to work. The shift is away from physical labour to exploiting knowledge in the so called 'knowledge economy'. As our knowledge continues to grow in ever-more focused and technical areas where few have expertise, the imperative is to share this knowledge and transfer information and understanding within groups, regions, nations and the world.

In 2007 the European commission released a document, (*Improving knowledge transfer between research institutions and industry across Europe*), stating the need for research institutions, governments and industry to collaborate more closely across national boundaries to enhance knowledge transfer and innovation. They believe, "the importance of improving knowledge transfer between public research institutions and third parties, including industry and civil society organisations was identified by the Commission as one of ten key areas for action". While European initiative is aimed at assisting with the innovation and development of new products it also reflects on the importance of knowledge transfer in areas outside the domains of product and service development. While collaboration practices are well developed within member states the EU is working towards breaking down national barriers to collaboration in an attempt to create and environment where Europe operates as a 'single market for knowledge.'

While the answer to the above question may seem to be easy based on the idiom, 'two heads are better than one' the alternative must also be contemplated as countered by the statement 'the camel is a horse designed by a committee' [2]

This suggests that collective wisdom may not always produce the best or even the intended result. You could even suggest examining the role of individual excellence in a paradigm favouring collective wisdom.

Remember there are various levels of collective wisdom that is, within a group, company, country, discipline etc.

Students should also consider hindrances to collective wisdom and sharing.

- How does intellectual property and industrial secrecy act against collaboration, at least in a broader context?

Exercises

Consider a product, project or system that has only been successful through large scale collaboration e.g. the Large Hadron Collider (LHC) at CERN.

In terms of failure of design by committee, students would have to look no further than the General Motors produced 'Aztec', considered by some to be 'one of the ugliest cars produced in decades' [3] and a financial failure. What other examples of design by committee can you find that resulted in failure?

References

[1] European Commission (EC) 2007, *Improving knowledge transfer between research institutions and industry across Europe, Embracing open innovation*, pp.6

[2] *Design by committee* March 2004, http://en.wikipedia.org/wiki/Design_by_committee, accessed June 2014.

[3] Weissman J 2005, *Biggest Automaker Needs Big Changes*, The Washington Post, from www.washingtonpost.com/wp-dyn/content/article/2005/06/10/AR2005061002188.html, June 2005.

5.5–PRODUCT LIFE CYCLE

ESSENTIAL IDEA

There are several key stages in the product life cycle.

© IBO 2012

NATURE OF DESIGN

Designers need to consider the whole product cycle of potential products, services and systems throughout the design cycle and beyond. Products may have an impact not only on the direct consumer but on society at large and the environment.

© IBO 2012

AIM

An understanding of the product life cycle allows the designer to design a product with obsolescence in mind. Doing this at the design stage can potentially eliminate the effect of a product on the environment when it is no longer in use.

© IBO 2012

Key stages of the product life cycle: launch; growth; maturity; decline

New products progress through a series of stages from: development to introduction, growth to maturity, and finally decline. This sequence of events is known as the product cycle or product life cycle and describes the dynamic relationship between product changes and sales. Figure 5.5.1 shows a typical product cycle graph where sales are plotted against strategic product development stages. All of the various stages of the product cycle have implications for marketing.

Designers clearly have a role in the product cycle in many stages. Early in the cycle, designers are busy generating ideas and testing alternative solutions before settling on a final concept ready for testing and eventually introduction to the marketplace. Designers re-enter the cycle to bolster flagging product sales through the introduction of new products developments, modifications and/or improvements. Throughout the process, designers are working with multidisciplinary teams including: manufacturers, accountants, machinists, marketing staff etc.

In the early stages of the product cycle, at product launch, manufacturers seek to raise product awareness. Pricing could be aggressive to capture market share and the product may be positioned in a premium price range to recoup research and development costs. At this point the target market is early adopters.

In the growth stage, product changes and modifications take place to stimulate the market. Increasing demand sees little need to modify pricing.

During the mature stage competition may appear and the pace of sales growth may slow. Market penetration should be good and manufacturers attempt to differentiate their product. Pricing may also be reduced to attract consumers away from competing products.

In the late stage, the product begins to decline in need, (due to competition or obsolescence), and therefore in sales, heavy discounting may occur, some new features may be added to recover flagging sales or the product may be discontinued.

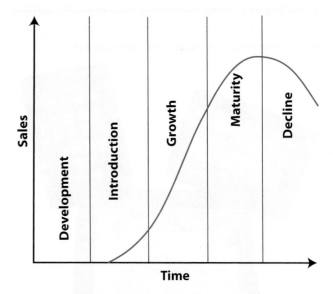

Figure 5.5.1   Product life cycle stages

Examples of products at different stages of the product life cycle

3D printers particularly for domestic sales are in the early stages of the product life cycle. Manufacturers are constantly entering the market with a new feature set, technology advances and software updates. There is yet to be a dominant player in the field with a design that embodies all of the desired market requirements. Particularly in this field, the technology is driving the product and the market needs or wants are yet to be fully determined.

Figure 5.5.2   Early market contender —3D printer

Tablet computers are still in the growth stage of the product cycle. They continue to disrupt the market due to a number of factors. Conventional technology such as the desktop is still being replaced by tablets as people transition from older personal computers to tablet devices. The technology is well developed now and a variety of devices are available at a range of pricepoints. As the power of tablet devices and their features continue to improve, purchases of new tablet devices are made at the expense of the personal computing market.

Figure 5.5.3   Tablet computer devices

The telecommunications service market is an example of a well developed mature market. Providers of mobile phone services are looking to bundle packages across devices and media. They are attempting to improve market penetration

by providing better coverage, faster speeds, and access to providers such as those in the entertainment industries.

There is an argument to be made that desktop personal computers are in market decline. Sales of desktop personal computers continue to fall. In 2013, technology research group Gartner, reported, "the 10% decline throughout 2013 is the worst in history for the worldwide personal computer market". The competition from hybrid computers and tablet devices continues to put pressure on the personal computer market.

Obsolescence: planned; style (fashion); functional; technological

Also known as 'built in obsolescence', planned obsolescence is a deliberate tactic employed by manufacturers to create products with a limited lifespan. It is designed to force consumers to purchase a product repeatedly. Planned obsolescence exists in such diverse product areas as computer software, mobile phones and automobiles.

The notion of planned obsolescence is not a new phenomenon and is documented as early as the 1930s, when General Electric improved the efficiency of flashlight lamps through a corresponding decrease in their lifespan. Engineers at the time were encouraged to build items with a limited lifespan to increase sales and boost the economy. The proposition was received with mixed responses but proponents accepted this new ethical paradigm with almost patriotic vigour.

Adopting a philosophy of planned obsolescence allows designers to create a desire for product replacement, or update, rather than repair. Design feature of planned obsolescence may include:

- low durability

- style obsolescence

- not easily or cheaply repaired

- difficult to disassemble thus restricting maintenance

- regular introduction of newer technologies or 'improved ' models.

The features listed allow manufacturers to cut costs and boost sales. This approach by manufacturers is known as 'value engineering', however, as markets develop and competition increases, pressure is brought about to increase product lifespans as consumers migrate to companies producing more reliable, more durable products.

Companies often use planned obsolescence to control costs, but other effects can include significant environmental impacts through consumers continuously replacing, rather than repairing products. This generates more waste, pollution, energy consumption and consumption of resources.

Advantages for the consumers when companies introduce new versions and generations of a product include opportunities to upgrade products as new technologies become available and the access to the latest in fashion trends. Strength in the consumer market through volume sales also has a knock-on effect in national economies and potential job prospects for the local population.

Disadvantages of planned obsolescence are around the constant need for replacement and associated inconvenience. Lack of repairability may mean consumers have to purchase a product before they are ready, or replace a model whose features they are entirely happy with. New models and new technologies often bring new ways of operating and this can also be disconcerting for some consumers. Increased consumerism through less durable goods wastes both energy and raw materials, while at the same time increasing pollution and greenhouse gases.

Predictability of the product life cycle

The rapid pace of technological change, fashion trends and global competition are factors that have affected the length of the product cycle. Manufacturers are always looking for a competitive edge. Incremental change through the incorporation of new technologies also continues to drive innovation. Additional to these forces are manufacturers' interests in planned obsolescence and society's propensity towards disposing of consumer items on a regular basis. Sustainable growth however can only come through new products and radical design. Products using microchip technologies have seriously shortened product cycles due to the regular availability of faster, smaller, more powerful and lighter processors. These developments continue to revolutionize product design making previous models, (sometimes only months old), no longer competitive.

Figure 5.5.4   Microchip image by M Olivander (own work) CC-BY-SA-2.0 - via Wikimedia

Product versioning/generations

Companies are constantly revising their products to feed market demand. The versioning or iteration of product developments attempt to better meet the needs of the target market. New generation products represent an improvement over the previous iteration of the product and are designed to maintain a loyal customer base while at the same time attracting new customers.

As the market continues to grow, manufacturers introduce a range of versions of the same product. This allows for greater penetration and market growth. Version variations cater for some or all of the following.

- Specific regional/cultural tastes.

- A range of price points in the market.

- Differentiation in product features from basic to extended.

- 'Special' or 'limited edition' releases marketed to an identified niche market.

INTERNATIONAL MINDEDNESS

The transition from a linear to a circular economy in the move towards sustainable societies has major implications for the ideas associated with product life cycle.

© IBO 2012

In his foreword to the Eurpopean Commission's report, Towards a Circular Economy, Janez Potocnik, European Commissoner for the Environment makes the point, '(the) challenge of the century will be to foster prosperity in a world of finite resources. Coming up with answers to this challenge will create competitive advantage'.

The circular economy is an all encompassing term referring to an industrial economy that is, configured in such a way to have zero sum impact on the environment. In this type of economy, materials consumption is composed of two streams:
- organic or biological materials, designed to re-enter and replenish ecosystems naturally and safely

- technical materials, which are designed to continually circulate through processes of recycling, re-purposing and refurbishment without entering the waste stream.

The traditional linear model of resource consumption that follows a 'take-make-dispose' pattern is a holdover from the past when resources were plentiful and easily accessible. Accumulating effects of pollution and finite resource depletion lead to no other conclusion than that these practices are unsustainable.

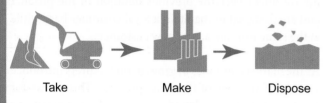

Take   Make   Dispose

Figure 5.5.5   Take-make-dispose model

While significant gains have been made in reducing waste, cutting resource consumption and improving energy efficiencies, more work is required in fundamentally rethinking the processes involved in the earliest stages of design to remove material/energy waste and materials disposal altogether.

Circular design could be the answer to this problem, by adopting a closed system based on designing out waste and actively designing in the re-use of finite resources throughout the product life cycle. Approaches to, and techniques employed in removing waste from the product cycle are being modelled on biological systems. There is no waste in nature as ecosystems constantly cycle energy and resources in a never ending closed system. The introduction of the circular economy extends beyond the design of objects and into how these objects are used. The transition to selling of services rather than products then impacts on the design process as the focus moves away from consumerism and volume of repeat sales towards design for extended life, repeat use through multiple owners, refurbishment and eventually recycling.

Frans van Houten, (CEO Royal Phillips), when writing for the Guardian in 2014, notes this transition "requires a new generation of materials as well as innovative development and production processes. In addition, we need to define new business models and redefine the concept of legal ownership and use, public tendering rules, and financial strategies."

In essence the circular economy is based on a few simple principles:

- Remove waste at the design stage. Waste should be designed out at the earliest stages of planning. Designing for disassembly, re-purposing and recyling as well as the specification of non-toxic, biodegradable materials all help to close the system while still in the planning stage.

- Use energy from renewable sources. The circular economy involves a shift from non-renewable fuel sources to the use of renewable energy. This not only preserves finite fossil fuel reserves but also reduces waste and greenhouse gas production.

- Design around 'systems'. Non-linear or feedback systems are a foundation of the circular economy, hence the name. Systems approaches including design for disassembly, cradle to cradle, and biomimicry all embody features of this approach.

- Consider cascade effects. Cascading is a value adding effect where embodied value in a material or product may be cascaded through another application to extract another use or an extended lifespan from the product, component or material.

THEORY OF KNOWLEDGE

Design considers areas other than man in its thinking. Are other areas of knowledge confined to human influence and values?

© IBO 2012

The fields of knowledge such as biology, physics, mathematics and cosmology are aimed at understanding fundamental laws of nature and the universe rather than human influence and values.

Specifically, theoretical physics and mathematics both employ models and abstractions of objects, systems and environments to rationalise, explain and predict natural phenomena such as space, gravity and the nature of matter.

Students should consider if there are areas of knowledge confined (at least in part) to human influence and values? Philosophy and ethics immediately spring to mind, Law would be another. Theology could be also argued to be aimed at understanding mankind's relationship with God.

5.6–ROGERS' CHARACTERISTICS OF INNOVATION AND CONSUMERS

ESSENTIAL IDEA

Innovations take time to diffuse into a target audience.

© IBO 2012

NATURE OF DESIGN

Rogers' four main elements that influence the spread of new ideas (innovation, communication channels, time and a social system) rely heavily on human capital. The ideas must be widely accepted in order to be self-sustainable. Designers must consider various cultures and communities to predict how, why and at what rate new ideas and technology will be adopted.

© IBO 2012

AIM

By categorising consumers, the designer can identify particular segments with a market sector to gain feedback. By engaging with these stereotypes, the designer can utilise their experiences with a prototype in order to guide further development.

© IBO 2012

Diffusion and innovation

Consumers make numerous purchasing decisions on a daily basis. These decisions are influenced by a number of factors including social contacts, multimedia and personal traits. Understanding what motivates consumers to make positive purchasing decisions and how decisions spread through markets is the theory of innovation diffusion.

Diffusion refers to the processes or mechanisms through which a new product or service is accepted by the market. Rates of diffusion are determined by how fast the innovation spreads between consumers. The diffusion of innovation is about not the changing of consumers or markets but about the innovations themselves.

Adoption is closely related to diffusion but deals with the thought patterns or psychological processing that takes place in individuals within mass markets. The success of innovation diffusion is studied carefully by marketers to try and maximise adoption rates by consumers.

Figure 5.6.1 demonstrates the relationship between market groups and their propensity to adopt an innovation. The black bell curve shows successive groups of consumers adopting a new product or service. The green curve indicates market share eventually reaching saturation point (100%).

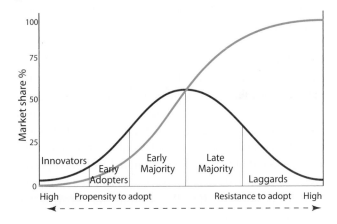

Figure 5.6.1   Adoption rates within market groups

The impact of Rogers' characteristics on consumer adoption of an innovation

Everett M. Rogers, (1931—2004), was an American sociologist and author best known as the inventor of the 'Diffusion of Innovation Theory' based on his research into how farmers adopted innovations in the agricultural industry. The theory attempts to explain how innovations are accepted by the market.

The impact of Rogers' characteristics on consumer adoption of an innovation can be considered in terms of relative advantage, compatibility, complexity, observability and trialability.

Relative advantage covers the degree to which consumers rate the merits of a new product relative to the product it supersedes. There are many factors to consider including prestige, functionality, fashion trends, features, etc. As a general rule, the greater the perceived relative advantage the higher adoption rate of the new product by the market.

The introduction of compact fluorescent globes to replace incandescent lamps provided consumers with direct comparisons between relative energy consumption, globe longevity, heat production, amount of light delivered per Watt and reduced carbon monoxide emissions due to lessened energy consumption. Relative advantage may be summed up by Ralph Waldo Emerson's famous quote, "Make a better mousetrap, and the world will beat a path to your door."

Compatibility refers to how well consumers determine that the innovation reflects their expectations in terms of their needs and wants, current practices and values. The greater the degree of compatibility, the higher the adoption rate. In the field of beauty products, cosmetics and hair care, many consumers will make a choice based on product testing protocols. In this context there is a group that will reject products that involve mistreatment of, or testing on animals.

Complexity encompasses degree of difficulty and may extend from consumers' difficulty in understanding the value of a product to the level of complexity of use. Simple concepts that are easier to understand and products that are user friendly have higher adoption rates than those products requiring new or complex skills. Software systems such as Windows® 8 may have suffered from complexity issues in the minds of consumers who listened to reports from early adopters that the software was proving too difficult to use efficiently.

Observability is the profile or visibility of positive results attributed to product ownership. Positive visible outcomes from product ownership lead to reduced anxiety and lower levels of uncertainty amongst friends, colleagues and acquaintances. More visible advantages to the ownership of a product translate into higher levels of adoption. The transition from videotape to DVD provided consumers with very obvious advantages in terms of media durability, storage capacity and, most visibly, picture quality.

Trialability is the level to which an innovation may be examined, tested or trialled on a limited basis to improve consumer confidence in the feature set, appropriateness or reliability of an innovation. Successful trialability builds confidence amongst consumers and leads to higher levels of adoption. Apple stores are full of products on display, readily available for customers to test and experiment with.

Social roots of consumerism

Consumerism is a set of behaviours found in all cultures predominantly based around the consumption of goods and services. It is also a means of transmitting information about societal values and norms through social interaction. These interactions take the form of 'handing down' values and cultural norms from one generation to another as well as transferring behaviours within social groupings.

Everett Rogers' research, (1996), on innovation diffusion theory is considered the benchmark in this field and his definition of diffusion is still considered relevant. "Diffusion is the process by which an innovation is communicated through certain channels over time among the members of a social system. An innovation is an idea, practice or object perceived as new by an individual or other unit of adoption. The diffusion of innovations involves both mass media and interpersonal communication channels".

In his essay *Diffusion of the Idea of Beyond War*, Rogers (1983) postulated that "most individuals evaluate an innovation, not on the basis of scientific research by experts, but on the basis of the subjective evaluations of near peers who have already adopted the innovation".

Issues for companies in the global marketplace when attempting to satisfy consumer needs in relation to lifestyle, values and identity

Rogers' work encourages innovators to focus on the market and the mechanisms by which consumers adopt new products. He argues that innovators need to pay particular attention to consumer contexts including lifestyles, values and identity. Through the identification of consumers' contexts and consumption patterns, the way innovations are perceived by specified groups may be linked to adoption practices.

This theoretical framework may be used to both analyse consumption and assist innovators when predicting product diffusion.

Lifestyle refers to social groupings of people based around how they use their resources such as time, space and money. These groupings aggregate around the multiplicity of daily conscious decisions occurring in everyday life. These decisions can be as simple as food and clothing choices through to house and car purchases.

Consumer value belief systems relate to people's attitudes, principles and core values about what is good and right, and notions of quality and desirability. Social environments are particularly influential in the development and testing of value systems. These social groupings may be based around the family unit, friends or work colleagues. Purchasing decisions or adoption of innovation in turn reflect these belief systems.

Identity is generated by an individual's background, personality, experiences and social interactions within a society. Cultural identities are often handed down between generations through the transmission of values, cultural norms and customs. In Eastern countries, collectivist cultures significantly influence the nature of adoption of innovation and must be considered carefully by those attempting to introduce innovation.

While the research may be used to identify common traits within the various adopter groups after diffusion has taken place, it has proven difficult to make a consistent and reliable means of predicting who the adopters within each group will be and what their specific characteristics may be for a given product.

The influence of social media on the diffusion of innovation

A social network is the pattern of friendship, advice, communication or support which exists among the members of a social system. The complexity and ever-changing nature of social networks make predictions about innovation diffusion and specific products very difficult. Research indicates, however, that a positive correlation between adoption behaviours and the behaviour of social contacts.

The transition from Web 1.0 to the more interactive Web 2.0 and the development of easy-to-access and use social media has made the sharing of information, experiences and opinions not only popular but almost instantaneous in its exchange and further distribution.

The appearance of social media has created an entirely new platform for personal communication. Businesses have seen and capitalised on this technology by placing the consumer at the forefront of the diffusion process.

While social media are still considered new phenomena compared to more traditional means of communication, it has permeated society to the point where its widespread use is an integral part of many people's daily lives. Social media for many provides a range of contacts that allow interactions relating to information, communication and self-expression. Social media is clearly another mechanism where individuals can communicate and validate the ideas and beliefs associated with the diffusion and adoption of innovation. The real power of social media are that they negate the need for face to face or even simultaneous contact. The nature of posting on social media sites and responders replying at their leisure, across the globe and timezones makes these communication media enormously flexible.

The influence of trends and the media on consumer choice

While Rogers, (1996), explains, "the diffusion of innovations involves both mass media and interpersonal communication channels", the chart shown in Figure 5.6.2 demonstrates the disparity between the impact of interpersonal communication and mass media. At the time the chart was constructed social media were not a consideration but they clearly fit into the field of personal interaction, albeit electronic.

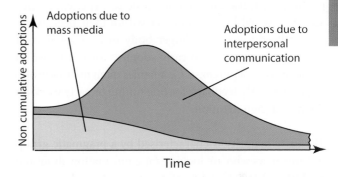

Figure 5.6.2   Bass forecasting model based on Mahajan, Muller and Bass (1990). New Product Diffusion Models in Marketing: A Review and Directions for Research. Journal of Marketing, 54, 4.

Categories of consumers in relation to technology adoption

Categories of consumers include innovators, early adopters, early majority, late majority and laggards.

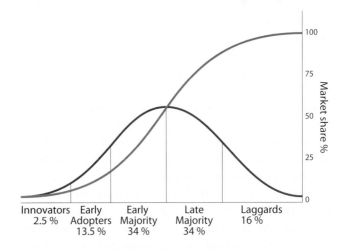

Figure 5.6.3   Categories of consumers

Innovators are the smallest group and the earliest to adopt of the consumer groups. They are characterised by individuals who are very well informed and highly adventurous in their purchasing patterns. They are excited by the prospect of owning something new and innovative. It has been suggested that they can be obsessive about innovation. This group has substantial financial resources, a high tolerance for risk and the ability to research and understand sometimes complex and technical knowledge about a product.

Early adopters, as the name suggests, are looking to be the first amongst the mainstream population to purchase new products. They enjoy being 'ahead of the curve'. While a risky strategy with new products, this group is generally well informed and has the financial resources to make purchases, often at premium prices. As a group, these people are vocal about their new product experience. They are often social leaders, popular within their peer group and well educated. The larger body of a target market population often look to early adopters for confirmation before making a purchase. Companies often use this group to provide early feedback for fine tuning or early work on the next design iteration.

The early majority is characterised by a pragmatic group of consumers who are looking for confirmation about the quality and functionality of a new product. This group will often deliberate for a period of time before making a commitment. While they are not leaders they still make a decision just before the majority of the market. Their major contribution to the network is to link early adopters with the rest of the market and contribute to the diffusion process.

The late majority is more cautious and sceptical about innovations. They will make a purchase only after the majority of the consumer group have paved the way. Their decision to purchase is often based around peer networks and the need to belong. This group may be financially challenged and may have to be convinced by their peers of the importance of the product to remove all uncertainty from their deliberations before adopting.

The last of the adoption social groupings are the laggards. This group is more resistant to change and its opinions are often based in the past on what has been proven to be successful. Their peer group is often of the same opinion and therefore reinforces their decision making processes. This group mostly has the least financial resources at their disposal and as such must be totally convinced before adopting. At this end of the product cycle, however, they will most probably acquire products that have been superseded, although they do often come at a discounted price.

INTERNATIONAL MINDEDNESS

The origin of Rogers' theory in one or two areas may lead to inappropriate application on a global basis. Positive and negative aspects may be opposite in different regions/countries.

© IBO 2012

The nature of innovation diffusion and cultural influence is a double-edged sword ie. innovation may influence cultures but there is also the consideration that cultural influences affect innovators and the adoption of innovation may be based around cultural values and attitudes.

Even Rogers was aware of the lack of certainty associated with innovation, "desirable consequence in one culture can be undesirable in another."

While unintended impacts of innovation in different cultures was investigated in topic 5.2, it is clear a designer from one culture would find it difficult to make completely objective judgments of the suitability and appropriateness of an innovation in another country. Conditions in a foreign culture often seem strange and unusual to an outsider and yet these customs, practices, beliefs, values and attitudes have benefitted from many years of evolution relying on experimentation and trial and error. It is this complex and invisible web of relationships forming a culture that make predicting the success and consequences (intended and unintended) of an innovation so difficult.

Conceptual models are required integrating both individual and cultural factors to better predict innovation diffusion rates. Such a model would consider the differences between individualistic and collective societies. In individualistic societies personal beliefs drive the decision making process opposed to a group consensus model of decision making more prevalent in collectivist societies.

There is continued debate in international marketing communities around the nature of innovation - globalisation versus local adaptation. While it is accepted there is growing convergence in preference around the world, there are still significant differences in cultural cognitive processes that lead to decision making, beliefs and preferences maintaining the need for cultural adaptation of innovation.

THEORY OF KNOWLEDGE

Design takes into account cultural differences. Are other areas of knowledge universal or culture specific?

While the concept of knowledge is universal across cultures, all areas of knowledge have a cultural bias or lens through which they are viewed. Morality, geometry, music, navigation, reasoning, and language are traditionally viewed as cultural achievements.

Can mathematics be considered as universal, that is do mathematical concepts remain true across cultures? The question above doesn't necessarily relate to whether all cultures develop all areas of knowledge to the same degree. Similarly, the ability to reason is a neurological condition common to humankind. The depth of reasoning may be a process of training, opportunity, education and culture, but the basic ability is universal.

Students should consider such questions and some of the reference material provided as a starting point for their investigations.

What is culture? English anthropologist E. B. Taylor (1871) indicates that culture is a complex whole that includes "knowledge, belief, art, morals, law, custom, and any other capabilities and habits acquired by man as a member of society". [1]

Do different cultures value, manage and communicate knowledge in the same ways? A starting point may be the thoughts of van Zolingen, Streumer & Stooker, "Culture defines not only the value of knowledge but also the internal organisation of this knowledge" (2001). [2]

Craig Rusbult, Ph.D. believes, "All activities in science, mental and physical, are affected by thought styles that are influenced by cultural-personal factors, operate at the levels of individuals and sub-communities and communities, and involve both conscious choices and unconscious assumptions". [3]

Students should consider how different cultural organisational philosophies may affect knowledge acquisition and transfer. Oyserman and Lee find that the cognitive tools used by members of cultures based on collectivism or individualism vary and that the cultural perspective or way of thinking then affects the knowledge produced. [4]

Hoftsede, 2001 further supports this assumption when he states "individuals in collectivistic cultures tend to give priority to the goals of the larger collective or group they belong to."

In the fine arts, cultural factors can influence an individual's appreciation of particular musical and artistic styles, themes and even the media through which works are created. Cultural influences may be seen in different musical styles between Chinese and Western music created using different tonal scales.

Hilary Charlesworth explores the nature of culture, faith and human rights in her article *Cultural Diversity in International Law* and poses such questions as, are the respect for cultural diversity, issues of faith and the protection of human rights mutually exclusive? [6]

While these questions offer some guidance for students they should also consider whether there are differences between and within cultures as to how knowledge is dealt with as well as the differences within and between areas of knowledge.

References

[1] Tylor E 1871, *Primitive Culture*, New York: J. P. Putnam's Sons. Volume 1, pp. 1

[2] van Zolingen SJ, Streumer JN and Stooker M 2001, '*Problems in knowledge management: A case study of a knowledge-intensive company*', International Journal of Training and Development, 5(3): pp. 168–184

[3] Rusbult C 1997, *A Detailed Examination of Scientific Method*. Retrieved 11 June, 2014 from www.asa3.org/ASA/education/ think/details.htm.

[4] Oyserman D and Lee WS 2008, Psychological Bulletin, 2008, Vol. 134, No. 2, pp. 311–342

[5] Ardichvili A et al. (2006), *Cultural influences on knowledge sharing through online communities of practice*, Journal of Knowledge Management, Vol. 10 Iss: 1, pp. 94 - 107

[6] Charlesworth H 1998, *Cultural Diversity in International Law. In Human Rights, Faith and Culture*. Proceedings of the Australian Bahá'í Studies Conference pp. 7-8

Exercise

How does science affect culture, and how does culture affect science?

5.7–INNOVATION, DESIGN AND MARKETING SPECIFICATIONS

ESSENTIAL IDEA

Successful innovations typically start with detailed design and marketing specifications.

© IBO 2012

NATURE OF DESIGN

Designers must establish clear parameters for a marketing specification in order to create unique and creative solutions to a problem. Designers need to collect valid and useful data from the target market and audience throughout the design cycle to ensure the specification includes certain essential components.

© IBO 2012

AIM

The ability to transform their research findings into a series of specifications is a skill that designers must develop to become successful. Being able to express parameters and requirements succinctly allows the designer to develop focussed solutions to their design problem and meet a client or the target market's wants and needs.

© IBO 2012

Target markets

How market sectors and segments can be used to establish target markets

A target market is a specific, well-defined group of consumers that an innovator, manufacturer or marketing team plans to target with its products or services. Market sectors are particular subsets of markets that share specific characteristics. Sectors are often large and could include such diverse fields as: pharmaceutical, household and automotive groupings.

Market segmentation involves the break up of markets into smaller divisions or segments. Consumers within market segments are identified as having similar characteristics. It is these characteristics that allow for careful targeting of goods and services. Traditionally markets have been divided using demographic characteristics such as age, gender, lifestyle or ethnic background. Also, attributes such as: location, income, marital status, children and even physical characteristics such as height or quality of hearing may be used.

Products targeting specific market segments create new customers in existing markets. This approach often builds on well-known brand names or market sectors.

The success of any product, in the marketplace depends entirely on its ability to meet the tastes, trends and requirements of the target market. To maximise the chances of product success and ultimately financial viability, meeting consumers' demands is paramount.

Initially, however, market surveys may be employed to determine:

- price placement

- current market solutions

- customer niche and demand

- brand recognition and product perception.

Once a market demand and initial product specification has been developed, production would be scaled up from bench scale to pilot-plant scale. This enables a larger volume trial production of product, allowing wider market testing. A range of methods may be employed by manufacturers to measure potential market acceptance before their products go to full-scale production.

Target audiences

How a target audience is used to establish the characteristics of users

A 'target audience' is a refined subset of the target market. Target audiences are identified through the special characteristic that your target audience might have, which may include language, culture, regional location, age, gender, seasonal and cyclical purchasing trends, etc. These characteristics are important because they create an understanding of how to develop and prioritise product requirements towards fulfilling a target audience's needs. A target audience can be the same as the brand's target market, but a target audience will be better defined.

Design contexts for different target markets and audiences

Bicycle manufacturers break their products down into specific target segments such as leisure, sports and competition. Segmentation of these markets would focus on men, women and children within these fields. An audience may be found within the male, competitive triathlon environment. This particular audience has many requirements beyond the bicycle itself and extends into swimwear, watches and footwear etc.

Australia is often characterised as an outdoor culture with many people enjoying the warm weather and large expanses of open space. Marketing to this group could include everything from portable barbeques to sporting apparel and equipment. A subset or segment of this outdoor market could be seen as the surfing segment. While many of the attributes of the outdoor market are still appropriate, this group requires very specific attention including a range of item from swimwear to surf craft.

Market analysis

Market research and analysis influences innovation and product development at all stages. Beginning with market investigation through to product evaluations, market research and analysis is critical for a product's initial and continued success. The following stages show where and how market research and analysis impacts innovation and product development.

- Identifying markets and user needs through surveys, crowdsourcing, interviews, focus groups, etc.

- Generating new product concepts and ideas, literature searches, reviewing patents, consumer feedback.

- Market testing and optimising of features through field testing, focus groups, user trials.

- Assessing product viability including costing, pricing, placement, etc.

- Gathering product reviews and feedback.

User need

Today's consensus is with the theories of Schmookler, who in 1962 decided user needs or market pull were the most influential drivers of successful innovation. In other words, successful innovation rests on identifying and understanding the needs and motivation of consumers before attempting to meet those needs through the development and introduction of a new product. Thomas Edison succinctly summed up this approach when he said, "I don't want to invent anything that nobody will buy."

The chances of an invention being developed into a market-successful innovation may be influenced by the following factors:

- expectations of demand

- magnitude of user needs

- expectations of profitability

- degree of positivity of market perception

- amount of intellectual property protection afforded by patents.

Consumer needs

The first part of the consumer purchase cycle is driven by the user identifying a need or a want and proceeding towards a purchase decision. There are a variety of causes associated with the creation of need recognition ranging from basic through to complex. Drivers of need recognition may be internal or external.

Out of Stock

Need recognition occurs when consumers deplete a supply of a product, (this is particularly the case with consumables, eg. foodstuffs, batteries, personal hygiene and cleaning products). The motivation is then to replace the product. The purchase choice is then often based on repetition of previous product brand choices.

Product dissatisfaction

Consumers recognise a need for change when a product fails to meet their expectations. Product dissatisfaction may arise from performance issues, changing fashions or through the introduction of new products with a superior feature set entering the market.

Change of circumstances

As consumer circumstances change so to do their needs. Improvements in salary, relocation and family growth all affect consumers needs. A simple example relates to the type of car required by a young single individual, opposed to a young married couple, contrasted with an older and larger family unit consisting of parents and a number of children.

Related Products/Purchases

Consumers may be encouraged to purchase add-on products once an initial purchase has been made e.g. window tinting or upholstery anti-stain treatments may be offered with the purchase of a new car or computer peripherals such as scanners, printers or wireless hubs with an initial purchase of a computer.

Marketer-induced needs

Marketing campaigns may induce consumer support through promoting changing fashion trends, perceived social status associated with product identity and/ or creating insecurities in consumers associated with personal hygiene or appearance.

New Products

Consumers identify needs based on availability of new products performing tasks previously not catered for e.g. tablet computers or modified products offering a new feature set. On occasions, new products are driven by technology. In this situation, known as technology push, consumers may be unaware of their need for a product until it appears on the market. Steve Jobs is famously quoted as saying, "people don't know what they want until you show it to them."

Competition

Competition research and analysis is aimed at identifying your competitors by market segment, target market and target audience. To understand the competitor's position in the market and the potential for the entry of a competitive player, the following questions need to be answered.

- What is the size of the market?

- Is entry to the market time dependent?

- What is the current level of market diffusion?

- Are there barriers to market entry; legislation, high investment costs, technology?

- What are the strengths and weaknesses of the new product and existing market solutions?

Research methods

Literature search

The starting point for any research project is the collection and evaluation of prior learning relevant to the topic. This is the aim of a literature search. The literature search therefore involves the systematic search for published material in order to establish the current levels of knowledge and criticism related to the topic of interest and to inform future research directions. This search is usually performed using sources of information recognised as being authoritative, such as; peer reviewed academic journals, books and published theses and patents, but may also include information published by consumer magazines, government agencies and industry. A properly conducted literature search will uncover the state of knowledge about a topic, preventing unnecessary duplication of effort, while highlighting areas of potentially fruitful study.

Qualitative and quantitative research

The type of information obtained from a research inquiry assessment can be divided into two broad groups; quantitative and qualitative. Qualitative research techniques are those that obtain information about some quality aspect of the subject being analysed. These include preferences or feelings about the product. Such assessments are often determined using instruments such as:

- interviews

- observation

- focus groups

- questionnaires

- telephone surveys.

These instruments aim to determine what the surveyed population feel about an idea/product/service – their level of satisfaction.

Quantitative research techniques are those that obtain some form of numerical data, and as such, determine a quantity. Quantitative research may use instruments such as those listed below.

- Data logging or data acquisition may be used to determine information surrounding product failure rates via durability tests, service data such as number of duty cycles, environmental conditions, etc. Data logging may record data from both destructive and non-destructive tests.

- Scale models. Scale models may be used as part of an evaluation strategy to assess shape and form. They may also be employed to obtain quantitative data on issues of strength, fluid flow, etc. using techniques of similitude. Similitude techniques allow models to be tested at less extreme temperatures and pressures to those required of the full size component. Experiments are performed on scale models because it is often faster, cheaper, or safer to perform experiments on a prototype or model before going into testing on the real product.

- Full-scale product testing allows for testing of final designs in small markets to assess the potential of the product in the market against competitive products. It may also cater for the last minute discovery of modifications required before going into full production.

- Questionnaires. A quantitative assessment of attitude towards an idea/ product/service can be obtained by attempting to determine the level or intensity of feeling. This is done by using questionnaires that ask for a rating scale usually organised from 'strongly dislike' through to 'strongly like' or 'strongly disapprove' through to 'strongly approve' etc. Such a scale can have a numerical value assigned to each choice for later analysis. Such a scale is known as a Lickert Scale.

- Computer simulations. Computer simulations use mathematical models for testing purposes. Simulation is one of the most widely used quantitative methods due to its flexibility and its capacity to yield a variety of results in a short timeframe. Through computer simulations we can gain a greater understanding of how current products perform, modified products would perform and how new systems would behave.

- Controlled experiments may be employed to gather quantitative data on the performance of a product under a range of variables ie. users, environments, duty cycles etc.

Design specifications

Successful innovations and new products don't just happen by accident, but by careful design. Successful designs and designers, start with a clear understanding of product context. Product or design context is a combination of factors including:

- characteristics of the target market

- purpose, goal or need for the product

- situation or environment within which the product will perform

- capabilities and limitations of appropriate technologies and materials.

Products that meet contextual needs have a better chance of being successful. Using this general information, a designer is better informed when developing a precise design specification.

A product specification should consist of information related to the product. This information should not just list design requirements but provide justification for their inclusion. This list should not direct the design but help focus the designer's attention towards fruitful investigations through the statement of a series of relevant restrictions. The nature of design requires that these statements need to be very specific and not include any vagaries that may lead to misinterpretation of the brief. Specifications must be achievable and provide an opportunity for measurement of success.

Specifications must be carefully developed through communication between designers, manufacturers and consumers. Product design specifications are produced after thorough investigation. This research process may use a variety of techniques including: market research, consumer surveys, patent investigations, literature searches and competition or SWOT analyses.

A design specification must be flexible enough to evolve throughout the design process. The final product design specification would include:

- appearance considering style and fashion trends

- pricing considerations including market placement

- user needs

- environmental impact at every stage of the life cycle

- physical considerations of size, mass and volume

- safe design of product for use and disposal

- functionality, features and performance issues such as durability

- specific materials and manufacturing requirements.

Marketing specification

Marketing specifications identify product user characteristics and may include the following.

- Target market - market sectors and segments.

- Target audience - clear refinement of subset group and its user characteristics.

- Market research and analysis - data gathering and analysis including potential users, current market solution status, costs, etc.

- User need - essential feature sets must be accurately identified based on targeted consumer group needs.

- Competition - consideration of current market solutions, price points, features, distribution and market penetration.

INTERNATIONAL MINDEDNESS

The characteristics of users in different countries/ regions need to be taken into account. Cultural differences may play a major role.

© IBO 2012

Understanding a culture is about recognising the shared values and beliefs of a group. From an innovator, designer or marketer's perspective the following categories or 'ingredients' must be considered:

- Material refers to the ownership of tangible possessions evidenced by not only the amount of 'stuff' owned but with a significant focus on brands and branding.

- Social environment refers to the level and types of social interactions taking place within a given society. Products in highly social societies thrive based not on a sense of ownership but on the benefit to the individual that is then directly or indirectly conferred on the group. Factors include safety and communication.

- Physical environment manifests itself in cultures in different ways. Some cultures venerate the natural environment and can have a religious connection with the earth while other cultures may see the physical environment as a resource to exploit. These different perspectives radically affect consumers and their purchase preferences. Physical environments may also affect whole cultures or smaller subsets e.g. Norway's 'outdoor' and 'skiing' cultures.

- Aesthetics. Colour is the most obvious expression of aesthetics in cultures. Depending on your perspective colour may communicate different meanings e.g., politically, red is often perceived as colour representing communism, however in commercial terms red is also

a significant part of the coca cola logo representing the values of the United States. Green may also be perceived as colour representing; Ireland, money (in the US), the environment or it may also be used to express the pallor of someone ill.

- Language is used by cultures to express how they perceive and interpret the world. Given an understanding of language, cultural nuances may be revealed and allow outsiders to gain a new perspective.

THEORY OF KNOWLEDGE

Design is evidence based. How do other areas of knowledge value the importance of evidence?

© IBO 2012

The Theory of Knowledge subject is concerned with what it means to know something. What are the conditions under which we can say we know or have knowledge? One of the conditions is evidence - so the student needs to consider what constitutes knowledge in the various areas of knowledge (ways of knowing) and how they value (or what they consider to be) evidence.

Design is based around evidence provided from qualitative and quantitative research and testing procedures. These appear in a range of forms including but not limited to opinion surveys, destructive and non-destructive product testing, field tests, prototype evaluations, materials testing and so on.

Paul Pardi (2011) when writing for *Philosophy News* [1] provides four conditions for something to be accepted as 'the truth'.

- Certainty- its hard or impossible to deny

- Evidence- it has to be based on something

- Practicality- it has to actually work in the real world

- Broad agreement- lots of people have to agree it's true.

The basis of inquiry in the natural sciences is the 'scientific method'. This is a means of investigating, measuring and testing information or knowledge in a way that is both objective and independently repeatable. The opportunity to verify results by reproducing 'evidence' is at the heart of the process.

In mathematics, a proof is a deductive argument or evidence that a mathematical statement is true. There are a number of ways of producing mathematical proofs such as directly, inductively or by showing contradictions.

The human sciences rely on gathering evidence to support assertions. This evidence may be in the form of physical fossilized remains, geological specimens, artefacts, tools, historical documents, verbal recounts and so on. The analysis and interpretation of this evidence is then distilled into knowledge. This analysis may, however, contain cultural, political or even socio-economic bias.

Consider how religious knowledge systems rely on faith based on evidence provided in documents such as the Torah, the Koran and the Bible. Christians view the Bible as a historical document whose writers are recording eye witness accounts of events thus providing reliable evidence for their faith.

Exercises

1. Examine a family heirloom and try to determine as much knowledge about the artefact as possible. Consider such questions as:

- What was the purpose of the item?

- Who owned the item and how did it come into their possession?

- From what is the item made and how was it manufactured?

- How old is the item and does it have any historical significance?

2. Students can examine religious documents and attempt to match up people and events through other historical accounts, thus identifying points of corroboration.

3. Students may examine how professionals deal with ethics and evidenced-based approaches. As an example, in the field of medicine and ethics, an evidence-based approach allows clinicians to have the best and most up to date information available to them to better inform their decisons. This evidence is gathered through the exchange of best practice, maintaining a reading program of published research and strong communication between colleagues and patients.

Reference

[1] Pardi P, 2011, *The Knowledge problem*, Philosophy news, from http://www.philosophynews.com/post/2011/09/22/What-is-Knowledge.aspx

SAMPLE QUESTIONS

1. The product cycle stage where prices are at their highest is most likely?

   A   introduction
   B   growth
   C   maturity
   D   decline.

2. Lone inventors operate best when working?

   A   independently
   B   leading teams
   C   consulting for organisations
   D   as part of a large multi-skilled team.

3. Technology pull is a market process where

   A   technology push plays no part
   B   markets have no say in product development
   C   market demand drives the development of new products
   D   a product is pulled faster through the product life cycle.

4. Circular economies

   A   are a natural occurrence
   B   are economically unsustainable
   C   never go forward only round and round
   D   are a means of securing sustainable practice.

5. Explain the differences between adaption, analogy and technology transfer.

6. Compare and contrast adoption and diffusion.

7. Explain the difference between target markets and audiences.

8. Explain why companies adopt an imitation strategy rather than developing new products of their own.

9. Identify the factors that have lead away from lone inventors and towards research and development teams.

10. Explain why successful inventions do not always translate into innovations.

11. Discuss the advantages and disadvantages associated with planned obsolesence.

LUNKENHEIMER
CASE STUDY

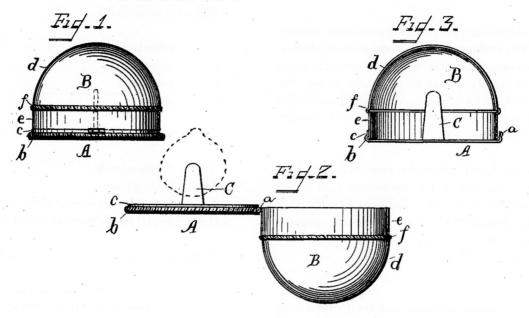

Figure 5.7.4   Lunkin's 1898 'Peggy' patent

Lunken's Peggy—An unsuccessful innovation

The Lunkenheimer Manufacturing Company also known as the Lunkenheimer Valve Company, gained a worldwide reputation for the steam valves, parts for steamboats, military equipment and other mechanical components that it produced. In 1892 Edmund Lunken, head of the company and multiple patent holder invented the 'Peggy'.

This highly decorated hinged brass container was easily manufactured using the company's equipment. The device consisted of two halves one domed and one hinged to a flat base with a spike attached at its centre.

It was designed to store used chewing gum ready for the next use. The owner could deposit and remove the gum using their teeth thus negating the need to touch the gum at any point. Lunkin had such confidence in his idea that he had it patented in 1898.

The device was marketed to the Wrigley gum company who unfortunately failed to see any commercial advantage in the product. From their perspective they were interested in increasing sales of gum, not finding ways of preserving, reusing or extending product life.

Ultimately the innovation was a failure and remains only as a curio in museums.

Figure 5.7.5   Lunkin's 1898 'Peggy'

CLASSIC DESIGN

CONTENTS

6

6.1–CHARACTERISTICS OF CLASSIC DESIGN

ESSENTIAL IDEA

A classic design has a timeless quality, which is recognized and remains fashionable.

© IBO 2012

NATURE OF DESIGN

A classic design is not simply defined by how well it functions or its impact. Classic designs can be recognized as from their design movement/era. Yet, originality—whether it is evolutionary or revolutionary—seems to be the trait that makes a product "timeless".

© IBO 2012

AIM

The iconic status of classic designs is often attributed to them being "breakthrough products".

© IBO 2012

Image, status and culture

Phaidon *Design Classics*, 2006, defines classic design as "an industrially manufactured object with timeless aesthetic value. It serves as a standard of its kind and, despite the year in which it was designed, is still up to date. It is characterised by simplicity, balance, and purity of form and has remained largely unchanged since its creation."

To ensure sustained success over an extended period of time, design classics must not only address functional and aesthetic requirements but also establish an emotional connection with the user/owner. The most successful designs convey a sense of satisfaction with ownership and may even bestow a level of prestige or social status upon the owner. Many examples across a range of product categories exist including the design examples offered below. These have often proven to be iconic reference designs against which others are judged over the decades. They each offer some national, social or cultural significance.

- Fender Telecaster electric guitar. In 1950 this was the world's first commercial solid-body, single-cutaway electric guitar. The 'bolt on' neck design not only made production easier but assisted with maintenance. In addition to the above features the Telecaster offered an instrument of impressive versatility due to its dual pickup configuration consisting of a pickup in the bridge and one in the neck; this meant that the Telecaster could be used by musicians from throughout the musical spectrum from Country to Blues and Rock. Just some of the musicians associated with the Telecaster are Elvis Presley, Muddy Waters, Otis Redding, George Harrison, Keith Richards, Eric Clapton and Bruce Springsteen. Fender today continues to produce a number of variants around the world.

- Eames lounge chair and ottoman. In continuous construction since 1956, hand-assembled and designed to last a lifetime, the Eames chair is considered by some to be one of the most significant designs of the 20th century. The design features a distinctive, moulded plywood shell and die-cast aluminium base that allows a stylish chair and matching ottoman to be manufactured using mass production techniques resulting in an affordable price.

- Porsche 911. Porsche is associated with the excellence and precision of German engineering. A Canadian study by DesRosiers Automotive Consultants Inc. recently showed that 97.4 percent of Porsches from

the last 25 years are still on the road, a testament to their design, engineering, longevity and robustness. Debuting in 1963, the 911 represented a radical change in automotive design with its swept-back design and rear-mounted air cooled six-cylinder engine. It quickly became a sports car favourite of the rich and famous with a sleek simple design that has remained largely unchanged. Since its introduction it has become the benchmark against which other sports cars are judged.

- Silver Cross baby pram carriages have connections with British royalty and therefore the associated social status that comes with ownership. The pushchairs have been in production since 1877 and have been characterised as hand made by craftsmen with a tradition of offering child comfort and parental usability.

Figure 6.1.1   Design classic collection

Porsche 911

Eames lounge chair and ottman

Fender Telecaster American Vintage 1952, image by Massimo Barbieri - own work., Creative Commons Attribution-Share Alike 3.0 via Wikimedia Commons

Obsolescence

Obsolescence, particularly planned obsolescence is a commercial ploy on the part of manufacturers and designers to boost sales, maintain a competitive edge and constantly refresh and improve products. Adopting a philosophy of planned obsolescence allows designers to create a desire for product replacement, or update, rather than repair. In terms of classic design it is the nature of the unchanging design that defies time allowing the product to cross generations and span decades of interest and use.

Michael Thonet's 19th Century No. 14 or bistro chair is one of the most recognisable pieces of furniture ever made. Originally designed in an attempt to make a durable cafe chair. The seat in particular was purposefully made from woven cane to allow the draining of spilt liquids. Earning a Gold Medal in the 1867 Paris World Exposition, the chair has been reproduced millions of times with over 50 million being sold between 1859 and 1930. Over the years the original No. 14 chair has inspired a range of variations and improvements. Noted Swiss-French architect and designer, Le Corbusier is quoted as saying "Never was a better and more elegant design and a more precisely crafted and practical item created."

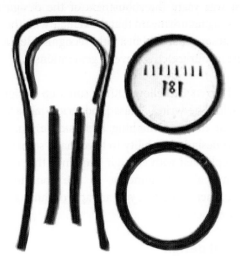

Figure 6.1.3   Thonet flat pack assembly

Today, Thonet style chairs use a variety of materials for the seat, contain additional components and have even evolved into benches and rocking chairs. Transcending its original purpose the manufacturing technique known as 'bentwood' has also inspired designs from coat racks through to lampshades.

Mass produced, ubiquitous/ omnipresent design

One of the key factors of design classic status is recognition. This comes about through market presence and volume sales. These sales can only be achieved through equally large numbers made possible by mass production. Mass production brings an economy of scale to manufacturing and therefore delivers cost benefits to consumers. Large production volumes and ease of availability also encourage consumers to make purchases.

Figure 6.1.2   Michael Thonet's cafe chair

Instantly identifiable by its simple design and bentwood construction, this chair is one of the best-selling pieces of furniture ever produced. What is not readily appreciated is that this may be the first example of flat-pack furniture.

Originally produced using only six pieces of steam-bent beechwood, formed in cast iron moulds, unskilled factory workers were able to mass-produce this design classic. Eight screws and a pair of nuts and bolts allowed the chair to be easily assembled. Figure 6.1.3 shows a disassembled version of Thonet's design.

While all of the products mentioned previously are worthy of the title 'design classic' the nature of mass production on a global scale and the seemingly ever-present nature of the VW beetle raises it to another level. The Volkswagen beetle or 'people's car' first went into small scale production in 1941 but by 2003 when it finished production over 21 million had been both produced and marketed in a variety of countries around the world.

The mechanical simplicity, quality of construction, performance of the rear mounted, air cooled 'flat four' engine and suspension design all contributed to its success. The vehicle's robust nature, tolerance for heat and near watertight construction saw it marketed in a variety of contexts including commuter vehicle, police car, racecar and military vehicle. In WWII the German armed forces used the car as transport and ambulance configurations.

CORE

In post war years the robustness of the design and its unchanging nature meant that the vehicle with the unique, curved design that was instantly recognisable, became a low cost favourite across several generations.

Writer Darren Bedfellow (2014) sums up design classic status when he writes "Mass production has a lot to do with what makes something a classic design. When it comes to design, the ability to have made something that can be replicated with enough frequency that it becomes ubiquitous, almost mundane in the constancy of its presence, then odds are, you are approaching something like a design classic."

Dominant design

Dominant design is the emergence of a product design that achieves market dominance through the provision of a particular feature set that is seen as essential to the product category.

In new markets it takes time for dominant designs to emerge and it is often the imitators or market colonisers that wait to capitalise on the research and development work of other firms. As the market matures and customer preferences develop, imitators enter and product development and improvement continues. Dominant designs with associated market-driven features often appear at this point.

Classic dominant designs are often difficult to change if the popularity of the product continues over an extended period of time. Additional to this, older classic designs are often associated with emotional connections and feelings of nostalgia reminding owners of past times or places.

6.2–CLASSIC DESIGN, FUNCTION AND FORM

ESSENTIAL IDEA

For a design to become a classic design, the form can transcend the function.

© IBO 2012

NATURE OF DESIGN

Classic design holds "form follows function" as a fundamental principle, but this is not always evident in practice. Some products are so well designed with function as their primary goal, that their use is intuitive. As designers develop new technologies, the lines between the form and function of a product continue to blur.

© IBO 2012

AIM

The balance between function and form is often an area of difficulty for the designer. If a product is purely functional, it may be lacking in appeal to consumers, no matter how good it may be at completing its job. Often we are drawn to products that have been developed with form as a primary consideration. The human psyche appreciates beauty.

© IBO 2012

Form versus function

'Form follows function' is a frequently used phrase, incorrectly translated and attributed to American architect Louis Sullivan who said, 'form ever follows function'. In this statement he identifies the inextricable links between functionality and aesthetics. The question is often asked, which is more important? In reality there should be no separation of form and function and it is not a question of choice but of balance and emphasis depending on the circumstances.

The Bauhaus school founded in Weimar, Germany in 1919 revolutionised approaches to design and architecture. Its focus was the merging of design with industrial practice. The key principle of Bauhaus design was 'form follows function' thus allowing the development of well-designed, utilitarian, functional items that evoked both simplicity and an appreciation for both art and industry.

Researchers Chitturi, Raghunathan, and Mahajan (2007) when writing for the American Marketing Association discuss the notion of 'precedence', where consumers place specific value on functional aspects of design before proceeding to consider aesthetics. As an example car buyers may weigh factors of safety, performance and fuel economy before switching their attention to vehicle aesthetics.

The researchers found, however, that if the consumer was evaluating a product solely based on its price rather functionality then aesthetics or fashion considerations come to the fore. Based on their research, Chitturi, Raghunathan, and Mahajan advise designers to ensure products 'deliver (a) certain minimal level of functionality first; however, they also suggest that after this level of functionality is met, marketers should focus almost exclusively on enhancing the hedonic appeal of their offerings'.

Retro-styling

Retro design is a term coined from the word retrograde or backward looking and is a style of design that appeared in the 1980s in New York. It incorporated nostalgic revivals of modernist European designs from the first half of the 20th century and quickly spread throughout the world.

Retro-designs often mimic a product or past experience to evoke feelings of nostalgia. Modern retro products may also use an old format to meet a new need.

An example of retro design is the reintroduction of film-based cameras or lomographs. Lomography is the use of low-fidelity analog cameras of simple construction that hark back to the days of celluloid film cameras and associated technologies. While similar photographic affects can be achieved digitally using software products such as Photoshop®, this defeats the whole purpose of the lomography experience.

Figure 6.2.1 shows a Soviet-era LOMO LC camera compared to a modern (2012) Belair X 6-12 panoramic lomo camera.

Figure 6.2.1   A Soviet-era LOMO LC, image by Jan Kratochvil Creative Commons Attribution-Share Alike 3.0-2.5-2.0-1.0 via Wikimedia Commons and a Lomography Belair X 6-12

The Sony XDR-S16DBP digital clock radio with stereo speakers uses modern digital technology encased in a retro looking wooden box. While there is still a digital display, the mechanical push button selectors, telescopic metal aerial, analog knobs and wooden case all combine to create an overall effect reminiscent of 60s style portable radios but with many of the advantages of modern technology. It has, however, no docks, usb ports, auxiliary inputs or any other form of connectivity.

Figure 6.2.2   Sony XDR-S16DBP digital clock radio

In comparison, digital radio offers more choice than AM or FM bands and also offers a clearer sound without the effects of interference caused by atmospheric conditions or electrical interference.

Figure 6.2.2   1950s vintage portable radio

Both the choice of material, aluminium, and the 1950s rocket shape of Phillipe Starck's design classic 'Juicy Salif' (shown in Figure 6.2.5) evoke a sense of nostalgia and retro-styling.

Conflict and compromise

The Bahaus School of Design (1919—1933), based its work on the premise that function should be the driving influence behind an object's design. Bauhaus furniture design was often simple and light. Proponents of this style believed purity of function would create simplistic, elegant design without elaborate decoration, following only the needs of the consumer.

Designers are constantly faced with the challenge of developing aesthetically pleasing, functional products for an identified market. When developing new products based on traditional or classic designs the challenges and compromises between form and function can be even more difficult to resolve than usual.

Practical function versus psychological function

Psychological function and responses

Psychological function involves the 'needs and wants' driven by fads, fashion and technological trends. There may be some form of social benefit from inclusion and even perceptions social status associated with the ownership of a particular product or brand.

On viewing an object a psychological response is often provoked. Even before the practical uses of a design can be evaluated, this psychological or emotional response may be good, bad or indifferent. There are a number of theories that explain how people respond to psychological design and the tools and techniques designers employ to solicit positive responses. Psychological design theories include;

- semiotics
- gestalt theory
- colour theory.

Semiotics

Semiotics is the study of signs and symbols. It includes the communication of information and meaning from source to receiver. Semiotics may be used in product design in the field of ergonomics through the development and refinement of user interfaces or more general applications where user interaction with a product may be improved. Semiotics also sees application in branding and logo development. A good deal of information about a product may be communicated simply through the strategic placement of a logo. Logos can convey much to the consumer about product quality, performance and even cost expectation. For example, consider what consumers would expect from a product branded with any of the following logos.

Figure 6.2.3   Semiotics and branding

Gestalt theory

Gestalt psychology was founded in the 1920s. *Gestalt* is a German word meaning 'unified whole' and is used to describe how individuals perceive visual input such as when viewing/using a product. Gestalt is the concept that 'the whole is greater than the sum of its parts.' The principles may apply to individual design elements or the whole.

There are a variety of interpretations of Gestalt theory. One classification of the elements is provided below.

- Similarity. This refers to repetitive elements that may be identical or similar based on values such as shape, size, colour texture etc. The greater the similarity between individual objects the greater the link or cohesion. Individual elements may also be highlighted by emphasising their dissimilar nature in a repetitive field of sameness. Using this effect is known as creating an anomaly.

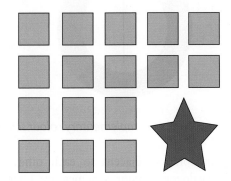

Figure 6. 2.4   Similarity

- Continuation. This principle uses design elements to draw the eye a long a path. In some cases the eye may be 'tricked' to continue or complete lines that are not actually part of the design. Lines are often used to focus or lead the eye to a specific design element or create layering effects.

Figure 6. 2.5   Continuation

- Closure. This technique is again about tricking the eye into completing objects. This approach is commonly achieved through the use of negative space which can give a stencilled effect. Figure 6.2.6 shows Taiwan's recycling symbol. Consider how, through the use of negative space, arrows are created to point both outwards (white) and inwards (green).

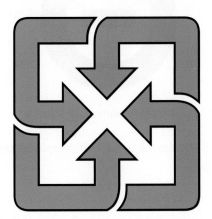

Figure 6. 2.6   Closure technique involving negative space

- Proximity. Proximity uses the closeness or grouping of objects to generate a relationship between individual elements. These elements may then often be seen as part of a larger or single whole.

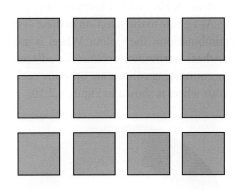

Figure 6. 2.7   Proximity

- Figure/ground. Figure and ground routinely uses light and shade to help create an image that appears from a group of shapes. Again employing a trick of the eye to see and then separate objects from the background. MC Escher used this technique to great advantage often in conjunction with tesselations.

Figure 6. 2.8   Figure/ground

- Symmetry and order. Design compositions should provide a sense of order and balance. The principle is based around the assumption that we perceive objects as symmetrical shapes that form around their centre. Our eyes quickly identify the order associated with symmetry and, as Figure 6.2.9 shows, symmetry takes precedence over proximity

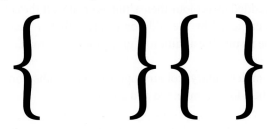

Figure 6. 2.9   Symmetry and order

Colour theory

Colour theory suggests that, within the colour spectrum, certain colours are aesthetically pleasing together, either because they harmonise with each other or provide a pleasing contrast, while other colour combinations are not as pleasing. As a guide to the selection of these aesthetically pleasing combinations, the Colour Wheel is used. Using the colour wheel, harmonious colours lie adjacent to each other while contrasting colours are opposite each other. A typical colour wheel is shown in Figure 6.2.10.

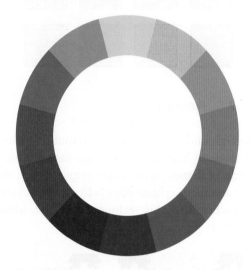

Figure 6.2.10   Example of a colour wheel

Kelly Berg, (2011) of AiInsite says, "Everything designed –by human or nature–has a colour and every colour creates an emotional response." Colour and the choice of associated colours play an important role in product design, packaging and branding. It can have a significant influence on how consumers view a product.

Appropriate colour combinations may be based upon the colour wheel which plots primary colours around a circle, mixing different primary colours to achieve secondary and on further blending to form tertiary colours. The colour wheel allows us to see at a glance various colour combinations such as:

- monochromatic–is a colour scheme consisting of various shades of a single colour including all colours, that is, tints, tones and shades of a single hue. If white is added to a colour then a 'tint' is created. If the colour is darkened by the addition of black then a 'shade' is the result. The addition of gray produces a 'tone'.

- complementary–colours opposite each other on the wheel for example: red and green.

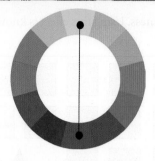

Figure 6.2.11   Sample complementary colour scheme

- analogous–colours adjacent to each other on the wheel. Analogous colour schemes are often found in nature. Colour schemes using three colours are regularly created with one colour dominating, a second supporting and the third (in conjunction with black, white or gray) as an accent.

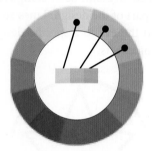

Figure 6.2.12   Sample analogous colour scheme

- split complementary–in a split complementary colour scheme, instead of just two opposite colours being used, three colours are selected in which one of the complementary colours is substituted for the colours on either side of it.

- triadic–three colours positioned at 120° on the wheel from each other. This book was coloured in this way.

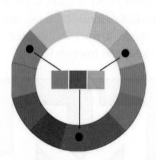

Figure 6.2.13   Sample triadic colour scheme

- tetradic–involes the use of two complementary colour pairings.

Functional design

Functional design represents a paradigm in which the prime purpose of a design is seen to be to provide the intended functions simply and with the intended user in mind rather than focusing on aesthetics.

Functional design, however, is not only about the competency of how well a product meets its intended function. The act of using a device may also provide a psychological response. In his book *Emotional Design,* Norman, (2005) groups these responses under the following categories:

- Visceral response. These design features evoke a physical response from the user. They involve sensations such as taste, smell, sound and touch. Examples include tactile feedback from a keyboard, the acceleration of a motor car or the weight of a piece of equipment. The visceral appeal of designs encourages consumers' 'wants' before they examine their 'needs'. A considerable number of products are purchased on appearances alone and this is where proportion, colour, texture, heft and materials selection play a major role.

- Reflective design responses are about fulfilling emotional needs. These emotional needs may involve inclusion, social status or self esteem. The ownership of high quality watches, motor cars, brand name handbags or shoes may meet these needs.

- Behavioural response is all about usability and functionality. User centric design, the intuitive nature of a product's use and degree of functionality rate highly in this category. The most important part of behavioural design is understanding how consumers will use a product.

Form versus function

In the post-modern era, the product aesthetic became the driving force. Objects took on creative or arbitrary forms. Functionality took a back seat to appearance. These products were often marketed as unique or collectable. The most publicised example of this style is the 1980s Philippe Starck designed lemon squeezer, or 'Juicy Salif'. This product soon became an iconic, albeit expensive 'must have' and is hailed as a design classic. Yet, when evaluated under performance-based criteria, the retro-style rocket ship device is notoriously difficult to use successfully. When fielding criticism of his creation Starck is alleged to have said, "My juicer is not meant to squeeze lemons; it is meant to start conversations".

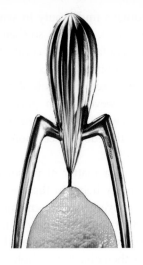

Figure 6.2.14   Phillipe Starck's 'Juicy Salif'

INTERNATIONAL MINDEDNESS

The emergence of retro-styling products as new technologies are developed relate to the emotional response that comes with nostalgia. This is often not only different between countries and between generations, but at the same time can transcend both.

© IBO 2012

The nostalgia associated with retro-styling is not limited to one generation or culture. While there may be specific cultural influences linking cultural groups, the nature of globalisation has spread cultural knowledge and influences around the world to generate shared appreciation.

THEORY OF KNOWLEDGE

Is aesthetic value purely a subjective matter?

© IBO 2012

Students should first clearly define the nature of terms subjective, objective and aesthetic value. Aesthetic value refers of course to the generic term for beauty or the appreciation of beauty.

Students should consider the ancient philosophers such as Plato and Aristotle who both regarded beauty as objective and yet disagreed on the specifics. Classical beauty was said to follow specific rules such as the 'golden ratio', a mathematical relationship against which to measure beauty. Would this be appropriate in all instances? Does this leave room for personal preference or opinion?

It is said that humans find beauty in symmetry, (a very simple geometric rule). If this is so then this rule when applied to the human face should comfortably determine a person's beauty. 'Anaface' is a computer program that uses an algorithm or set of rules to determine so called human 'beauty'. However, when perfectly symmetrical faces produced this way are viewed, many find the images unsettling because they do not seen normal.

Subjective beauty is a matter of personal opinion. The very nature of 'beauty being in the eye of the beholder.' It is however the convergence or agreement of many that tends to suggest that something may in fact be beautiful. Are there then rules to determining aesthetic beauty and can these rules be then objectively applied or even tested.

The works of both Hume and Kant (18th century philosophers) are worth considering as they examine both the subjective and objective nature of 'taste'.

Any investigation into this topic should also consider the various ways of knowing or appreciating beauty. Certainly sense perception, culture, education, memory, emotion, reason and even faith are ways of perceiving, recognising and experiencing beauty. Does the manner of appreciation affect the objectivity or subjectivity of the observer?

Exercise

Examine examples of beauty in nature that adhere to the 'golden ratio'.

SAMPLE QUESTIONS

1. Dominant designs:

   A   are the highest in quality
   B   are always first to market
   C   have recognised essential features
   D   imitate the best features of other designs.

2. Retro-styling involves:

   A   designing for old products
   B   designing for aesthetic appeal
   C   re-using old technologies
   D   designing products to evoke feelings of nostalgia.

3. Four elements of Gestalt theory are:

   A   nominal, ordinal and interval
   B   similarity, proximity and closure
   C   continuous, relative and comparative
   D   symmetrical, continuous and nominal.

4. Semiotics is the study of:

   A   religion
   B   signage
   C   symmetry
   D   signs and symbols.

5. Mass production may be defined as

   A   manufacturing by hand
   B   manufacturing one-off unique items
   C   the use of automated assembly lines to produce customised orders
   D   the production of large numbers of standardised parts, usually at low cost.

6. Explain the relationship between obsolescence and classic design. Provide examples.

7. Choose a classic design and discuss how it meets consumers' needs of image and status within a particular cultural context.

8. Explain how pyschological design uses people's emotional responses to promote sales.

9. What makes classic designs successful?

10. Compare and contrast a modern retro-styled product with the original design.

USER-CENTRED DESIGN (UCD)

CONTENTS

7

7.1–USER-CENTERED DESIGN

ESSENTIAL IDEA

The fundamental principle of UCD is that understanding the needs of the users is the key to designing the best products and services.

© IBO 2012

NATURE OF DESIGN

A designer must consider the needs, wants and limitations of the end user within every element of the design cycle. The ability to identify how users will interact with a product, service or system is vital for its success. To achieve this, designers must be able to acquire and analyse valid data without making assumptions about how the product may be used.

© IBO 2012

AIM

The ability to put aside one's own ideas and bias is essential for UCD. Designers must act with integrity and not project their own ideas of what the user requirements are when trying to create technological solutions to their problems.

© IBO 2012

The designer needs to have a deep understanding of the user, task and the environment.

The term user-centred design (UCD) or human- centred design (HCD) has its origin in the 1980s with the US cognitive scientist Donald Norman. The concept became widely known through his publications *User-Centred Design: New Perspectives on Human-Computer Interaction* and *The Psychology of Everyday Things* later to be renamed *The Design of Everyday Things*. In developing the concept of UCD, Norman took issue with the multitude of consumer devices that were not only difficult to use but that often incorporated design style changes solely for style sake and which in so doing reduced usability. The inclusions of functions that are not required by the consumer can lead to:

- increased cost

- increased complexity

- reduced efficiency of use.

The foundation of UCD is that good design requires that the needs and capabilities of the users are determined and incorporated into the design process from the start through to the finish.

While the inclusion of a wide variety of functions can often be accomplished relatively cheaply, their inclusion can lead to confusion and ultimately reduce rather than increase usability and customer satisfaction, particularly when things go wrong.

This is particularly the case with electronic interfaces. Many electronic interfaces from consumer products such as microwave ovens to TV remotes and smart phones have complex functionality available that can far exceed the requirements of most consumers. This increased functionality is also often achieved at the expense of intuitive operation leading to confusion, particularly on the part of the casual user. In most instances, such confusion is little more than frustrating. However, if it is associated with critical equipment, the potential for errors can be dangerous.

Interfaces intended for use by a wide range of users such as Automatic Teller Machines (ATMs) need to be of a relatively standardised lay-out, large displays and limited functionality to avoid confusion. By comparison, the design of more complex consumer products needs to have those functions used often displayed prominently and intuitively accessed or, in the case of modern electronic devices such as smart phones, the programming options need to be intuitive and allow easy customisation of the interface.

Similarly, designs need to take into account the environment in which they are to be used. Most electronic equipment includes information regarding the temperature range in which it should be operated and the need to shield devices from strong magnetic fields to avoid damage. Of possibly greater danger is the use of standard functions in unintended situations such as the practice of 'texting' while walking. Over one third of young people are reported to have had an accident in such a situation (The Guardian, World News, Australia, 23 Jan 2014) and deaths due to texting while walking are reported to be increasing (KLA-Los Angeles, 9 August, 2013). Increased use of speech recognition software may obviate the effect of such distracted walking practices.

If the designer has a clear understanding of the user, task and environment only those features truly required and desired by the customer will be incorporated into the product. In addition, instructions for use will be written in clear simple language.

The process is iterative led by the user and developed through user-centred evaluation.

UCD requires an iterative approach in which the consumer is surveyed at a number of stages throughout the product design process. At each point, problems are identified and the design modified until a finished product is arrived at that meet consumer needs.

The product must address the whole user experience.

Design should make it easy for the user to:

- determine actions possible at any time

- see the options and results of actions

- determine current system state

- follow intuitively from intention to action.

UCD design teams are multidisciplinary

Norman argued that only by incorporating into the development process the concerns and expertise of the user and production teams that manufacture, distribute, maintain and market the product could a good design emerge. The UCD process therefore represents a fundamental change in the traditional design process where designs were developed largely in isolation.

The five stages of UCD: Research; Concept; Design; Implementation; Launch

Research

This stage of the process involves the defining of the problem and establishing the criteria the new design needs to fulfil. This stage is often undertaken by psychologists, ethnographers and anthropologists who observe the way in which humans undertake tasks and interact with products. Focus groups and market research strategies will be used to determine the likely market opportunities and challenges.

Concept

The initial design concept is typically developed by a team of industrial designers, psychologists and engineers. They aim to create a design concept that will fulfil the needs of the user as defined during the research phase.

Design

The concept drawings and models of the product should allow factors such as scale and feel to be accessed and the design modified cheaply and quickly.

Implementation

User testing of the model with a broader range of end users is undertaken often under the guidance of psychologists who monitor the user experience. This information is again fed back into the design process and the writing of instruction manuals.

Launch

The product is introduced to the general market accompanied by advertising and sales begin. At this stage customer feedback in addition to questionnaires designed to gain a wider response to usability issues and ideas for improvement may be sought.

In his book *Invention by Design: How engineers get from thought to thing,* Henry Petroski recounts the release of the easy opening stay-on-tab can top in the 1970s. Because it was an innovation, beverage companies required consumer studies be performed to assess acceptance before they would adopt the change from the throw away tab design. In addition, early cans were imprinted with instructions of how to open the top.

The stages of UDC are shown graphically in Figure 7.1.1

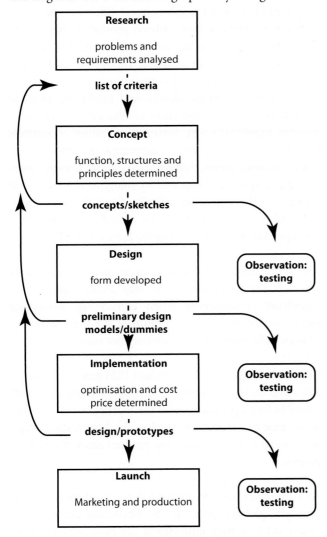

Figure 7.1.1   The UCD process (adapted from Den Buurman, R. (1997). User-centred design of smart products. Ergonomics, 40:10, 1159-1169)

At each stage and their various iterations the user experience is sought using a number of techniques such as focus groups, field studies, etc. The International Standard 9241-210(E) provides some guidance in the implementation of UCD.

Inclusive design

Inclusive design is an extension of UCD in that it aims to include those members of the community who might otherwise be forgotten during the product design process, such as those who are pregnant, elderly, disabled, or injured.

Inclusive design principles (sometimes called 'Universal Design', 'Universal Usability Design' 'Accessible Design' and 'Design for All') are increasingly being incorporated into building codes. The term Universal Design was originally used by Ron Mace, (1998), and was coined to meet the needs of people of all ages and abilities.

The Centre for Universal Design defines the term as, "... the design of products and environment to be useable by all people, to the greatest extent possible, without the need for adaptation or specialised design. The intent of universal design is to simplify life for everyone by making products, communications, and the built environment more useable by as many people as possible at little or no cost."

Centre for Universal Design, 2005.

Universal design takes into consideration people of all ages, genders and abilities, and through design attempts to improve the life of all people. In the past it has been misconstrued as 'one size fits all'. This is clearly less than its full intention. Through legislation and public education campaigns designers have come to realise their social responsibilities and the recognition that good design reflects the needs of a variety of users and makes accommodation for this range. The main features of Universal Design may be interpreted as:

- equity in use

- flexibility in service

- allow tolerance for error

- simple and intuitive operation

- communicate unambiguous information

- need low physical effort to function

- provide space for operators and use.

In many industrialised nations legislation exists covering and enforcing consideration of people with a disability. Human factors research drives and informs designs based on these legislative requirements. Just some of the countries with legislation requiring consideration of individuals with a disability include:

- Australia, the Disability Discrimination Act 1992

- Canada, the Ontarians with Disabilities Act of 2001

- US, under the Americans with Disabilities Act of 1990

- South Africa the Promotion of Equality and Prevention of Unfair Discrimination Act 2000

- India, Persons with Disabilities (Equal Opportunities, Protection of Rights and Full Participation) Act, 1995.

In developing countries, formal legislation may not be enacted, but through a series of informal guidelines and international standards promoted by NGOs and government agencies, disability issues may be addressed to some degree.

Instances of everyday items where inclusive design can be found is in the design of currency, where coins of varying size, thickness and edge detail allow those with poor sight to avoid confusion. Similarly, many countries have adopted notes with differing sizes, colours and textural details that assist the vision impaired.

INTERNATIONAL MINDEDNESS

Even though the task addressed through UCD may not change from region to region, there can be an impact on the success of a global product due to variations in users and environments.

© IBO 2012

While UCD attempts to take into account the needs of the user, the testing and evaluations undertaken are often restricted to the major market. The issues identified and solutions developed are then often assumed to be applicable to an international user. This is, however, not always the case.

Many marketing campaigns by some of the World's leading companies such as General Motors, Ford, Mitsubishi, Pepsi and Coca Cola, etc., have suffered from words changing meaning when translated into another language. These failures to understand the individual cultural and linguistic traditions of the importing countries were at the

time both embarrassing and amusing, but largely harmless with the possible exception of their impact on sales. This is not always the case.

In 1971, a shipment of wheat and barley seed grain was sent to Iraq from North America to allow farmers to grow their own crops. The grain itself was not intended for consumption and had been treated with the fungicide alkyl mercury to prevent spoilage. To emphasise its toxicity the grain had been dyed red and the bags contained a warning in English along with a Skull and Cross bones symbol recognised in the West as an indication of danger.

However, most of the farmers of the region could not read English and were not familiar with the meaning of the Skull and Cross bones symbol. Thinking only the red dye was associated with the chemical treatment, the dye was washed out of the seed and used to make bread. As a result of ingesting the grain 459 deaths occurred and over 60 000 peasants suffered neurological damage.

Because of the language and cultural differences that exist in world markets, a standardised product is not always successful and can be the antithesis of UCD. A process known generally as localization should be undertaken in which the customs and conventions of each country are determined and the design and marketing adjusted accordingly. These changes may involve a change of name, colours, graphical icons, textures, operation of controls and even smell. In her book *Customer Sense: How the five senses influence buying behaviour*, Aradhna Krishna notes that the new car smell prized by many in the West, and created by the release of volatiles from the upholstery, is found to be objectionable by the Chinese who often attempt to remove it by drying tea leaves in the car.

The time, money and resources needed to adequately research the differences that may exist, represents a significant commitment when considering marketing products globally. In many countries the local resources to undertake usability research may not exist.

In the marketing of a new product IBM has a 'rule of ten' that suggests that for every $1 spent on solving a problem found before a product enters the market, it will cost $10 to fix that same problem during the beta testing stage, and $100 if not found until the product enters the market proper.

As companies seek to expand the size of their market through globalization, it is becoming increasingly important that they understand the particular needs of local environments and culture and localise their products and marketing appropriately.

7.2-USABILITY

Essential idea

Usability is about how easy it is to use a product or system.

© IBO 2012

Nature of design

A design team should be 'user' driven and frequent contact with potential users is essential. To understand how a product, service or system may be used, the designer must consider the prior knowledge and experience of the user, as well as their typical psychological responses. Evaluation methods that utilise appropriate testing and trialling strategies must be used to determine these aspects.

© IBO 2012

Aim

Designers must consider the limits of population stereotypes. Through recognising these limits, the designer can critically assess the appropriateness of their product in relation to those who will use it.

© IBO 2012

Usability of objectives

The International Standard ISO 9241-11 defines usability as: "the extent to which a product can be used by specified users to achieve specified goals with effectiveness, efficiency and satisfaction in a specified context of use."

The primary objectives of usability are:

- Ease of use.

- Efficiency of use.

- Unambiguous feedback.

- Clarity of human interface.

Enhanced usability

Enhanced usability is any development that expands and extends the usability of a product. Speech recognition software on smart phones satisfies this requirement by providing those with limited dexterity or familiarity with the keypad a means of easily creating a text message.

Similarly, options to increase font size on computer screens provides improved clarity for the vision impaired as do text to speech functions.

Icons or Graphic User Interfaces (GUI) on computer screens can be useful, particularly those that are universally recognised such as print and save, however it has been found that they can also be a source of confusion, requiring the memorisation of the relationship of a wide variety of images with functions often used infrequently. To correct this situation and enhance usability, text is now commonly associated with an icon to clarify its purpose.

One of the simplest ways of enhancing usability is through the simplification of controls and interfaces. The 2013 London Design Museum award for the Best Design of the Year was won by the UK government website Gov. uk which achieved this by creating a single site using a straightforward, uniform design with limited graphics and colours that made searching for information uncomplicated. This site superseded thousands of sites maintained by individual departments all of which used different screen formats that had made searching for information from one department to another confusing and time consuming.

Characteristics of good user-product interfaces

Most consumers want to use a product 'straight out of the box.' Easy to use intuitive interface design allows new operators to quickly become competent in the basic operations. Good user interface design can be the discriminating factor for consumers. Levels of customer satisfaction or frustration in their interactions with the interface can tarnish the reputation of an otherwise sound product. This can be the contributing factor between product acceptance and failure in the marketplace.

Poorly designed, less intuitively organised interfaces require a high level of learning through trial and error. They also increase the memory burden placed on consumers who may use the product intermittently and be destined to repeat the learning process over.

When simple operations require higher levels of concentration or memory, the full feature set of a product tends to be under exploited. An easy to use interface with

AHL

high levels of success generates confidence in the user and encourages further use of the device.

Good user-interface design exhibits the following features:

- low user error rate

- high levels of user satisfaction

- easy to learn–simple uncomplicated, uncluttered interfaces

- easy to use–intuitive design, controls appear where anticipated and actions perform as expected

- easy to remember functions and operations are performed over time with an ease of repeatability and high level of competence retention.

Converging technology offers the benefits of the incorporation of a variety of technologies into a single device, providing increased functionality. Where these technologies are incorporated without rationalisation of the controls into a uniform solution, however, confusion can arise regarding operation particularly under conditions of stress.

Population stereotypes

Assumptions and associations are made by the population of a particular culture regarding how equipment and products operate. Such assumptions include the direction a handle should turn to open or close, or the direction a switch moves for on or off. These are not associations that are intrinsic to the machine but are established as a factor in machine standardisation within a society.

Because of this, it is often the case that different paths to standardisation have been taken leading to different population stereotypes. In the UK and Australia for instance a light switch is pushed down for on and up for off while in the USA it is the reverse.

Which side of the road drivers use varies around the world between left and right. While over 60% of the world favours the right, the reason for the variation remains unclear. Historical references to driving side choice include Roman charioteers, medieval knight battle tactics, Napoleonic conquests and even courtesy to female passengers.

Some countries have even made the change from one side to another: Canada in the 1920s, Sweden (1967), Burma (1970) and Samoa (2009).

INTERNATIONAL MINDEDNESS

Population stereotypes based on cultural expectations contribute to human error and designers must consider this when designing good user-product interfaces.

© IBO 2012

If population stereotypes are incorporated into product design operations can often feel more intuitive as they conform to expectations based on past experience.

The displacement of a population stereotype, however, means that an operation does not conform to user expectations. Such a displacement might be the turning of a knob clockwise for ON rather than anti-clockwise. With a little effort the alternate operation can be learned, however, under conditions of stress or tiredness, reversion to the population stereotype can emerge.

Under conditions of stress working memory is occupied and the patterns of action learned over a lifetime reassert themselves and the chances of an error increases or an increased delay in response can occur. One such situation can arise if a motorist has learnt to drive in a vehicle in which the turn indicator control is on the right hand side of the steering column, and the windshield wiper controls on the left. If this motorist then occasionally drives a European vehicle in which these controls are on the opposite sides of the steering column, confusion will result in the wipers being activated when a turn signal was intended.

7.3–STRATEGIES FOR USER RESEARCH

ESSENTIAL IDEA

The designer needs to understand the reasons behind the behaviours, wants, and needs of the user.

© IBO 2012

NATURE OF DESIGN

Designers should select research strategies based on the desired user experiences in the context of the product, service or system. The purpose of user research is to identify needs that reveal the complexities of personae. Real-life scenarios that simulate "actual" user experiences can generate new findings.

© IBO 2012

AIM

The various strategies for user research can be used by the designer to explore the true nature of a problem. Through the use of personae and use cases, the designer can build a range of possible scenarios with which to explore the problem in detail.

© IBO 2012

User population

The user population is simply that group expected to make use of or 'use' an item, instrument, product or data.

Classification of users

Large groups can be defined in terms of common characteristics such as age, gender, physical condition, handedness, ethnicity etc. In user research groups, classification tends to be defined in terms of common goals or needs. A group defined in this way is referred to as a user population. In usability research, a profile or persona is often created to describe the group. In developing a group persona, heavy reliance is placed on information obtained from field trials recording user experiences and requirements.

The personae developed represent a generalisation of a group and allow designers to test their designs against the requirements of a defined user group.

The use of personae, secondary personae and anti-personae in user research

Personae are fictional constructs derived from ethnographic research and field trials that allow those involved in user research to focus on the behaviour of a user group with common goals and identify general issues and themes. As suggested above, while personae are fictional constructs they are not hypothetical in nature as they embody the results of extensive ethnographic research.

A persona, therefore, embodies the information obtained during observation of a group rather than what group members say they would do as might be recorded using focus groups and surveys.

By constructing a persona from a group with common goals, designers can:

- Allow design activities to be prioritised.

- Focus development activities on user goals.

- Gain an understanding of customer motivations.

- Identify opportunities and shortcomings within a market.

- Test and validate design concepts against user requirements.

- Evaluate designs without the need for numerous usability tests.

- Avoid costly and time consuming research surveying the whole user community.

- Create a standardised reference available throughout a project to provide consistency and reduce disagreements.

In any survey of user needs, it is common for a number of interrelated groups to be identified, with many common as well as differing requirements. In this instance, several persona can be created representing the primary user population, and secondary populations identified as the Primary and Secondary Persona respectively.

The goal of the design process is then to satisfy the requirements of the primary persona while extending

AHL

usability to incorporate the extended needs of the secondary persona where possible.

In contrast to primary and secondary personae, user research also defines an anti-persona for whom the design is not intended.

Scenarios provide physical and social context for different personae

In order to make the personae seem real and build empathy for them within the design team, a physical and social context is typically produced, often including a photograph intended to put a 'face' to the persona. Information included in the profile of a persona might be:

- age

- health

- gender

- interests

- activities

- life goals

- education

- motivation

- employment

- expectations

- marital status

- organizations/affiliations.

Use case

A use case is a written description of the manner in which a user will interact with a product /design as seen from the user's perspective. This analysis allows an insight into the usability of the product /design as experienced by the user. While personas have found extensive use in usability research and design they are not without their critics who point out that:

- The size of the user group that a particular persona represents cannot be verified.

- The validity of the persona as an accurate representation of the user population cannot be independently assessed.

- The persona method still awaits peer review evaluation of its validity.

- Personas often contain ambiguities, allowing various interpretations that can lead to team conflict.

- Personas may represent stereotypical images of user populations which are damaging to the design process.

INTERNATIONAL MINDEDNESS

User population behaviours, wants and needs may vary from one community of potential users to another, which may result in the development of a product family.

© IBO 2012

A product family represents a group of products developed around a common core or product platform. Using this common platform, a variety of products are developed for various segments of the market.

Groupings include the elderly, students, maternity, vegetarian, lactose or gluten intolerant, alternative medicines, religion, life-style, gender, age.

Perhaps one of the most commonly differentiated groups is simply between male and female, with many products that are ostensibly the same being marketed to each group and then further differentiated for particular perceived needs. An example of this is provided in Figure 7.3.1 in which a popular brand of antiperspirant is differentiated by user needs.

Figure 7.3.1   An example of a product family

THEORY OF KNOWLEDGE

> Design considers the needs of individuals as paramount. Is this the case in other areas of knowledge?
>
> © IBO 2012

In answering this question the student might find a useful starting point to be some justification of the statement regarding design. To what extent and in what way does design consider the needs of individuals paramount?

The question can be restated as: those with design knowledge consider the needs of the end user as paramount when developing a design.

Essentially the question is one of the intent of those with knowledge toward those who will use or benefit from the products of that knowledge. Unless we are talking about bespoke designs, the individuals referred to are personae, which the designer aims to accommodate, and therefore can potentially encompass a large segment of the community.

Students can outline other knowledge areas in which the needs of the individual are paramount, medicine, law, physiotherapy, accountancy etc. These professions often deal with individuals at times of need or distress and the specialised knowledge they have is focused on the helping of that particular individual.

Even in the area of faith and religious knowledge it could be argued that the spiritual needs of the individual are of paramount concern.

Fields of knowledge that encompass what might be considered the creative arts such as Music/ Art/ Poetry are somewhat more problematic. These areas of knowledge/ skill are certainly appreciated by many individuals but were they necessarily created by the artist with the needs of those individuals as paramount? The converse could certainly be argued, that the paramount need was that of the artist to create. The Sciences such as Physics, Chemistry and Mathematics, more clearly, don't consider the individual as paramount but rather the pursuit of knowledge for its own sake.

Exercise

Review two products, one where the needs of the individual are considered and another where the needs of the individual have been less well catered for.

7.4–STRATEGIES FOR USER-CENTRED DESIGN

ESSENTIAL IDEA

> The user has a central role in evaluating whether the product meets their wants and needs.
>
> © IBO 2012

NATURE OF DESIGN

> For a designer to successfully integrate usability into the design process they require a holistic understanding of how a product, service or system is used. The designer must identify user requirements through the use of careful observation and interviews. A clear strategy for UCD will improve acceptability and usability, reducing costs and effort, whilst fulfilling user requirements.
>
> © IBO 2012

AIM

> By including potential consumers in the testing of designs and prototypes, designers gain valuable data relating to how they will interact with a product.
>
> © IBO 2012

Field research

Field research involves observing people in their natural environment to obtain an understanding of their needs and normal behaviour and is typically carried out early in the design process. Techniques commonly employed include:

- field trials

- ethnographic interviews

- observation of everyday activities.

Because field research is conducted in the natural environment

- data is obtained in context of use

- previously unrecognised issues are discovered

- there are no artificial effects generated from evaluations such as those occurring in laboratory testing.

Method of extremes

As the name implies the 'methods of extremes' looks at the extremes of the user population distribution. These positions along with the mean are used to design equipment used for general use.

Doorways, ladders, escape hatches are based on the 95th percentile of males while the forces required to operate control panel buttons are based on the 5th percentile of females. By adopting these extremes the greatest number of users is accommodated.

By its nature this form of design will not include those members of the population that lie beyond the extremes chosen.

Observation, interviews and focus groups

Observation

Observation involves watching people as they use a product. Observations may be undertaken in the controlled environment of a laboratory or in the field within the normal environment of the user.

The purpose of observation is to gather information on the way a product is used and any problems of usability that are encountered.

In order for observation to be an effective usability technique, the effects that the presence of the observer may have on the actions of the user need to be recognised and steps taken to minimise such effects. Some advantages of observation are listed below.

- It can uncover previously unrecognised usability problems.

- Products are tested under actual conditions of use.

Disadvantages of observation

- Data can be complex to analyse.

- Noise represented by the environment may disguise small effects.

- Observation is usually only performed on finished products/systems.

Interviews

Interviews involve the observer interacting directly with the user to ask questions regarding issues of usability and can take a number of forms, they can be structured, semi-structured or unstructured.

Unstructured interviews use predominantly open ended questions. These are questions that require more than one or two words to answer and allow the respondent to answer in their own words. Typically these questions take the same form as examples listed below.

- What did you find were the most useful features?

- Were there other features you would have liked?

- In what situations do you think this product would be most useful?

Because some idea of the issues known to be of concern have already been discovered, questioning can be more specific but still seeks comprehensive answers from the subject being interviewed. While the questions asked may still be open ended in nature, the interviewer will attempt to restrain answers to the topic and may prompt responses where necessary.

Structured interviews typically ask closed questions for which a set of fixed responses are provided or only a simple yes or no reply is required.

- Did you like the positioning of the sound controls?

Alternatively, the interviewer may ask for the items in a list to be ordered from most to least useful or ask for a rating of an item on a Lickert type scale which asks for an evaluation on a scale typically ranging from 1 to 5, where 1 is most useful and 5 is least useful.

- How would you rate this product?

Because the range of responses is limited, the structured interview can be used to obtain quantitative data.

Advantages of interviews include:

- The interviewee has the opportunity to ask for clarification if the intent of the question is not clear.

Disadvantages of interviews include:

- interviews can be time consuming

- relatively small groups may not represent all issues with usability

- respondents are not anonymous and therefore answers may be influenced by an attempt to please the interviewer.

Focus groups

Focus groups are an evaluation tool commonly used in market research and usability testing to gauge the opinion and experiences of the public in relation to a specific topic. Focus groups are generally small with no more than 8-12 participants facilitated by a leader. The focus group leader/facilitator has a number of duties:

- to introduce the topic

- maintain the discussion should it begin to stall

- ensure all participants have an opportunity to express their opinion

- redirect the discussion on topic without stifling interaction between the participants.

Advantages of focus groups include that they can:

- uncover previously unrecognised usability problems

- be used throughout the design process, but are particularly useful in the early design stages.

Disadvantages of focus groups include:

- data is predominantly qualitative in nature

- difficulties in group dynamics can arise which may be disruptive

- relatively small groups are interviewed which may not represent all issues with usability.

Questionnaires

Self-administered questionnaires consist of a printed list of questions that are provided to a respondent to be read and completed by the respondent without any outside interference.

As was the case for an interview the questions again generally fall into one of two groups:

- Fixed-response.

- Open ended response.

Fixed response questions: are aimed at obtaining quantitative data and consist of questions with a selection of responses, from which the respondent is asked to choose, or a rating scale in which level of agreement or disagreement is sought. A commonly used fixed response questionnaire of this type uses what is known as a Lickert scale which is usually organised from 'strongly dislike' through to 'strongly like' or 'strongly disapprove' through to 'strongly approve' etc. Such a scale can have a numerical value assigned to each choice for later analysis.

In these questionnaires, a final summation and averaging of the responses provide an overall determination of the participant's evaluation. The evaluation of this participant can then be analysed along with responses from other participants using statistical methods for factors such as age, gender, etc.

A primary requirement of fixed response questionnaires is that they have been evaluated for reliability and validity. Reliability relates to the repeatability of the response to the question, while validity is concerned with the degree to which the question measures what is intended. Such instruments can take considerable time to construct and validate, since the aim of being able to determine a final overall number requires that the questions be of equal value.

When measuring usability there are a number of standard fixed response questionnaires available that have been evaluated for reliability and validity. One of these is the System Usability Scale (SUS) developed by John Brook in 1986.

The SUS represents a widely used example of a Lickert Scale employed to evaluate product usability. An example of the type of questions included in this questionnaire is provided in Figure 7.4.1.

1. I think that I would like to use this system frequently

   1   2   3   4   5

2. I found the system unnecessarily complex

   1   2   3   4   5

Figure 7.4.1 Sample of two questions from the ten question System Usability Scale (SUS), ©Digital Equipment Corporation, 1986. [www.usabilitynet.org/trump/documents/Suschapt.doc]

Open ended questions: in contrast to the fixed response type, questionnaires using open ended questions allow the respondent to answer in their own words. While these questions have the advantage of potentially uncovering previously unexpected information, they also require considerably more time to analyse.

Questionnaires that use open ended questions tend to gather qualitative data and are often useful when a designer is attempting to determine the important issues. Open ended response questionnaires are therefore particularly useful in the early stages of the design process, compared to fixed response questionnaires which tend to be used in later evaluations of the design.

Advantages of questionnaires include:

- they can cover a wide geographic area

- interviewer observation bias is eliminated

- a large number of questionnaires can be sent potentially surveying a large sample group.

Disadvantages of questionnaires include:

- unless respondents are guaranteed anonymity, accurate information may not be provided

- typically only a fraction of the questionnaires sent out are returned

- those questionnaires that are returned may represent a biased population in that only those interested may respond.

Affinity diagramming

Affinity diagramming is an analysis technique, usually undertaken by a team, and is a form of 'brainstorming'. Each member of the team writes an idea or concept on a card and continues until each member of the team has exhausted their contributions. Those cards are then collected and arranged such that those containing related concepts (in other words those with an affinity for each other) are formed into groups and sub-groups.

Affinity diagramming can be used to analyse customer usability, uncover previously unrecognised relationships, highlight areas of concern and identify areas for further research and development.

An example of an affinity diagram is illustrated in Figure 7.4.2.

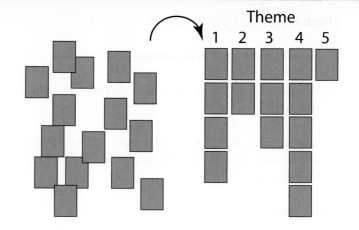

Figure 7.4.2   Affinity diagramming

Advantages of affinity diagrams include:

- simplicity

- builds teamwork

- cost effective means of obtaining team ideas

- allows for consolidation of customer data into design criteria.

Disadvantages include:

- time consuming.

Participatory design, prototype and usability testing sessions

Participatory design

Participatory design is a relatively recent development and aims at integrating the user more closely into the design process. As such it has found application in offices and factories where new designs for workplaces or computer systems are being contemplated in order to improve efficiency. User centred design (UCD) involves the user in the design process as mediated by researchers who, through various research techniques such as observation, focus groups, interviews and questionnaires, determine the needs of the user and convey them to the designer.

In participatory design, designers actively seek to discover the working conditions of those who will be affected by the design and to discuss their experiences. At the same time the designers discuss the various technologies available. In participatory design the social networking systems are accessed to determine design requirements. By accessing user experiences with products and their desires, designers can incorporate them into the design process. Design prototypes are examined in the workplace.

Prototype

A prototype is a conceptual design or early model of the product under development. As such it functions as a test bed for new designs.

Prototypes may be drawings, Web designs, or physical models made from cardboard, polystyrene, wood, clay or increasingly 3D printed items.

Physical models, in particular, allow designers to assess dimensional attributes and experiment with the location, colour, texture and size of function controls. Dyson are well known for the use of cardboard models in the design process. Examples of just two of the many cardboard models constructed by Dyson engineers in the development of the DC08 vacuum cleaner are shown in Figure 7.4.3 and 7.4.4. By using cardboard, prototypes can be created quickly and cheaply. As design concepts are gradually developed, the sophistication of the prototype increases with the addition of smoother lines, textures and colour.

Figure 7.4.3   Cardboard prototype of a Dyson vacuum cleaner, image courtesy of Dyson Australia

Figure 7.4.4   Advanced prototype of a Dyson vacuum cleaner, image courtesy of Dyson Australia

Usability testing sessions

Usability testing sessions typically involve small groups of people who will be observed completing a task in a test laboratory environment. The test sessions are moderated by a facilitator who explains the purpose of the session and answers any questions the participants may have before beginning.

While the participants work through the task assigned, observers record their actions. In some instances participants may be asked to vocalise their thinking process as they perform their tasks, a technique known as 'Concurrent Think Aloud' or CTA.

Following completion of the tasks, the participants are typically asked to complete a questionnaire or are interviewed for the opinions regarding usability of the product under evaluation.

Natural environments and usability laboratories

Usability testing in the natural environment, that is the environment in which the product is ultimately intended to be used, is called a 'field trial' (sometimes called a product-in-use trial) and takes the concept of a user trial into the general market place to observe how people 'actually' interact with the product. Participants are generally unaware that they are being observed.

This sort of investigation is important because consumer behaviour (what they do) is often different to what they say they would do. This data may not be detected during laboratory based user trials. Analysis of field trial data, however, can be time consuming and interpretation sometimes difficult.

In his book *Set Phasers on Stun* Steven Casey gives two poignant examples of inadequate field testing.

The first of these was the radiotherapy treatment of a patient in 1986 who received three blasts of high intensity radiation from a new medical linear accelerator known as the Therac-25 that led to his death four months later. The cause of this tragedy was the use by the operator of a simple combination of key strokes that corrected an incorrect input. Unfortunately the rapid entry of this sequence of key strokes had not been tested during development and resulted in a computer malfunction that left the machine in a hybrid high energy state that delivered 25 000 rads instead of the intended 200 rads. It was subsequently found that the same situation had arisen in three other clinics.

The second example was the death on re-entry of the three man crew of the Soyuz capsule in 1971 because a pressure equalisation valve could not be closed in the seconds available to the crew to perform the task. Although intended for use in an emergency, the parameters that would exist in using the manual control had not been adequately considered during the design stage.

Testing houses versus usability laboratories

Testing houses represent third party test organisations that can provide an independent testing service. Because testing houses offer these services to a wide variety of customers they are able to maintain laboratory facilities and trained personnel. Usability testing can be performed in isolation from the designers, with a report issued to the design house, or have members of the design team in attendance to view sessions first hand.

An advantage of testing houses is that they can be located in geographically disparate parts of the country or world and can, therefore, provide information on culturally based usability issues.

INTERNATIONAL MINDEDNESS

Testing in the environment where a product will be used is often extremely important for the design of products, especially where the problem to solve occurs in a country foreign to the design team.

© IBO 2012

The application of human factors research, methodologies and resulting recommendations is critical to the development of successful products in emerging economies. In 2005, the 'UN Millennium Development Goals' documented the importance of making the benefits of new technologies and materials available to developing economies. It has become apparent, however, that it is not just a technological fix that is required but a unique approach to developing countries, taking into account social considerations and cultural contexts. It is the consideration of these human factors, neglected in the past, that researchers believe is the key to sustainability in cross-cultural environments. Greater consideration is therefore required when transferring goods and technologies from developed nations to emerging economies.

Human factors requiring additional consideration in these situations include:

- social context and cultural setting

- suitability and relevance of the perceived need

- use of appropriate technology and infrastructure.

THEORY OF KNOWLEDGE

Is it ever possible to eliminate the effect of the observer?

© IBO 2012

In answering this question students need to reflect on what is meant by the 'observer effect' and the context in which elimination is in fact desirable.

There are a number of iterations of the observer effect.

The observer effect is typically understood to relate to the effect the act of observing has on the actions/response of the observed. This effect has been reported in widely divergent areas of human inquiry. In physics, the observer effect relates to the extent that instrumentation used to record physical data influences that data, as might be the case of measuring tyre pressure which is difficult to do without releasing some air and therefore affecting the pressure measured [1]. This form of the observer effect is sometimes called 'measurement bias'. While the effect might be small if performed carefully, and for practical day-to-day circumstances could be said to be negligible, the effect is present and must be considered when more delicate measurements are required [2].

In the sociological and psychological sciences the observer effect is identified with the way that actions of human subjects can be influenced by the observer. This is sometimes referred to as the Hawthorn effect which refers to research undertaken from 1924-1932 at the Hawthorne Works of Western Electric, outside Chicago in the USA. During this research, a number of workers performing different tasks were placed in a room and their productivity measured as their working environment was gradually changed. It was found that as changes in lighting and furniture occurred, productivity improved. It was concluded that this improvement in productivity resulted from the assessment by the participants that management cared about them and their working conditions.

Students need to take care when using the Hawthorne effect as an example of the Observer effect as the results remain controversial [3, 4, 5].

Another version of the observer effect is related to the observers themselves and what they see/interpret from their observations. Students could introduce the theory of science famously proposed by Thomas Kuhn, that an examination of history shows that science does not proceed by a uniform process of discovery and correction of theory (what Kuhn called 'normal science'), but rather through a discontinuous process in which a common theoretical framework or paradigm operates until sufficient anomalies accumulate that a revolution occurs and the old paradigm is replaced with a new paradigm that explains the anomalies [6]. Observer effects in this context relate to the interpretation the observer makes about an observation, as filtered through expectation and the theoretical paradigm existing [7, 8, 9, 10]. An interesting extension here is that when several observers make observations of the same situation, considerable differences can emerge [11].

The observer effect is of course not always detrimental. Some have argued particularly in ethnographic research that it can have beneficial effects in uncovering otherwise hidden information [12]. The observer effect is central to the effectiveness of deterring some behaviours as seen in the use of red light and speed cameras [13].

1. *Observer effect (physics)*. Wikipedia. [Available online at: www.en.wikipedia.org/wiki/Observer_effect_(physics)].

2. Mytkowicz, T., Sweeney, P.F., Hauswirth, M. and Diwan, A. (2008). *Observer effect and measurement bias in performance analysis*. University of Colorado at Boulder, Technical report CU-CS 1042-08. [Available online at: www.digitool.library.colostate.edu///exlibris/dtl/d3_1/ apache_media/L2V4bGlicmlzL2R0bC9kM18xL2 FwYWNoZV9tZWRpYS8xNjgxMjg=.pdf].

3. Crane, J. (2013). *The Hawthorne Effect*. IB Psychology. [Available online at: www.thinkib.net/psychology/ blog/15068/the-hawthorne-effect]

4. Macefield, R. (2007). *Usability studies and the Hawthorne effect*, Journal of Usability Studies, Vol.2(3), pp145-154. [Available online at: www.upassoc.org/upa_publications/ jus/2007may/hawthorne-effect.pdf]

5. Evans, D. (2014). *The Hawthorne Effect: What Do We Really Learn from Watching Teachers (and Others)?* [Available online at: www.blogs.worldbank.org/ impactevaluations/hawthorne-effect-what-do-we-really-learn-watching-teachers-and-others].

6. Naughton, J. (2012). *Thomas Kuhn: The man who changed the way the world looked at science*. The Observer, Sunday 19 August. [Available online at: www.theguardian. com/science/2012/aug/19/thomas-kuhn-structure-scientific-revolutions

7. Rensink, R.A., O'Regan, J.K. and Clark, J.J. (1997). *To see or not to see: The need for attention to perceive changes in scenes*. Psychological Science, Vol. 8(5), pp368-373. [Available online at: www.aegean.psychology.uiowa.edu/ classes/31133/readings/Rensink_etal_97.pdf]

8. Dror, I.E. and Hampikian, G. (2011). *Subjectivity and bias in forensic DNA mixture interpretation*. Science and Justice, Vol. 51, pp 204-208. [Available online at: www. cognitiveconsultantsinternational.com/Dror_SJ_ Subjectivity_and_bias_in_DNA_mixture_interpretation. pdf]

9. Thompson, W.C. (2009). *Interpretation: Observer effects*. [Available online at: www.law.northwestern.edu/faculty/ conferences/workshops/cognitivebias/documents/ Thompson_2009_Observer_Effects.pdf]

10. Brewer, W.F. and Lambert, B.L. (1993). *The theory-ladenness of observation: Evidence from cognitive psychology*. Proceedings of the Fifteenth Annual Conference of the Cognitive Science Society. Institute of Cognitive Science, Univ. of Bolder Colorado, Boulder, pp254-259.

11. Hertum, M. and Jacobsen, N.E. (2001). *The evaluator effect: A chilling fact about usability evaluation methods*. International Journal of Human-computer Interaction, Vol.13(4), pp421-443. [Available online at: www.citeseerx. ist.psu.edu/viewdoc/download?doi=10.1.1.88.2791&rep= rep1&type=pdf].

12. Monahan, T. anf Fisher, J.A. (2010). *Benefits of 'observer effects': Lessons from the field*. Qualitative Research. [Available online at: http://torinmonahan.com/papers/ Qualitative_Research.pdf].

13. Retting, R.A., Williams, A.F. Farmer, C.M. and Feldman, A.F. (1999). *Evaluation of red light camera enforcement in Fairfax, Va., USA*. ITE Journal, Vol.69, pp30-34.

Exercise

Ask three people to observe another person performing a task. Question two of the observers separately, in-depth, immediately after the trial to obtain details of their observation. Question the third in an identical manner two days later. Compare and contrast the results between and within groups.

It is undeniable that language can have a significant effect on the results of a questionnaire and students should have no difficulty in finding suitable references. The question

To what extent does the language used on questionnaires shape the results?

© IBO 2012

of extent to which language shapes the result can be interpreted as the degree to which language affects test validity. Validity is a measure of the extent to which a questionnaire measures what it intends to measure. If the questions are not clearly understood by the respondent or not phrased in a neutral or respectful manner, inaccurate information will be collected and test validity will decrease. It should also be remembered that language can be both verbal and non-verbal. Graphic non-verbal language when applied to questionnaires can refer to font type and size, colour, and layout (including background). The length of each question and its complexity can place demands on memory, literacy and comprehension. In order to avoid some of these issues, a number of basic considerations need to be kept in mind:

- Technical language or jargon can lead to confusion and irritation of the respondent.

- Double-barrelled questions in which two or more questions are joined will cause confusion e.g. Will you be leaving A to study B?

- Ambiguous phrases need to be avoided that may be interpreted differently by different respondents.

- Leading questions contain within them information that subtly suggests a particular response. For example, a question asking how tall someone is often leads to greater estimates of height compared with questions asking how short they are.

- Unbalanced questions offer limited alternatives from which to choose and therefore suggest that no other options are valid or available.

- Recall/memory error questions that require the respondent to remember details experienced some time in the past can be subject to considerable error.

- Intrusive (sensitive questions)–such questions can be embarrassing and may exceed what the respondent feels is a legitimate area of interest.

Students will need to discuss the various effects of language on the validity of the questionnaire and how this might be mitigated.

7.5–BEYOND USABILITY– DESIGNING FOR PLEASURE AND EMOTION

ESSENTIAL IDEA

Usability is not the only factor for a designer to consider; products can be designed to evoke pleasure and emotion.

© IBO 2012

NATURE OF DESIGN

A designer's ability to provide satisfaction through aesthetic appeal and pleasure can greatly influence the success of a product, service or system. Understanding attitudes, expectations and motivations of consumers plays a significant role in predicting product interaction. Designers need to be empathetic and sympathetic to user emotion, which acts as a critical component to determine how they interpret and interact with a product, service or system.

© IBO 2012

AIM

The ability to express emotion through a product can not only build appeal for the consumer, but also build affinity between a product and consumer. It can enable a product to communicate how one should interact with it.

© IBO 2012

The four-pleasure framework: socio-pleasure, physio-pleasure, psycho-pleasure and ideo-pleasure

In 1992, anthropologist Professor Lionel Tiger, proposed a system describing the range of positive, human, pleasurable experiences. This framework became known as the, 'four pleasure framework' and included socio-pleasure, physio-pleasure, psycho-pleasure and ideo-pleasure.

Socio-pleasure

Socio-pleasure deals with interpersonal and social relationships such as families, workmates, sense of community and social status.

Socio-pleasure may be obtained from services that ease or facilitate communication such as mobile phones, email, Facebook, Twitter, Skype and so on.

Physio-pleasure

Physio-pleasure involves physical pleasures of the body and senses including taste, touch and smell. It also includes pleasure associated with achievement of physical tasks. Physio-pleasure is derived in a variety of ways dependent on the product, for example:

- taste of a dessert or fresh fruit

- smell of perfume or fragrance of soaps

- weight, shape, fit and solid feel of a drinking glass in the hand.

Psycho-pleasure

Psycho-pleasure relates to the psychology of the mind, cognitive challenges and positive emotional responses to stimuli.

Psycho-pleasure deals with pleasure derived from cognitive challenges and successful use of products. Successfully negotiating a complex manual for a new piece of equipment or facilitating the efficient use of a new product through trial and error would both produce positive psych-pleasure reactions.

Ideo-pleasure

Ideo-pleasure incorporates personal taste, values and ethics, attitudes, belief systems and self-image.

Products that embody an individual's values and attitudes promote positive ideological belief responses. 'Green' or sustainably designed products would promote ideo-pleasure responses in those with a strong commitment to the environment. Companies that support charitable organizations would also solicit positive ideo-pleasure responses from consumers.

The 'four pleasure framework' provides a structure to support design and marketing staff when attempting to meet the needs of consumers. Taking into consideration all of the positive psychological elements associated with

produce purchase and use, designers and marketing personnel become more successful at enhancing the overall experience of consumers. In this fashion, a greater understanding of the consumer brings with it a product that fulfils both practical and emotional needs. Companies successfully employing the 'four pleasures' principle include: Harley Davidson, Starbucks and L'Oreal.

Design for emotion

Design for emotion aims at increasing the desirability of the product by arousing an emotional response in prospective users.

Designs that invoke an emotional response in the user create a strong bond of attachment toward a product that can relate to:

- usefulness

- ease of use

- aesthetic appeal

- product status.

Those products that subconsciously meet emotional needs of the consumer will be successful such that a relationship or attachment to the product can form. When design for emotion is successful we make value judgments about the product that can extend to other products by the same designer or brand.

The attract/converse/transact (ACT) model

The ACT model describes the process through which an emotional response can be stimulated and some of the factors that should be considered when designing for emotion. The model suggests that product design that produces an emotional response begins with attracting attention through features such as colour, texture, sound, etc.

Once the user's attention has been gained, the product design must create feelings of control and reliability. In other words the user must be able to converse with the product. It must conform with our sense of usability.

Finally, if the product satisfies the requirements of usefulness and functionality, the consumer will move to commit to its continued use, in other words a transaction will occur between the user and product.

A schematic illustration of the ACT model is presented in Figure 7.5.1

AHL

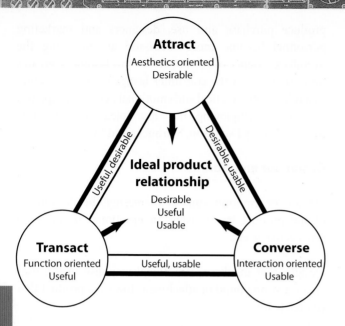

Figure 7.5.1   A.C.T. Model (van Gorp, 2009)

THEORY OF KNOWLEDGE

Are emotions purely physiological or are they culturally bound?

© IBO 2012

The 'naturalist' view of emotions is that they are natural processes that have an evolutionary basis and therefore should be physiologically common to all cultures. This view was promoted by Charles Darwin, although Darwin accepted that cultural factors would affect emotional responses. An alternative 'constructivist' view of emotions is that they are derived from cultural interaction and will therefore differ to some degree from culture to culture. Students should consider whether it is the emotions themselves that are influenced or just their expression. That is, is it the emotion (happiness, fear, anger sadness, grief etc.) that is in question or the expression of those emotions and the appropriateness of that expression in various contexts that will be influenced by the prevailing culture.

Students will need to review the naturalist and constructivist concepts of emotions and whether there is a universal or cultural basis to the feeling, expression and perception of emotions across cultures.

Exercise

What if anything do those who have uncontrolled emotionally activity (psychotic-spectrum) and those with low emotional activity (autistic spectrum) tell us?

SAMPLE QUESTIONS

1. Positive responses to a product that are generated by human senses are examples of?

    A   ideo-pleasure
    B   socio-pleasure
    C   physio-pleasure
    D   psycho-pleasure.

2. Universal design may also be called

    A   exclusive design
    B   inclusive design
    C   acceptable design
    D   all for one design.

3. An analysis technique, usually undertaken by a team, similar to 'brainstorming' is called

    A   mind mapping
    B   affinity diagramming
    B   infinity diagramming
    D   morphological analysis.

4. The 'method of extremes' is used to cater for

    A   designs for general use
    B   designs for the median group
    C   extreme conditions of product use
    D   the population outside of 'normal limits.'

5. Describe the advantages associated with testing houses compared with usability laboratories.

6. Explain how the term 'universal design' includes more than 'one size fits all.'

7. Identify and describe the features of good user interface design.

8. Explain the potential pitfalls associated with designs that are developed without applying the principles of user centered design.

9. Describe the qualities of primary, secondary anti personae.

10. Explain how the principle of convergence has affected the development of new technologies.

SUSTAINABILITY

CONTENTS

8

8.1–SUSTAINABLE DEVELOPMENT

ESSENTIAL IDEA

Sustainable development is concerned with satisfying human needs for resources now and in the future without compromising the carrying capacity of the planet.

© IBO 2012

NATURE OF DESIGN

Designers utilise design approaches that support sustainable development across a variety of contexts. A holistic and systematic approach is needed at all stages of design development to satisfy all stakeholders. In order to develop sustainable products, designers must balance aesthetic, cost, social, cultural, energy, material, health and usability considerations.

© IBO 2012

AIM

Triple bottom line sustainability does not only focus on the profitability of an organisation or product, but also the environmental and social benefit it can bring. Organisations that embrace triple bottom line sustainability can make significant positive effects to the lives of others and the environment by changing the impact of their business activities.

© IBO 2012

Triple bottom line sustainability: environmental, economic and social

Interest in sustainable development first appeared in the 1980s. Researchers were responding to political debate and increasing public awareness of the ecological consequences related to the patterns, pace and style of human development. This research was a direct consequence of the environmental movements of the '60s and '70s.

The term sustainable development is attributed to the report, *Our Common Future*, (1987), by the World Commission on Environment and commonly known as the 'Brundtland report', so named after the Chair of the Commission, Gro Brundtland. Delivered in Geneva, Switzerland in June 1987, the report offered the following definition;

"Sustainable development is development that meets the needs of the present without compromising the ability of future generations to meet their own needs."

The term 'triple bottom line' (TBL) is attributed to John Elkington, (1995), and refers to the need to consider the economic, environmental and social regions of human activity together in order to attain sustainability. The TBL approach forces organizations to deal with environmental and societal issues and not just the economics of profit making. It has been popularized through a variety of catch phrases such as, 'economy, environment, equity' or 'planet, people, profit'.

The interlinked relationship between financial sustainability, social responsibility and environmental sustainability is shown graphically in Figure 8.1.1. The overlapping sustainable portion of the diagram represents the concept of triple bottom line sustainability.

Each of the components is described below.

AHL

Environmental sustainability – involves maintaining the integrity of an ecosystem by assessing and working within its capacity while at the same time recognizing and respecting biodiversity.

Social sustainability – includes empowering the local population through maintenance of cultural identities, implementation of equitable principles and practices, creating a stable environment.

Financial sustainability – incorporates the principles of economic development through responsible growth while improving productivity and efficiency.

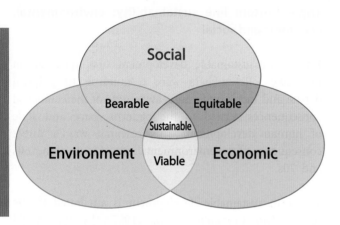

Figure 8.1.1   Triple bottom line diagram, image by Johann Dréo [Creative Commons Attribution- Share Alike 2.0 Generic] via Wiki Commons

At its best TBL encompasses all the values, attitudes, performances and processes that a company implements to maximise financial, social and environmental benefits. Cynics claim TBL is little more than an opportunity for corporations to pay lip service to the environment through the application of a framework for reporting purposes.

Decoupling: disconnecting economic growth and environmental impact so that one no longer depends on the other.

Whereas the triple bottom line concept emphasised the union of environmental, economic and social concerns to achieve sustainability, decoupling emphasises the need to concentrate on economic considerations.

Decoupling involves the disconnection of economic growth as measured by GDP from environmental resources and social well-being. This decoupling is also referred to as 'dematerialisation of the economy', as the rate of resource use is reduced per unit of economic activity.

The disconnection of economic growth and environmental impact is seen as crucial if sustainability is to be achieved in a climate of increasing demand and reducing availability of resources.

In 2011, the United Nations Environmental Programme (UNEP), International Resource Panel report *Decoupling Natural Resource Use and Environmental Impacts from Economic Growth* identified four classes of material resources that require economic decoupling if sustainability is to be achieved.

- Construction minerals.

- Ores and Industrial minerals.

- Fossil fuels.

- Biomass.

Economic decoupling can occur in two ways:

- Resource decoupling- in which the rate of use of a resource is decreased through greater efficiency of use.

- Impact decoupling- in which the impact of resource use on the environment is reduced even as resource use increases.

Impact decoupling is tied to life cycle analysis in reducing waste. While this form of decoupling reduces environmental damage, it does not address issues of scarcity and sustainability.

Resource decoupling also faces the potential problem that as efficiency increases a rebound effect can occur, resulting in the paradoxical increase in resource depletion.

The use of International and national law to promote sustainable development

International and national laws can have a major impact on the product and innovation decisions of manufacturers. Through regulation, governmental authorities establish the standards against which products and processes will be judged. Manufacturers constrained by new legislated limits of product stewardship and waste management are forced to innovate. Without the imposition of absolute targets to promote sustainable practices there is often little incentive for industry to change.

Regulations concerned with the handling and disposal of waste including prohibitions on transboundary transportation discussed in Chapter 2, for example, have had significant effects on decisions regarding sustainable design, materials choice and production processes. Laws that include reference to the precautionary principle similarly influence business decisions and research directions. Many international treaties contain references to sustainable development and the precautionary principle, such as:

- The World Heritage Convention- dealing with the protection of natural and cultural heritage of World significance.

- The Ramsar Convention- concerned with the conservation and sustainable use of wetlands.

- The Convention on Biological Diversity- concerned with the conservation of biodiversity.

All of these treaties however only require adherence to agreed minimum standards and have no enforceable value unless included in domestic legislation.

Further reading

Millar, I. (2009). *The environmental law framework for sustainable development – Principles of sustainable development in international, national and local Laws.* Paper presented to the Sustainable Future Project, Workshop Six: Economics and Administration for Sustainability, Canberra. [Available Online].

Preston, B.J. (2006). T*he Role of the Judiciary in Promoting Sustainable Development: The Experience of Asia and the Pacific.* Paper presented at the Kenya National Judicial Colloquium on Environmental Law, Mombasa, Kenya 10-11 January. [Available Online].

Sustainability reporting

Sustainability reporting represents a means by which companies attempt to describe the various operations undertaken, that are not covered in financial reporting, that describe the effects their actions have on the environment and to elucidate their future plans. Variations exist, however, in the way that sustainability reporting is performed. Some countries have adopted the United Nations Global Compact (UNGC) and included sustainability reporting into their supply chain management systems, while others have adopted guidelines governing disclosure established by the Global Reporting Initiative (GRI). The GRI represents a set of guidelines in terms of performance indicators for reporting, intended to overcome one of the major problems with sustainability reporting; namely the lack of standardisation with regard to the data that must be collected. The motivations for and against sustainability reporting are indicated in Figure 8.1.2.

Arguments supporting sustainability reporting
Improved staff morale.
Benchmark for the future.
Facilitation of environmental policies.
Enhanced progress tracking against targets.
Improved communication of efforts and standards.
Improved credibility within the community through greater transparency.
Better organisational awareness of environmental issues.
Arguments against sustainability reporting
Will not increase sales.
Doubts about benefits to the organisation.
Customers and shareholders are not interested.
Expensive and data can be difficult to collect.
Concern actions might not meet intentions leading to damage to corporate image.

Figure 8.1.2   Motivations for and against sustainability reporting [Adapted from Kolk, A., 2004]

Further reading

Adams, M., Thornton, B. and Sepehri, M. (2012). *The impact of the pursuit of sustainability on the financial performance of the firm.* Journal of Sustainability and Green Business. Vol.1, pp. 1-14.

Ioannou, I. and Serafeim, G. (2014). *The consequences of mandatory corporate sustainability reporting: evidence from four countries.* Working Paper 11-100, Harvard Business School. [Available Online]

Jackson, A., Boswell, K. and Davis, D. (2011). *Sustainability and triple line reporting-what is it all about?* International journal of business, humanities and technology, Vol.1 (3), pp. 55-59. [Available Online]

Kolk, A. (2004). *A decade of sustainability reporting: developments and significance.* International journal of environment and sustainable development, Vol.3 (1), pp. 51-64. [Available Online]

Product stewardship

Product stewardship involves those involved with a product accepting responsibility for the end of life phase of the product in terms of environment, health and safety. This includes using eco design or design for sustainability (DfS) principles to make recycling easier.

In the planning for end-of-life recycling, consideration needs to be given to how consumers can be encouraged to present the product for recycling. Consumer container-deposit schemes are a familiar form of stewardship encouragement.

These schemes involve the inclusion of a small additional cost when purchasing the product that represents a deposit on the container (Figure 8.1.3). When the empty container is returned for recycling, the deposit is reimbursed. This scheme constitutes a voluntary scheme in the sense that, while legislation is enacted to require reimbursement of the deposit at a collection point, the decision to return the container and reclaim the deposit is encouraged, but voluntary. Because of the monetary reward, the scheme also encourages the collection of containers that have been discarded by others and would otherwise be contaminating the environment.

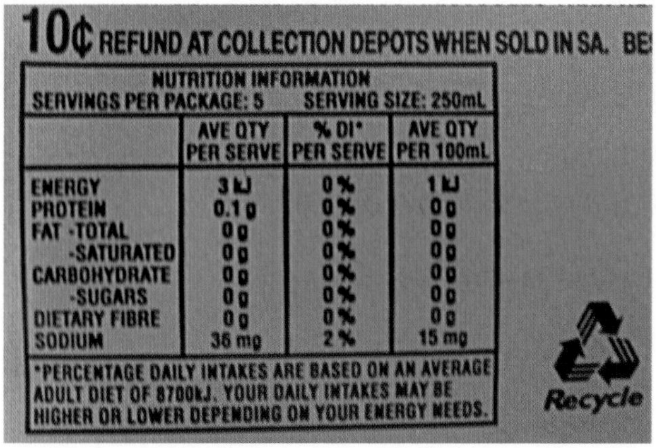

Figure 8.1.3   Example of a container-deposit notice on a soft drink container.

Product stewardship legislation has been introduced in a number of countries that requires certain industries to provide drop-off points for the recycling at end-of-life recycling of their products. Although a financial reimbursement is not usually associated with their return, the consumer is provided a location for the free disposal of such items, which can attract a charge if otherwise delivered to a landfill site.

Stewardship legislation is presently in existence or under consideration for the following products.

- Paint.

- Tyres.

- Packaging.

- Televisions and computers.

- Mercury containing lamps.

- Refrigerators and air conditioner (with small gas charge).

- Batteries (less than 2kg in weight),

In the area of tyre manufacturing, opportunities for reuse and recycling of scrap tyres continues to grow. In the USA alone, at the end of 2003, reprocessors existed sufficient to cope with 80% of scrap tyres. This figure shows a dramatic increase from the 17% in 1990. This process allows tyres, or their constituents, to be retreaded and/or reused. In Australia, a national tyre stewardship industry group has been established. Launched in January of 2014, the aim of the program is to increase domestic market recycling of tyres and expand the opportunities for tyre-derived products. Guidelines have been established to ensure end-of-life tyres are put to an environmentally sound use. The scheme is funded through levies on participating tyre importers and repurposing charges are passed on to consumers in place of disposal charges currently in force. In total, monies gathered will fund the running costs and administration of the scheme, research and market development.

Figure 8.1.4   Tyre dump, image by TUBS CC-BY-SA-3.0 (http://creativecommons.org/licenses/by-sa/3.0/), via Wikimedia Commons

INTERNATIONAL MINDEDNESS

> Changes in governments sometimes result in the reversal of sustainable development policies leading to different approaches to international agreements.
>
> © IBO 2012

Despite the findings of the International Panel on Climate Change (IPCC) and widespread concerns regarding resource depletion, many people remain unconvinced that such problems exist, or in the case of climate change, are the results of human activity. Scepticism regarding the science is particularly found were solutions are proposed that will result in increased energy costs and disruption to industry may result. In this respect the fossil fuel industries face particular difficulties in transitioning to 'greener' operation.

Scepticism also exists regarding the ability of alternate energy sources such as Solar and Wind to replace fossil fuels while proponents of nuclear energy have been affected by the Fukushima nuclear plant disaster.

Given the controversy that has arisen within the community it is understandable that the division will be reflected between government and opposition parties of representative governments leading to differing responses.

THEORY OF KNOWLEDGE

> Design involves making value judgements in deciding between different ways of interacting with the environment. Is this the case in other areas of knowledge?
>
> © IBO 2012

What is a value judgement?

What does it mean when we say we value something?

Value systems represent the criteria by which societies are established and include aesthetic, legal, ethical, religious, political and moral attitudes passed on within family units and communities and as a result of personal growth and reflection. A value system reflects the way in which various criteria are ordered.

This question could be narrowly defined in terms of exploring whether other areas of knowledge make value judgements with regard to different ways of interacting with the environment or more broadly about the degree to which value judgements are more generally involved in the various areas of knowing.

Further reading

Keat, R., and Urry, J. (1982). *Values, Theory and Reality.* Social Theory as Science, 13-31.

Kuhn, T. S. (1973). *Objectivity, value judgment and theory choice.* [Available online]

Lacey, H. (2001). *The ways in which the sciences are and are not value free. Presented at the conference, 'Value Free Science: Illusion or Ideal?',* Center for Ethics and Values in the Sciences, University of Alabama at Birmingham. [Available Online]

Lacey, H. (2003). *The behavioural scientist QUA scientist makes value judgements.* Behavior and Philosophy, Vol.31, pp. 209-223. [Available Online]

AHL

8.2–SUSTAINABLE CONSUMPTION

ESSENTIAL IDEA

Sustainable consumption focuses on reducing the use of resources of a product to minimise its environmental impact.

© IBO 2012

NATURE OF DESIGN

Designers develop products, services and systems that satisfy basic needs and improve quality of life. To meet sustainable consumption requirements, they must also minimize the use of natural resources, toxic materials and waste, and reduce emissions of pollutants at all stages of the life cycle.

© IBO 2012

AIM

It is not only the role of designers to create markets for sustainable products. Consumers need to change their habits and express a want and need for these products.

© IBO 2012

Consumer attitudes and behaviours towards sustainability: Eco-warriors; Eco-champions; Eco-fans; Eco-phobes

Many ancient cultures express a belief that they are part of nature, and live in harmony with it, taking only what they need to survive. The impact of these cultures is therefore generally taken as being sympathetic with the local ecosystem and the principles of environmental sustainability. If this is true, these cultures may represent only those civilizations that have faced environmental issues of their making, and found a solution. There is much evidence to suggest that many ancient civilizations collapsed from the ecological change brought about by their own actions and ignorance of its environmental consequences.

Until recently, most modern cultures have seen themselves as separate from nature and that through technology they have been liberated from such primitive concerns. With the onset of the Industrial Revolution this mastery over nature was becoming more evident. At that same time, a small number of people also began to express disquiet at both the rate of change of society and the local environment. Authors such as the Englishman Thomas Malthus (1766– 1834) warned that population growth, if unchecked would exceed the capacity of the earth to provide food, a position again proposed by Paul Ehrlich in his 1968 publication, *The Population Bomb*. Projections of the date at which such calamities would occur were averted however, by technological changes that increased food production. The American author Henry David Thoreau (1817–1862), promoted the benefits of a simple life and advocated the conservation of virgin forest as a standard by which change could be measured. Industrialization as a rule, however, proceeded with little regard for its impact on the environment.

Widespread concern for the environment is a relatively recent consideration. The origins of popular awareness and understanding of environmental degradation probably lie with the publishing of *Silent Spring* by the biologist Rachel Carson in 1962. Carson noted the effects of the use of DDT to control mosquitoes, on the environment and the food chain. Expanding on the theme, *The Closing Circle: Nature, Man & Technology*, by Barry Commoner (1971), detailed a number of instances of environmental degradation by industrial pollution. Commoner also proposed what he called the four laws of ecology:

- nature knows best

- everything must go somewhere

- there is no such thing as a free lunch

- everything is connected to everything else.

In 1971, Greenpeace was established, initially to oppose US atomic bomb tests, and subsequently became involved in the environmental movement more generally. Greenpeace rapidly became a focus group for protests against environmental pollution. Environmental concerns were further raised by a number of revelations regarding the disposal of toxic waste and the inadequacy of many safety control systems, among them: Minamata (1968), The Love Canal (1978), Three Mile Island (1979), Bhopal (1984), Chernobyl (1986), and the Exxon Valdez (1989).

In 1979, scientists James Lovelock and Lynn Margulis published *Gaia: A new look at life on Earth*, in which they proposed a controversial hypothesis that the

Earth could be considered to be a super-organism that could respond to changes using a self-regulatory, or homeostatic, process. This hypothesis added support to the suggestion that human activity might not only change the local environment but might set in train changes on a worldwide basis that might be irreversible. About this time, concerns about a rise in atmospheric carbon dioxide and its possible influence in global warming began to appear in the popular press. Today, we categorize people based on their attitudes to green issues.

Eco-warriors

Eco-warriors are individuals who take a proactive role in championing causes for the environment by caring for the natural world in their daily lives and decision-making. The term may have its origins in the protests of 1978 to 1983 to stop the controversial Gordon-below-Franklin River Dam in an area of Tasmanian wilderness subject to an application for World Heritage listing. The Tasmanian government planned to use the new dam to generate hydro-electricity for the state in order to attract industry with cheap power. The protest gained world wide support from environmentalists many of whom joined the street protests and media campaigns or travelled to the isolated site in 1982 for the months long blockage of heavy equipment. Although non-violent, 1 217 arrests were made with nearly 500 protesters sent to jail including the well-known British botanist David Bellamy. No charges were eventually laid.

An influential part of the campaign was the photograph of the Rock island bend on the Franklin River by Peter Dombrovskis shown in Figure 8.2.1.

Figure 8.2.1   Rock island bend on the Franklin River by Peter Dombrovskis

The project was cancelled in 1983 with the help of the Federal government based on the 1982 UNESO World Heritage Listing and provisions of the UNESCO Convention for the Protection of the World Cultural and Natural Heritage which Australia had signed in 1974.

The eco-warrior movement in Australia developed a flag in the 1990s, (Figure 8.2.2), symbolizing their ethical stance. The flag has fours colours. Red, yellow and black represent indigenous cultures worldwide, while green is indicative of nature and the environmental movement. In the centre of the flag is a tripod symbol representing unity. This flag first appeared in the late 1990s when environmental activists gathered to protect an area of high ecological value at the Timbarra Plateau in northern NSW Australia against the use by the Ross Mining company of cyanide leaching to extract gold. The action was peaceful but included blockading access to the mine. The NSW government and Ross Mining were eventually forced to abandon the project in the face of growing opposition from protestors and several government departments, including the National Parks and Wildlife Service.

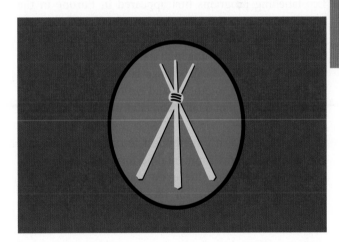

8.2.2   Eco warrior flag, image by Ecopeter at en.wikipedia (Transferred from en.wikipedia) [CC-BY-SA-3.0 (www.creativecommons.org/ licenses/by-sa/3.0)], from Wikimedia Commons

Eco-champions

Eco-champions are individuals who promote awareness of environmental issues within organizations. As an example, Cardiff University Wales, encourages members of staff to embrace sustainable practices. The university's website outlines a program inviting staff to nominate an eco-champion whose responsibility is, "To promote and encourage the reduction in unnecessary energy and water consumption, minimise waste production and ensure efficient recycling of unwanted resources."

Eco--fans

Eco-fans are defined by their enthusiasm to adopt environmentally friendly practices as consumers. They seek to help others in applying these same principles. Eco-fan groups around the world aim to spread the practice of environmentally friendly consumption and lifestyle.

Eco-phobes

Eco-phobes objectify the environment and see it as a machine that produces resources and energy for the use and control of mankind. Eco-phobes champion technological solutions to problems and see environmentalists as resisting progress. In these terms, environmental protection is seen as an inefficiency that only increases company costs, causes delays and reduces profitability.

Eco-labelling and energy labelling schemes

Eco-labelling schemes

Eco-labelling programs first appeared in Europe in the late 1970s, targeting the promotion of products and packaging designed to minimize their environmental impact while maintaining high standards of performance. The use of the EU eco-label logo is a trusted brand and allows consumers to quickly and easily identify products meeting its stringent quality and environmental criteria.

Eco-labelling is also a method of testing, certifying and communicating environmental performance of products or services based on life cycle considerations. Due to the independent nature of the certifying bodies, eco-labelling differs from so called 'green' labels developed by manufacturers. The vagaries of manufacturer's claims such as; natural, safe, environmentally friendly and green have now been replaced through the use of third party, verifiable certification which in turn has improved consumer confidence in eco-labelling.

Eco-label programs have been developed and implemented worldwide. Large ranges of eco-labels exist that take a variety of forms including: logo style stamps of approval, performance indicators and certifying statements. Environmental labelling can be a determining factor when deciding whether items are suitable for import or export. Using ISO-based labelling programs and benchmarks makes it easier for governments to grant approval and for consumers to make informed buying choices. Eco-labelling allows manufacturers to promote their green credentials measured against a set of well-known independent standards through the use of highly recognizable symbols such as the EU flower logo (Figure

8.2.3). The EU flower is affixed to household appliances, garments, services and even accommodation.

Figure 8.2.3   EU flower eco-label

The EU's Integrated Product Policy supports industry in its efforts to design products with: more efficient water use, extended life and increased use of recycled and recyclable materials. The program is aimed at developing greater consumer awareness and growing market demand for green products. Advantages associated with eco-labelling programs include the ease by which consumers can:

- compare products across a range

- obtain a measure of quality assurance

- identify environmentally friendly products.

Eventually the EU aims to extend this program to have companies report to the public in a fashion modelled after the principles of the 'triple bottom line' (see section 8.1). This reporting style would have companies include information on environmental impacts, economic performance and social sustainability.

The International Organization for Standardization (ISO) recognizes three types of voluntary eco-labels.

Type I ISO 14024: Environmental label suitability determined by product category life-cycle analysis based criteria assessment.

Type II ISO 14021: Information based, self-regulated environmental claims. The danger with self-regulated schemes is that, even though they may be based on genuine life cycle analyses, companies may choose to ignore phases of the life cycle where their product underperforms and only report on the more favourable aspects. This leads to inaccuracies where labelled products may not necessarily be class leaders in overall life cycle performance. In this case comparison between products in the same category could prove difficult. Examples of such labels are those that contain reference to being made from *x*% recycled material.

Type III ISO 14025: Quantified environmental information and data based around predetermined guidelines conforming to life cycle assessment specified in ISO 14040. Certified by authorized independent third parties, the eco-labelling program is both well established and ever expanding. It covers 23 major areas from product manufacturing categories through to campsite services. Product groups under development include buildings and wooden furniture. Items specifically excluded from the eco-labelling program include:

- pharmaceuticals

- foodstuffs and drinks

- specified medical devices

- materials classified as dangerous

- products developed using techniques harmful to the environment or individuals.

Type III eco-labels however are not comparable between products.

Australia employs 'The Good Environmental Choice' product label program (Figure 8.2.4). Administered by the Australian Environmental Labelling Association, this non-profit organization certifies local and imported goods selling in the Australian market.

Figure 8.2.4   Good Environmental Choice product label

The Australian eco-label system operates under guidelines comparable to ISO 14024. This voluntary program is the first of its type in Australia and fills a gap in consumer knowledge that has been available overseas for a number of years. A simplified life cycle assessment approach is used to identify the areas of greatest environmental impact. Specific criteria are then selected to judge environmental performance. Criteria used in this product assessment program are based on similar protocols to those in use by Australia's major trading partners.

The North American eco-labelling scheme EcoLogo™ was founded in 1988, has widespread acceptance in the USA and is recognized worldwide. Over 7 000 products and services from 120 categories bear the EcoLogo™ trademark shown in Figure 8.2.5. The EcoLogoTM program is a Type I eco-label and thus meets or exceeds the criteria outlined in ISO 14024.

Figure 8.2.5 EcoLogo™ seal

In Europe, eco-labels are awarded to products (including packaging) and services that have been investigated for their environmental impact throughout their entire life cycle including their manufacturing, transport, in use and end-of-life disposal phases. An independent body must verify the results of these investigations before the eco-label can be attributed to the product. The EU eco-label is the only validated environmental impact program using life-cycle analysis to assess goods and services.

Household appliances awarded the European Eco-label not only use energy and water more efficiently than standard unlabelled products, but the manufacturer also backs them in terms of durability and future parts supply.

Energy labelling schemes

Many consumer items for domestic use, particularly whitegoods, carry an energy rating which is designed to give consumers information regarding the energy efficiency of the appliance. Such information is important as, over the lifetime of the appliance, running costs can exceed the initial purchase price.

A typical energy rating tag from Australia/New Zealand is shown in Figure 8.2.6.

Figure 8.2.6   Energy rating tag (washing machine)

The energy tag system allows consumers to compare appliances based on energy efficiency and consumption. The tag shows the energy consumption that might be expected for an appliance in kWh per year along with efficiency usually in terms of a six star scale, where the more stars highlighted, the more efficient the appliance.

One star represents a base energy consumption (BEC). Each additional star is awarded for a defined energy reduction factor (ERF) which may be anywhere from 15% to 30% depending on the product group.

As the general efficiency increases, the BEC value is re-evaluated and lowered appropriately, resulting in a recalibration of the label. This reduces the need to add additional stars to the label as efficiency improves. However some appliances, such as televisions, improve faster than others and these products use a ten star label.

Since its mandatory introduction in 1992, this labelling system has seen a substantial improvement in energy efficiency of whitegoods driven by consumer knowledge and preference for energy efficient products.

Comparisons may be made between the Australian and EU energy label systems. An example of an EU energy rating label for a refrigerator is shown in Figure 8.2.7. Energy efficiency is indicated as well as volume of cooling

and freezing sections in addition to noise generated (quoted in decibels - dB)

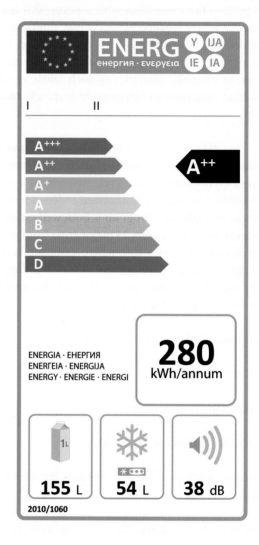

Figure 8.2.7   EU energy label, image by Flappiefh (Own work) [CC0], via Wikimedia Commons

Further reading

Horne, R.E. (2009). *Limits to labels: The role of eco-labels in the assessment of product sustainability and routes to sustainable consumption.* International Journal of Consumer Studies, Vol. 33, pp 175-182.

Creating a market for sustainable products: pricing considerations; stimulating demand for green products; production of green products

Pricing considerations

The pricing of any product represents a combination of considerations such as production and material costs, legislative compliance cost, distribution costs, marketing costs, sales volume and profit.

New products and suppliers have an added burden of gaining consumer trust in the quality and value for money of the newcomer among the mass of competing products. Environmentally sustainable products are no different in this respect from other products on the market. Despite numerous surveys finding that a large number of consumers would consider buying green products, it is only a relatively small percentage of committed individuals who actually follow through on a regular basis.

A survey of 6 000 consumers undertaken by Deloitte in 2009, on behalf of The Association of Food, Beverage and Consumer Products Companies (GMA), found consumers could be divided into five categories (Committed, Proactive, Influenced, Unsure and Unaware), see Figure 8.2.8.

The survey found that while 54% of consumers indicated a leaning toward 'green' products only 2% could be considered committed 'green' shoppers. The other shoppers (Proactive and Influenced) were affected largely by other factors such as price and availability and were influenced by sustainability claims as a deciding factor when two products were seen as similar.

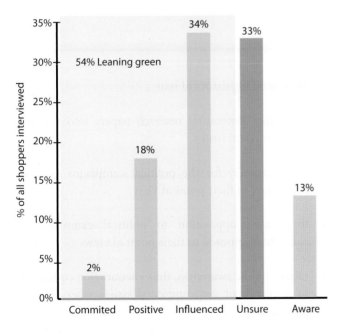

Figure 8.2.8   Green purchasing stages of development [Source: 2009 GMA/Deloitte Green Shopper Study]

These results are in basic agreement with numerous other surveys of the purchasing intentions of consumers, although indications are appearing that as messages of the need to adopt sustainable production increase, buying practices are moving toward greater commitment and in some cases a willingness to pay a premium for such products.

Stimulating demand for green products

Creating and maintaining demand for green products can be broken down into five stages.

- Awareness raising through advertising and promotion of a product is the first step in making consumers aware that a green product exists.

- Consumers must be convinced the green product is of similar quality to purchases previously made before they will commit.

- Consumers of green products may be sceptical of the products' environmental credentials. Marketing campaigns can be misleading or difficult for consumers to verify. Creating a rigorous, credible and respected eco/energy labelling scheme to reliably inform consumers will build consumer confidence.

- Price sensitivity is a strong influence on consumers. On many occasions green products are dearer but savvy consumers are looking for value for money. Some of that value can be attributed to the relative greenness of the product.

- Green products as alternatives are not always easy to locate or find available in supermarkets. Convenience and availability also affect consumers purchasing decisions.

Production of green products

The production of 'green' products as distinct from those of conventional production relies on the premise that cradle-to-grave or cradle-to-cradle philosophy is adopted.

While 'green' production is often used interchangeably with sustainable production this is not necessarily the case. Concerns for environmental degradation, and government legislation is however leading many companies to adopt triple bottom line practices and to pursue sustainable manufacturing practices.

Increasingly manufacturers are adjusting their processes to improve their environmental performance as illustrated in Figure 8.2.9. In this figure the changes in the approach to preventing environmental degradation can be traced, from end-of-tailpipe solutions to pollution control in the 1970s through the introduction of clean technologies in the 1980s to design for the environment (DfE) programmes and triple bottom line (3BL) reporting of the 1990s.

AHL

AHL

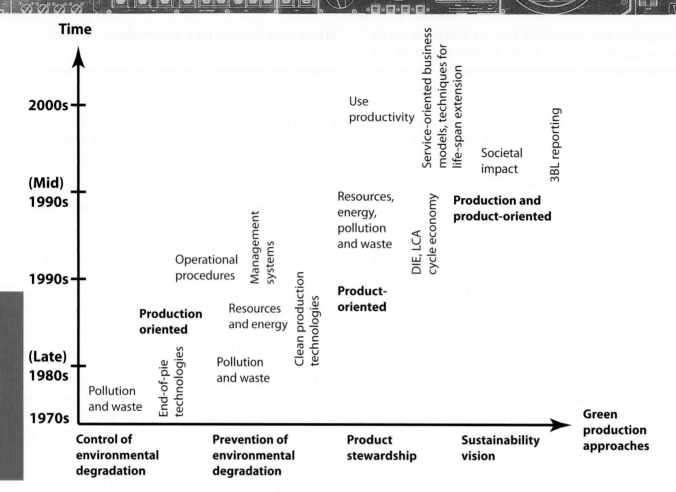

Figure 8.2.9 Evolution of the green production, (Adapted from Bains, T. et.al., 2012).

Environmental sensitivity is now not only a legislative requirement. Many corporations see a reputation for environmentally sustainable manufacture as a positive message that allows differentiation with competitors and increases employee morale. Rankings of many of the World's largest corporations with regard to the sustainability of their operations can now be found in publications such as the *Dow Jones Sustainability Indexes* and the *Climate Counts Company Scorecard*.

Further reading

Baines, T. et.al. (2012). Examining green production and its role within the competitive strategy of manufacturers. Journal of Industrial Engineering and Management, Vol.5(1), pp.53-87.

Pressure groups

Pressure groups, (also known as lobby groups), represent an organised group of people with a common interest in seeing a particular political outcome achieved. By joining together, such groups can gain access and influence over the political agenda by:

- informing legislators of issues

- academics generating research papers into sensitive environmental issues

- raising money for the political campaigns of those supportive of their point of view

- threatening opposition to political campaigns of candidates opposed to their point of view

- raising public awareness, thus encouraging consumers to think about environmental issues when making purchases

- financing advertising campaigns and public protests.

Lifestyle and ethical consumerism

Purchasing decisions made by consumers have the potential to influence producers and increasingly companies are adjusting their products and marketing to appeal to concerns for the environment. However, while it is true that consumers have become more informed and sophisticated in their understanding of environmental issues this consciousness does not necessarily translate into the purchasing of sustainable alternatives. Consumer purchasing decisions can be a complex mix of the following influences:

Product:

- Price.

- Quality.

- Eco-label.

- Availability.

- Product origin.

- Company reputation.

Consumer:

- Habit.

- Trust.

- Income.

- Life stage.

- Political values.

- Religion/culture.

- Brand recognition.

- Consumer lifestyle.

- Living arrangements.

- Environmental awareness.

- Time available to make decision.

Consumer research has found that 30% of those identifying themselves as a green consumer found it difficult to translate their concerns into green purchases.

The purchasing of white goods has been found to be influenced by the energy rating ecolabel, and consumers are willing to pay a premium for products with higher efficiency ratings. Even here, however the selection has been found to often be made from within the consumers preferred criteria of brand, availability and price. The decision to purchase the product with the highest efficiency may also be influenced more by considerations

of cost savings over the life of the product than a reduction in greenhouse gas emissions.

Similarly, brand recognition and a reputation for reliability are found to be more influential in making purchases of small electrical appliances than sustainability. By comparison the market share for ethical foods which includes the organic sector of the market, although growing, represents only about 5% of sales.

The complexity of purchasing decisions means that even those that describe themselves as green or ethical consumers, at some time and under certain condition will make purchases that do not satisfy the conditions of an ethical or sustainable choice.

Further reading

Carrigan, M. and Attala, A. (2001). *The myth of the ethical consumer-do ethics matter in purchasing behaviour?* Journal of Consumer Marketing, Vol.18(7), pp.560-578. [Available Online]

McDonald, S. et.al. (2009). *Comparing sustainable consumption patterns across product sectors.* International Journal of Consumer Marketing, Vol.33(2), pp.137-145.

Shaw, D. et.al. (2005). *An exploration of values in ethical consumer decision making.* Journal of Consumer Behaviour, Vol.4(3), pp.185-200. [Available Online].

Young, W. et.al. (2010). *Sustainable consumption: green consumer behaviour when purchasing products.* Sustainable Development, Vol.18, 20-31. [Available Online].

Implications of take-back legislation for designers, manufacturers and consumers

Historically, disposal of discarded packaging, refrigerators, cars and electronic products has long been the responsibility of governments. Traditionally these unwanted items have been buried in landfill or incinerated with little consideration given to reuse or recycling. Not only is this process wasteful of many materials that may be recycled but also has serious impacts on the environment. Suitable landfill sites close to the source of waste materials are increasingly difficult to find and consume land that would otherwise be public space. Even when appropriate sites are found, the burying of community and/or industrial waste generates its own set of problems including:

- risk of subsidence

- generation of odours, flammable and toxic gases

- attraction of scavenging bird and vermin populations

- release of pollutants into the atmosphere in the event of a fire

- pollution of surface and groundwater through run-off and leaching.

Take-back legislation or extended product responsibility (EPR) requires manufacturers to either manage their own waste or engage a third party to be responsible for managing waste products and packaging over the entire product life cycle.

The product life cycle starts with materials acquisition and finishes with product end-of-life and waste disposal. This period is often referred to as 'cradle-to-grave'. Legislation now requires a product specific approach, however, one immediate result is the reduction or elimination of landfill and incineration as the primary means of dealing with product end-of-life waste.

Take-back policy has implications for manufacturers and designers across the entire product life cycle. The legislation essentially aims to reduce environmental impacts through a three-stage process:

- increasing recycling rates

- reducing or eliminating pollution at every stage

- reducing the volume and toxicity of waste disposal.

Typically, EPR strategies used by designers and manufacturers include:

- producing more durable products

- identifying materials to aid recycling

- choosing materials that recycle more easily

- reducing the amount of materials used in products

- eliminating toxic materials in the product design stage

- developing and managing recovery, reuse and recycling systems

- designing modular or component-based construction, assisting repair or maintenance

- improving ease of recycling through design for disassembly approaches e.g. using clips.

Because manufacturers are financially responsible for the management of their products entire life cycle, these costs must be included within the retail price. To remain competitive in the market, companies and therefore designers have to make this process as efficient as possible. Consequently there is an incentive for innovation as designers and manufacturers strive to reduce toxic waste materials while incorporating recyclable and recycled materials into their products. It should be noted however that waste management programs can add to production costs, if not carefully integrated into designs.

INTERNATIONAL MINDEDNESS

There are many different eco-labelling and energy-labelling schemes across the world that could be standardised.

© IBO 2012

Eco-labelling and energy labelling schemes have become increasingly popular in recent years in response to the growing consumer concerns regarding issues of environmental degradation. In 2014, the ecolabel index contained reference to 450 eco-labels, from over 211 countries and covering 25 industry sectors. The earliest of these, the 'Blue Angel' was introduced by Germany in 1977 and is one of the most widely recognised and trusted labels in Europe (Figure 8.2.10). Access to the label is evaluated by an independent third party that only awards the label to products that exceed the average, with products being reassessed every few years.

Figure 8.2.10   The Blue Angel eco-label

Eco-labelling systems have been accepted as a guide to consumers that allow them to make a contribution in arresting environmental degradation through the purchasing choices they make. The lack of standardisation and transparency regarding the methodology used to establish environmental impact means that the comparison of the eco-friendly nature of products can be difficult for the consumer to assess.

As more companies and products vie for consumer attention, and the lack of an eco-label becomes a potential barrier to sales, concerns arise regarding the advertising of some products with exaggerated claims of compliance with eco-friendly principles or 'green washing'.

The ISO Type I, II and III classification system is an attempt at providing some standardisation in the field. Eco labels that comply with these standards provide confidence in the accuracy and transparency of the claims.

Further reading

Ecolabel Index
http://www.ecolabel index.co./ecolabels/

Allison, C., and Carter, A. (2000). *Study on different types of environmental labelling (ISO Type II and III labels): Proposal for an environmental labelling strategy.* DG Environment, European Commission. [Available Online].

OECD (1997). *Eco-labelling: actual effects of selected programmes.* OECD/GD(97)105. [Available Online]

Perfrement, T. (2010). *What's in a name an exploration into eco labels and environmental product declarations.* [Available Online]

Simi, T.B. (2009). *Eco-labels: trade barriers or trade facilitators.* Discussion Paper, CUTS Centre for International Trade, Economics & Environment.

THEORY OF KNOWLEDGE

Sustainable consumption focuses on reducing the use of resources of a product to minimise its environmental impact.

© IBO 2012

This question asks the student to examine the conditions under which people are driven to break the law to express their point of view. It is a question essentially about Civil Disobedience.

What is the role of a citizen with regard to respect and compliance for the law, and under what conditions would this role as a citizen justify knowingly and deliberately breaking the law?

If laws are made by a legitimately established government, which implies it is recognized by the community as a legitimate law-making authority, then disobedience of those laws must be based on a political/moral assessment of the greater social good. The power of civil disobedience is based on the assumption that the moral underpinnings of the protest are shared by the majority or would be if made aware of the situation. The action then is about publicity and willingness to accept the consequences of breaking the law.

It would therefore be argued that the rightness of the disobedience follows from the wrongness of the law.

How do we decide the rightness or wrongness of a situation and calibrate this against breaking the law?

One of the most famous expressions of the principle of civil disobedience is by the American philosopher and environmentalist Henry David Thoreau the author of *Walden* (1854). In 1849, Thoreau published *On the Duty of Civil Disobedience* (1849), in which he argued that peaceful opposition to an unjust law was a moral duty. This is said to have influenced Mahatma Gandhi's sit-in protests against British rule and Martin Luther King Jr's campaign of civil disobedience against racial discrimination.

"If the injustice is part of the necessary friction of the machine of government, let it go, let it go; perchance it will wear smooth—certainly the machine will wear out. If the injustice has a spring, or a pulley, or a rope, or a crank, exclusively for itself, then perhaps you may consider whether the remedy will not be worse than the evil; but if it is of such a nature that it requires you to be the agent of injustice to another, then, I say, break the law. Let your life be a counter friction to stop the machine. What I have to do is to see, at any rate, that I do not lend myself to the wrong which I condemn." (HD Thoreau, 1849).

While many praise Thoreau's points of view, others have characterised them as anarchistic and in times of national emergency actions can easily be misinterpreted.

While acts of civil disobedience are generally peaceful, this is not always the case. Students might explore the dividing line between what might be considered peaceful civil disobedience and actions leading to damage to property and violent confrontation. Can such cases be justified?

The 'Boston Tea Party' of 1773 famously led to the destruction of Tea in Boston harbour by colonists protesting against the imposition of taxes (specifically the Tea Act) by the British Parliament in which there was no elected American represented. It has been raised by some as an example of an act of civil disobedience, although private property was damaged. A complicating factor is that the 'Sons of Liberty', who carried out this action, were disguised as Indians.

Can acts of destruction in which the participants do not identify themselves be considered acts of civil disobedience or are they by today's terminology acts of terrorism?

Perhaps even more fundamentally in relation to the premise of the question regarding eco-warriors, can the justifications for civil disobedience be extended to environmental protests? Unjustness is usually considered to relate to a person; from where does the concept of an unjust law with regard to the environment arise?

Further reading

Brown, J. (2012). *Eco-warriors: An invisible line.* Australian & New Zealand Maritime Law, Vol 26 (2), pp152-162. [Available Online].

Bell, L. (2009). *What is called ecoterrorism. Journal of Theory and Criticism*, Vol.16, pp153-166. [Available Online]

Cohen, C. (1966). *Civil disobedience and the law.* Rutgers Law Review, vol.21 (1), pp 1-17. [Available Online]

Rant, S. (2007). *Should we ever disobey the law?* Richmond Journal of Philosophy, Issue 14. [Available Online]

Sabl, A. (2001). *Looking forward to justice: Rawlsian civil disobedience and its non-Rawlsian lessons.* The Journal of Political Philosophy, Vol.9 (3), 307-330. [Available Online]

Smith, D.D. (1968). *The legitimacy of civil disobedience as a legal concept.* Fordham Law Review, vol.36 (4), pp 707-730. [Available Online]

Thoreau, H.D. (1849). *On the Duty of Civil Disobedience.* Elegant Books ebook, Created by José Menéndez. [Available Online].

Vanderheiden, S. (2005). *Eco-terrorism or justified resistance? Radical environmentalism and the "war on terror".* Politics & Society, vol.33(3), pp 425-447. [Available Online].

Welchman, J. (2001). *Is ecosabatage civil disobedience?* Philosophy & Geography, vol.4(1), pp 97-107. [Available Online].

8.3–SUSTAINABLE DESIGN

Essential idea

Sustainable design is a philosophy of developing products in line with social, economic, and ecological sustainability principles.

© IBO 2012

Nature of design

The first step to sustainable design is to consider a product, service or system in relation to eco-design and analyse its impact using life cycle analysis. The designer then develops these to minimise environmental impacts identified from this analysis. Considering sustainability from the beginning of the process is essential.

© IBO 2012

Aim

Datschefski's five principles of sustainable design equip the designer with a tool to use not only to design new products, but also to evaluate an existing product. This can lead to new design opportunities and increase the level at which a product aligns with these principles.

© IBO 2012

Green design versus sustainable design

Manufacturers are increasingly recognizing the advantages of pursuing green design not just from legislative or social concerns but also in an effort to capture the growing 'green consumer' market. The concept of sustainability has however been harder to convey and in many instances green design and sustainable design are terms that are often used interchangeably. This is in fact inaccurate.

Essentially green design refers to products that have a benign or reduced effect on the environment whereas sustainability deals with the more complex intersection of economics, environmental health and social equity. As such green design may be seen as a subset of sustainable design. Green design is generally easier to achieve than truly sustainable design.

A major difference between the two concepts is that green design is concerned only with environmental improvement, and typically with single products. Sustainable design by comparison requires consideration of the interaction between the environment, economic vitality and social justice systems to ensure the availability of raw materials into the future.

William McDonough and Michael Braungart explain in *Cradle to Cradle: Remaking the Way We Make Things*, sustainability is more complex than green design in its larger systems oriented integration of the product life cycle into a product's development and realisation.

Further reading

Friedman,T (2008). *Hot, Flat, and Crowded: Why We Need a Green Revolution- and How It Can Renew America.* Farrar, Straus and Giroux, New York.

Yanarella, E.J., Levine, R.S. and Lancaster, R.W. (2009). *Green versus sustainability: from semantics to enlightenment. Sustainability,* Vol.2(5), pp.296-302. [Available Online]

Datschefski's five principles of sustainable design: cyclic; solar; safe; efficient; social

In 2001, Edwin Datschefski published his book *The Total Beauty of Sustainable Products* in which he outlined five parameters or principles by which he maintained design should be judged to determine its sustainability credentials. He developed these principles in response to the rise in 'greenwashing.' Greenwashing is the promotion of products that have minor environmental or green credentials as sustainable. He felt consumers were being misled by advertising and the use of media in general and subsequently developed five principles of sustainable design. These principles are outlined below:

Cyclic: Products should be part of a recycling system either by natural processes such as composting or recycled as part of the material stream.

Solar: Energy required to operate the manufacture and use the product should come from renewable energy sources in any of its forms.

Safe: Products should not contain hazardous materials or in their creation produce hazardous by-products.

Efficient: Designs should aim through efficiency of material choice and operation to use one tenth of the materials and energy previously used. Designs that provide multiple functions reduce the impact of multiple devices.

Social: Production should incorporate safe work practices and conditions and observe fair trade principles.

Using these principles Datschefski showed how new designs could be assessed for sustainability using currently accepted product designs as a benchmark. A selection of products follow in Figures 8.3.1 to 8.3.5, that are provided to illustrate Datschefski's sustainability rating scale.

Datschefski acts as a sustainable design consultant and has proposed a 100 cubed project—100% of products to become 100% sustainable by the year 2100.

Raw material is off-cut branches from certified plantation timber, previously burnt as waste. Steel nails recyclable.

Solar grown raw materials. Hand sawn frame.

Treated with natural preservative (linseed oil) only.

Good durability, less mechanical processing.

(Baseline: Outdoor furniture wooden bench)

Figure 8.3.1   Bush furniture by Morpeth Gallery Australia

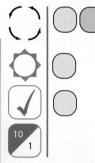

Grown and compostable in commercial facility.

Solar grown but fossil-driven manufacture.

Reduced emissions from oil refinery. emissions offset by carbon credits.

No reduction in energy.

(Baseline: Plastic disposable cutlery)

Figure 8.3.2   Disposable PLA Bio-cutlery (70% Starch, 30% Polypropylene)

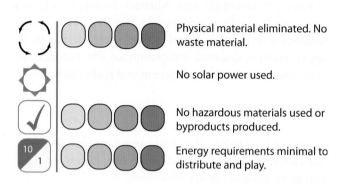

Physical material eliminated. No waste material.

No solar power used.

No hazardous materials used or byproducts produced.

Energy requirements minimal to distribute and play.

(Baseline: Compact disc)

Figure 8.3.4   Figure 8.3.4 Apple iTunes logo

Grown and compostable.

Solar grown but fossil-driven manufacture.

No emissions from oil refinery.

Fewer ink miles per pen.

(Baseline: Plastic disposable pen)

Figure 8.3.3   Bio pen

Plastic parts more recyclable; biodiesel is more recyclable.

Biodiesel is from plants, a form of solar power

A big reduction in exhaust pollutants.

Huge improvement in fuel efficiency.

(Baseline: 1990 VW Polo petroleum fuelled)

Figure 8.3.5 Volkswagen Lupo

INTERNATIONAL MINDEDNESS

The application of Datschefski's social principle of sustainable design can have different effects across different countries.

© IBO 2012

Most countries are making progress with regard to recycling and improving energy efficiency, however, the use of solar energy and other renewable sources of energy remains problematic. Countries such as Australia, the USA, Russia and Brazil have large reserves of fossil fuels which provide cheap base load power and significant export income. The application of Datschefski's principle of the use of solar energy and other renewable sources of energy for production will severely disrupt their economies if they have not made progress toward reducing dependency on fossil fuels or solved the technological difficulties associated with carbon capture and storage

THEORY OF KNOWLEDGE

Datschefski developed his five principles of sustainable design to help designers structure their approach and thoughts. In what ways and areas would the absence of experts most severely limit our knowledge?

© IBO 2012

In an era of globalisation the internal policies of the larger economies can have a significant effect on trade. In the 1966 in response to the air pollution from cars California required all new vehicles to have an exhaust control device fitted. Requirements for reduced exhaust emissions were further extended in the 1970s by the US Clean Air Act. By 1975 California required all new cars to have a catalytic converter installed. These policies had significant effects on engine designs internationally. Restrictions on the use of certain pesticides have meant that changes in farming practices have been required by exporters if the meat and cereals trade was to continue. Similarly, the banning of products containing asbestos and other toxic materials by trade partners has from time to time required changes in materials and design by the country of manufacture to comply.

Anon (1999). *The history of reducing tailpipe emissions.* United States Environmental Protection Agency, EPA420-F-99-017. [Available Online]

8.4–SUSTAINABLE INNOVATION

ESSENTIAL IDEA

Sustainable innovation facilitates the diffusion of sustainable products and solutions into the market place.

© IBO 2012

NATURE OF DESIGN

Sustainable innovation yields both bottom line and top line returns as developing products, services and systems that are environmentally friendly lowers costs through reducing the resources required. Designers should view compliance with government legislation as an opportunity for sustainable innovation.

© IBO 2012

AIM

As energy security becomes an ever more important issue for all countries, designers, engineers and inventors need to develop new ways of efficiently generating energy. As new energy production technologies become available, designers need to harness them to be used in new products to improve their energy efficiency.

© IBO 2012

Complexity and timescale of sustainable innovation

Manufacturers and governments have difficulty in achieving close relationships due to differing understandings of the concept of sustainability and the timescales necessary for its achievement and maintenance.

Sustainability is also a widely contested concept that in its broadest application implies any development is controlled by the limits imposed by the ecosystem's ability to preserve its diversity and the timeframes required to

AHL

253

repair and replenish resource depletion. Alternative, more specific definitions however, endorsed by a variety of groups, place hierarchical emphasis on one or more elements of sustainability in a variety of timeframes; for example maintaining economic, social or ecological values now or in the future.

Governments as representatives of current and future citizens are challenged to cater for a wide variety of interests; even as groups or individuals call for their concerns to be of primary importance. For example, manufacturers can validly argue that government support financially, or legislatively, can increase productivity which can in turn build a healthy economy and provide a means to increase social sustainability for the current generation. However, a holistic approach requires balanced emphasis on all elements of sustainability including the needs of generations to follow. Such an approach emphasises the need for a close collaborative relationships between manufacturers and governments in order for sustainable development to occur for current and future generations.

The road to achieving sustainable use of the planet's resources is therefore a complex one in which many inter-related interests are involved and strategies to achieve such a goal are still developing. Two commonly discussed strategies taken from the world of economics are 'top-down' and 'bottom–up'.

Top-down strategies: are those strategies implemented at the top of the system typically involving government implementation and often concerned with global issues of sustainability. These strategies generally incorporate the Brundtland Commission recommendations that strategies should be introduced to ensure that concerns for the needs of the present generation do not compromise the needs of future generations.

Such a goal requires a system-wide evaluation of resources and rates of depletion versus rates of consumption in order to develop solutions that ensure sustainability for future generations. Those resources that are non-renewable need to be managed and replaced with renewable alternatives. The top-down approach therefore aims at establishing targets and measures for sustainability. Criticisms of this strategy have involved the lack of clear strategies for achievement and responsibilities for implementation and enforcement.

Bottom-up strategies: are strategies introduced at the regional or local level. Campaigns such as 'Think Globally and Act Locally' might be thought of as bottom–up strategies that aim to encourage local action by asking people to forget for the moment about the scale of the problem and the affect change locally. For example, the 'Clean-up Australia' campaign

Local schools and organisations such as Lions and Rotary have adopted programmes of clean up campaigns to protect local bush land and promote community pride.

Landcare initiatives to plant trees, and grasses to stabilise coastal sand dunes against erosion have been established.

Further reading

Cairns, J. Jr. (2003). *Integrating top-down/bottom-up sustainability strategies: an ethical challenge. Ethics in Science and Environmental Politics.* Inter-Research 2003 www.int-res.com [Available Online]

Plummer, R. (2005). *A review of sustainable development implementation through local action from an ecosystem management perspective,* Journal of Rural and Tropical Public Health, Vol. 4, 33-40.

Government intervention in innovation

Critical to the success of sustainable development is the role governments play in establishing legislative frameworks enabling manufacturers to continue to profit albeit in an environmentally responsible fashion. These frameworks must be implemented through a negotiated process that brings manufacturers and governments together in a partnership of shared and common goals.

Sustainable development requires legislation sympathetic to its principles while simultaneously encouraging and supporting manufacturers towards adopting sustainable production methods and products. Without enforceable legislation, manufacturers are able to choose which practices they will implement.

Governments must offer incentives for business to make the transition to sustainable practices and not just rely on fines or the threat of punitive litigation to enforce adherence. Clear legislative rules provided by governments not only encourage manufacturers to comply but they promote equity, maintain a competitive marketplace, give consumers confidence and yet may still be used to penalize non-conforming companies. Governments must also issue clear information on standards and accreditation to avoid confusion for consumers when making choices based on a manufacturer's sustainability claims.

All governments face challenges when seeking to introduce legislation to cover the complex aspects of sustainability.

Three reasons for these challenges include:

A global economy with competing states, whereby each has different criteria for the advancement of their own interests, makes consensus difficult. Here the notion of 'good governance' is challenged by agreements that benefit particular groups, such as corporate profit over wider human or ecological concerns.

Judicial systems are often powerless to impose the penalties that are sufficient to enforce sustainable practices on non-conforming companies. This is particularly relevant when companies locate their core business outside the jurisdiction of the host nation's borders.

A lack of consensus by the scientific community, and thus scientific understanding on the effects of human action on biophysical interactions, promotes misunderstanding and conflicting notions of how to achieve sustainability.

Under these circumstances, governments are reluctant to be deterministic for when confusion and conflict become embedded in legislation and policy documents, 'loopholes' are created undermining the purpose of their construction and the government's integrity.

Further reading

Ashford, N.A., and Hall, R.P. (2011). The importance of regulation-induced innovation for sustainable development. Sustainability, 3, pp 270-292. [Available Online]

Macro energy sustainability

Macro energy sustainability focuses on how nations utilise energy in a sustainable manner. An example might be the Kyoto Protocol.

The introduction of alternative sources of energy production, such as solar, wind, tidal and geothermal with low GHG emissions involves macro energy decisions. Similarly, system integration to produce a 'smart grid' that can take power from multiple sources as required and the development of products such as hybrid and all electric vehicles constitute issues of macro-energy sustainability.

Micro energy sustainability

Micro energy sustainability focuses on local initiatives undertaken by individuals and business to improve energy utilisation. Such measures include the use of CHP systems and the installation of roof top solar panel power generation.

Other measures include the installation of sensors to turn lights off automatically if no one is in the region serviced by the light and the replacement of incandescent light globes with energy efficient alternatives such as compact fluorescent globes and LED lights.

Energy security

The increasing reliance of many countries on the importation of fossil fuels such as coal, oil and gas means that interruptions to those supplies is a cause for concern. In order to reduce concerns, a number of actions are taken including the following.

- Diversification of supply: access to multiple suppliers to reduce the effects of supply disruption from individual sources.

- Sustainable energy: the development of alternate energy supplies in the form of Wind, Solar, Nuclear, etc.

- Strategic reserves: the maintenance of a limited supply of fuel accessible in the event of short term interruptions of supply

- Integration: co-ordination of supply and flexibility during emergencies

- Information: fast reliable communication networks provide market confidence and reduce the tendency for panic.

Further reading

Jewell, J. (2011). The IEA model of short-term energy security (MOSES): Primary and secondary fuels. International Energy Agency Working Paper. [Available Online]

Yergin, D. (2006). Ensuring Energy Security. Foreign Affairs, Vol.85(2), pp. 69-82. [Available Online]

Anon (2006). The new energy security paradigm. World Economic Forum [Available Online]

SAMPLE QUESTIONS

1. Renewable resources are:

   A   easily purchased
   B   more expensive to obtain
   C   available in limited supply
   D   consumed at a lesser rate than natural processes replace them.

2. Green designs:

   A   always employ a LCA
   B   involve the choice of colours
   C   develop products with zero emissions
   D   reduce product impacts on the environment.

3. Design for dis-asssembly products would feature:

   A   welded parts, circlips, specific tooling requirements
   B   bolted sections, epoxy adhesives, soldered connections
   C   modular components, snap fittings, minimal axial lines of assembly
   D   all of the above.

4. Which of these combinations are not environmentally friendly:

   A   reuse, recycle, repair
   B   reduce, renovate, reclaim
   C   replace, repurchase, remake
   D   refurbish, restore, recondition.

5. Compare eco-labelling schemes with energy labeling programs.

6. Explain the differences between sustainable and green design.

7. Explain the concept of 'the triple bottom line' and how it assists sustainability.

8. Explain how Datschefski's five principles of sustainable design can be used to evaluate products.

9. Outline strategies that maybe employed by designers and manufacturers when dealing with extended product responsibilities.

10. Explain why it is difficult for governments to agree on the guidelines for sustainable development.

INNOVATION AND MARKETS

CONTENTS

9

9.1–CORPORATE STRATEGIES

ESSENTIAL IDEA

Companies and businesses can utilise a range of different strategies to develop products, services and systems.

© IBO 2012

NATURE OF DESIGN

The success of a company relies heavily on the strategies they adopt. The evaluation of products, services and systems can inform the selection of the most appropriate strategies to follow that will enable a company to achieve its objectives.

© IBO 2012

AIM

The designer must consider the ethical implications of imitating the products of others and their implications on a cultural, economic, and intellectual property level.

© IBO 2012

Pioneering strategy

A pioneering strategy, as the name suggests, involves charting a new or innovative course. Many manufacturers believe there is a competitive advantage to being 'first to market', with a product or service. It is this approach that drives the pioneering strategy. Market pioneers not only need to carefully identify their market, in some cases they need to create one where none exists due to the ground-breaking nature of their product. They must generate sales as quickly as possible to justify the often large research and development costs involved in bringing a product to market.

A good example of product pioneering occurs in the development and introduction of the first cell phone. In 1973, Motorola vice president and division manager Martin Cooper made a phone call on the company's new DynaTAC 8000X cell phone from the front of the New York Hilton. In 1984, Motorola offered the first commercially available cell phone and soon found itself a leader in the field of mobile communications. Motorola's device was the start of a revolution in mobile communications, first untethering consumers from fixed line phones and eventually connecting them to the world through the internet. The relentless development of mobile communications continues to impact on the general public and the business world alike. Of interest is the fact that little remains of Motorola's dominant cell phone division that has largely been absorbed by Google.

Imitative strategy

Markets early in the product cycle are very volatile. Until a clear set of parameters are determined as to what constitutes a successful and marketable design, many companies will hold off entering. This is how the imitative or market colonising strategy comes into play. In new markets it takes time for dominant designs to emerge and it is often the imitators or market colonisers that wait to capitalise on the research and development work of other firms. As the market matures and customer preferences develop, imitators enter and product development and improvement continues. Dominant designs with associated market-driven features now appear. Corporations applying an imitative strategy to entering the market regularly avoid high levels of risk associated with innovation and side-step the large costs associated with early research and market development. The financial advantages and technological benefits here may be considerable.

The relative success of pioneering and innovative strategies

Economist Bronwyn Hall, (2003), states in her paper, *Business Method Patents, Innovation and Policy,* "In both the United States and Europe, firms rate superior sales and service, lead time, and secrecy as far more important than patents in securing the returns to innovation. Patents are usually reported to be important primarily for blocking and defensive purposes."

Unfortunately, research shows that the majority of product and service pioneers rarely reach market dominance. Examples abound in a range of industries of market innovators being unable to capitalise on their early entry to the market to produce a dominant design from a significant innovation. The Xerox Corporation is an example of such a company unable to reap the benefits in the PC market after developing a personal computer operating system interface, at its PARC research centre. Sony's Betamax failure to capture market dominance is another high profile example of an imitator such as JVC achieving market success.

Hybrid approaches

In 1998 the MpMan music player appeared in stores as one of the first mass-produced portable digital audio players. Manufactured in South Korea, it consisted of a flash memory driven portable player that required linking with a docking station to encode and load music into the 32 MB player.

Figure 9.1.1   Digital audio player, image by Michele M. F., CCA-Share Alike 2.0 Generic license

Over a short period of time, (approximately 3 years), multiple companies attempted to capture the growing Mp3 player market. A number of these were successful including the Diamond Rio PMP300, Creative Nomad Jukebox and Sony's Vaio MC-P10 Music Clip.

It wasn't until 2001 when Apple® released its own Mp3 player, the iPod with a unique set of features that captured the mass market. Constant improvement and refinement through the introduction of new technologies saw Apple® first colonise this market then continue to innovate and dominate market share for more than a decade.

Market development

Market development is the process of developing sales, new products or new markets. It is designed to grow a business in a variety of ways including:

- introducing new products or services to existing customers

- generating new products and/or services to new customers

- establishing a greater market base by attracting new customers

- educating consumers, particularly when introducing new product lines

- creating new applications for existing products, for example, nylon was originally developed for parachutes.

Product development

Product development involves product evolution through the addition of new features and technologies. Product development is mostly aimed at the existing customer market but may also attract new or first time purchasers.

One example of product development is in the field of household cleaning products. Cream, liquid and spray delivery systems continue to be the most popular modes of delivery for these products. In recent times, these and other companies have identified market segments that have induced product development to meet a very specific market.

The introduction of cleaning wipes, (disposable, cleaner-impregnated cleaning cloths), have been developed for busy households where cleaning time is considered the factor motivating purchasers. Other developments involve the inclusion of anti-bacterial agents designed to sterilise surfaces as well as remove dirt, an example of which is shown in Figure 9.1.2.

Figure 9.1.2   Product development

Market penetration

Market penetration is a tool used to determine the potential growth available for product sales. It is often reduced to a simple mathematical calculation:

$$\frac{\text{product sales}}{\text{total market potential}}$$

A range of product promotion strategies may be employed including: discounts, celebrity endorsements, bonus offers, etc.

Company acquisition is also a strategy employed by companies to improve their market penetration. Along with increased sales, additional technologies, personnel and intellectual property may also be acquired.

Product diversification

A product diversification strategy involves the modification of an existing product so that its market potential can increase. Its aim is attract a new customer base and thus increase sales. It can be done by leveraging the reputation of existing products as well as developing new platforms to be able to produce and eventually sell the modified or the innovative products.

The premium accommodation provider Marriott have diversified through the mechanism of product extension. The generation of the 'Courtyard by Marriott' group has leveraged the brand recognition associated with Marriott hotels but targeted business and budget travellers to widen their market appeal.

In another case, product diversification has taken the form of producing a new but related product, on sale to the same target market group. The Reebok shoe company has entered the bottled water market through its Rebook Fitness Water™ product.

Nike™, has also ventured out from its original core business of manufacturing sports shoes to generate sales in the areas of fashion, sporting equipment and associated technologies such as pulse monitoring watches as shown in Figure 9.1.3.

The product diversification strategy is different from product development in that it involves creating a new larger customer base, designed to expand the market potential of the original product. Effective product diversification requires accurate market targeting and careful attention to product differentiation in order to prevent cannibalising of existing product markets. Its aim is to increase overall sales and profits of the company.

Figure 9.1.3   Nike™ watch product diversification

Corporate social responsibility

Corporate strategy refers to a company's planned approach for the future. It often involves an assessment of the current situation and mapping of policies and procedures to achieve predetermined goals. These goals may be long or short term, production-based, environmental, financial or deal with external factors such as competition. In simple terms a corporate strategy is a company's strategic vision for the future.

The responsibility of every business is to make money for owners and shareholders, however, many companies are also embracing corporate social responsibility, (CSR), principles and practices. Broadly this involves undertaking activities that improve society and are not damaging to the environment. Sustainable, environmentally friendly practice, if implemented correctly, can reduce costs, wastage and refuse. Pro-environmental practices are often seen as a positive by consumers thus boosting the company's public approval ratings. Companies also exhibit CSR through the enabling of programs to 'give back' to the community. These may take the form of sponsorship or donation of materials and or resources.

Having a strong CSR program makes good business sense. The 2013 CSR RepTrak® 100 study revealed only 17% of consumers were prepared to recommend services or products from a company with a poor CSR record. The study measures consumers perceptions of a company's quality of contributions towards citizenship, corporate governance and the quality of workplace environment.

The 2013 survey again named Microsoft as the company with the best overall CSR reputation along with The Walt Disney Company, Google, and BMW in a four way tie. Individually Google was identified as having the most desirable working conditions for employees while The Walt Disney Company scored the highest in its support for community and the environment. BMW faired best in the corporate governace division where it was perceived as the most ethical, open and transparent in its business dealings.

Microsoft's CSR program has not always been as highly regarded. Microsoft started its program in 2004 yet as late as 2008 it was accused of anti-trust activities detrimental to competitors and competition. In February 2008 the European Commission fined Microsoft 899 million euros, after it deemed Microsoft had failed to comply with its 2004 ruling, stating, "Microsoft's tying of Internet Explorer to the Windows operating system harms competition between web browsers, undermines product innovation and ultimately reduces consumer choice."

Similar to CSR programs is *Corporate Responsibility Magazine's* annual review of large capital companies. The magazine examines the corporate world's management of social responsibility but also includes managerial and financial aspects. It produces a list of the '100 Best Corporate Citizens' and a 'Black List' reporting on demonstrated poor corporate performance or failure to disclose policy in one or more of the following areas:

- philanthropy

- governance and accounting transparency

- climate change, sustainable practices and broader environmental policies

- employee relations, quality of working conditions and worker benefits programs.

The author of the article, Jay Whitehead, makes the link between good corporate citizenship and good business when he observes, "the irony is that 'Black List' companies

significantly under-performed both the S&P 500 and the '100 Best Corporate Citizens List' companies in three-year total return." Outside of the leaders in the CSR RepTrak® 100 study the Starbucks Coffee Company has an excellent CSR reputation due to its commitment to ethical sourcing, environmental footprint reduction practices and the supporting of tea and coffee growers in developing countries.

INTERNATIONAL MINDEDNESS

Adoption of corporate social responsibility by multi-national companies can be used as a distraction from their core business practices.

© IBO 2012

A major criticism of CSR programs is the notion that anything that takes a businesses focus away from making profit is inefficient. Criticism is also levelled at CSR programs alleging that they are employed in a cynical fashion to garner public support and thus add to the company's bottom line. In some cases CSR programs are seen as add-ons and easily reversed under periods of economic hardship.

Joel Bakan, a professor of law at the University of British Columbia believes that CSR programs may allow businesses to avoid governmental regulations by presenting a positive public image of compliance with social and environmental issues. He is concerned that both government regulators and the public are distracted by superficialities rather than investigating the substance of what is actually transpiring. He continues to argue that businesses use this approach to manipulate market forces in place of government oversight, potentially leaving businesses to self regulate.

THEORY OF KNOWLEDGE

The designer must consider the ethical implications of imitating the products of others and their implications on a cultural, economic, and intellectual property level.

© IBO 2012

It has always been possible to find markets where copies of products or blatantly counterfeited designs complete with imitation company logos are readily available. In the United States, functionality of products is protected but not design or style. Elsewhere around the world this level of protection may not even be available. In these environments imitation or even blatant counterfeiting is either tolerated or unenforced.

As documented previously, when considering companies using imitative strategies, some companies choose to use the intellectual property of others not only to enter a developed or developing market but also to avoid the large costs associated with early research and market development. The financial advantages and technological benefits here may be considerable. Counterfeiting is the extreme in this circumstance where companies trade not only on another's intellectual property but duplicate branding and reputation through the application of bogus logos, often while proffering inferior goods.

China, in particular, is often seen as a 'copycat' culture. There is a figure of speech within contemporary China referring to the 'Shanzai'. The term has multiple meanings, in contemporary culture. It refers to the act of copying or parodying while in historical terms it literally refers to a mountain stronghold or hideout for bandits. William Hennessey writes in the *Campbell Law Review* about the lack of time modern China has had to develop rigorous enforcement of intellectual property rights.

The counter argument may be proposed that enforcement of intellectual property to the extreme may in turn raise consumer costs by creating monopolies free of competition making it difficult or impossible for new firms to enter the market.

Exercise

Choose a product that you know is readily copied and distributed without the original owners permission. Common examples include, music, video media, etc. Examine the motivations behind both the original owner and those distributing without permission. What are the ethical issues associated with both parties?

9.2–MARKET SECTORS AND SEGMENTS

ESSENTIAL IDEA

Designers must research and consider the target market sectors and segments in the design of their products.

© IBO 2012

NATURE OF DESIGN

Designers must consider the market when targeting their product, service or system. The smaller the sector the more the target audience will have in common. Companies may decide to compete in the whole market or only in segments that are attractive and/or familiar. A designer's understanding of the identified market is essential.

© IBO 2012

AHL

AIM

By identifying the market sectors and segments a product will be designed for, a designer can gain data directly from the perspective of the potential consumer.

© IBO 2012

Categories of market sectors and their influence

Market sectors are particular subsets that share specific characteristics. They essentially consist of the classification of markets broadly into geographical and client-based sectors. These sectors are generally defined by the characteristics listed below.

- Geographical sectors identify purchasers in a particular region. Characteristics within the sector may be region-specific but could also include purchasing power, cultural values, climatic differences, etc. As an example, customers' needs vary from one climatic region to another. Insecticides often require different compositions based on the regional climate and the variety of pests to be targeted.

- Client-based sectors focus on consumers, whether they be individuals or groups, industry related, commercial or government run enterprises. Watchmakers target specific income groups when developing products for high end or mass market appeal. Swiss watchmakers Patek Philippe and Swatch manufacture timepieces for very different clients.

Classifications of consumer market segments: income; profession; age; family; values; behaviour

Market segmentation involves the break up of markets into smaller divisions or segments. Consumers within market segments are identified as having similar characteristics. It is these characteristics that allow for careful targeting of goods and services. Traditionally markets have been divided using demographic characteristics such as age, gender, lifestyle or ethnic background but attributes such as: location, income, marital status, household size, stage in the family life cycle and even physical characteristics such as height or quality of hearing may be used. Products targeting specific market segments create new customers in existing markets. This approach often builds on a well-known brand names or market sectors. Examples include:

- high performance prestige sports cars
- vacuum cleaners specifically for pet owners
- insurance packages tailored for 'mature' drivers.

The development of a product family

When companies manufacture a group of related goods or services, they are often grouped together under the title of a 'product family'. The leveraging of consumer loyalty across product families allows companies to both maintain and build their client base. Product families encourage consumers to purchase other products in the range if they have had a positive experience with the brand. Products gathered together under the product family banner are often bundled together at discounted rates as part of promotional packages designed to introduce consumers to other products within the family.

Young people purchasing their first motor car will often continue to stay with a known brand if other models in the product family over time meet their needs for increased family size, improved financial status or changes to vehicle purpose, such as of-road requirements.

Adobe's Creative Suite product family contains a series of fully independent software packages combined to form an integrated solution. Available independently for very specific markets, or as a product family, the technologies

have the same familiar interface and seamless compatibility leading to improved workflow.

INTERNATIONAL MINDEDNESS

Two broad categories of market sectors are geographical and client-based, with specific segments varying greatly.

© IBO 2012

Geographic dimensions relate directly to where people live. While this sector would be broken down considerably into a range of sectors it would be no surprise to see sales of water-related equipment and clothing be higher in coastal regions than those further away. Items such as surfboards, swimming costumes, scuba gear, etc. alternatively mountainous areas above the snowline would have greater sales in snow related equipment and apparel such as snow skis, snow mobiles, winter thermal leisure wear, etc. Client-based sectors examine divisions or sub-markets for products and services based on the identified needs of the individual, commercial, government and institutional market. The critical step in market segmentation is clearly and accurately defining the target market. A simple example is the passenger car market. The market is easily broken into multiple groups including trade vehicles, family cars, mini-vans or people movers, sports cars, etc. These divisions may be broken down even further based on engine size, number of doors, body configuration and so on. To continue the passenger vehicle analogy, age may be the segmentation criterion under consideration. If so, many young people purchase their first car based on price, peer recommendation, styling and fuel economy. Older drivers may choose their car based primarily on brand name, reliability, servicing costs and safety issues. Hair shampoo types may be broken down into men's, women's or children's hair shampoos. Further market division may be made based on hair types such as oily, colour treated, etc. Shampoos purchased for commercial use in hotel chains could be broken down by a branding or cost basis dependent on the hotels target market.

THEORY OF KNOWLEDGE

Gaining information on market sectors often employs many of the methods of gaining knowledge most closely associated with the human sciences. What are these methods of gaining knowledge, and how do they compare to the methods used in the natural sciences?

© IBO 2012

This topic was dealt with earlier in Chapter One.

9.3–MARKETING MIX

ESSENTIAL IDEA

The marketing mix is often crucial when determining a product or brand's offering.

© IBO 2012

NATURE OF DESIGN

Empathy for, and understanding of the target audience is developed through thorough analysis of the market chosen. This informs several factors: the standards that end users demand; how and where to distribute and sell the product; how much they are willing to pay for a certain product and its quality; and how to communicate the launch of a product. Correct analysis of these factors could determine the success or failure of a product, despite its quality.

© IBO 2012

AIM

Marketing is often a new area for designers to consider. Exploring unfamiliar aspects of innovation improves their understanding of the market needs of the products they are designing.

© IBO 2012

Marketing mix – The 4Ps: product; place; price; promotion

The 4Ps of marketing are also known as the marketing mix. Individually they are product, place, price and promotion. These four controllable variables act in concert to maximise profit potential. The marketing mix is designed to improve consumer awareness and demand for a product and assist with creating promotional marketing strategies including their execution.

Marketing mix

- Product—precise targeting is imperative to meet the needs of the identified market. The variables in this field are quality, styling, branding, packaging, warranties, etc.

- Price—price must be considered relative to perceived product value and the niche market targeted. Variables include list price, discounting, payment methods and terms of credit.

- Place—refers to the location where a product can be purchased ranging from physical stores through to virtual stores on the internet. Some of the variables here include distribution, location and accessibility.

- Promotion— deals with informing potential customers of the availability of the product, its price and its means of availability. Variables in this field include direct marketing, discount sales, advertising, package deals and special offers.

Trigger and incremental products

Trigger or decision products attract consumers on their own merit while incremental products engage consumers in purchasing add-ons. These high margin add-on purchases are rarely considered by customers when making the initial purchase decisions. Independently, the incremental products have little or no intrinsic value.

Computer hardware requiring software to add functionality is an example of trigger and incremental product. Shipping and handling on Internet purchases, buying a USB charging cable for your new phone or purchasing external speakers for digital music players are all examples of incremental products.

Figure 9.3.1   Incremental product, image by Cate Scott

Products and standardisation

The role of state-based legislation is to guarantee quality assurance for the benefit of the consumer irrespective of the product source. Children's toys are an example of individual governments providing legislation to reduce potential risk to the end user of the product.

Figure 9.3.2 Children's toys require specific regulation, image by The Children's Museum of Indianapolis [CC-BY-SA-3.0, via Wikimedia Commons

Component standardisation allows for the interchangeability of components across products and markets. Improved efficiency at a manufacturing level may be achieved through economy of scale and simplifying manufacturing processes. Component standardisation is often a feature of mature markets. Standardisation assists with quality assurance, component supply and cost overheads. Standardisation may be challenged by some product/component suppliers invoking lack of competitive differentiation and opportunities to innovate.

Industry-wide standards play a major role in an increasingly globalised world. They offer the advantages of reduced risk and physical costs associated with expensive research and development and give companies confidence to develop products for world markets. Companies well placed in the standards development process may also be able to favourably influence the development of the standard protocol.

Place: implications of internet selling for a company in relation to its supply chain and distribution network

Place is concerned with the range of methods employed for distributing the product to the market. Traditionally this has involved warehousing, transport networks and bricks and mortar outlets. Increasingly companies are presenting their products for sale alternatively, or in some case exclusively, for sale over the internet. Overheads may be reduced through the use of centralised warehouses or sales directly shipped from the manufacturer to the consumer's home. Online companies may carry little stock and simply place orders through suppliers on a needs only basis.

Strategies of setting price: cost-plus; demand pricing; competitor-based pricing; product line pricing; psychological pricing

Cost-plus adds a standard percentage of profit above the cost of producing a product. Accurately assessing fixed and variable costs is an important part of this pricing method.

Demand pricing is based on the consumer's perception of the product value. Prestigious branding allows manufacturers to price the product at a premium. Rarity or scarcity may be a feature of this style of marketing. Products that pose a competitive or innovative edge can also command premium prices.

Competitor-based pricing is based on the common market or 'going rate' price as charged by competing firms. Firms often offer an incentive to consumers if they can find the same product at a cheaper rate, thus engaging them in up-to-date market price investigation. Predatory pricing is a variation of this style where firms deliberately undercut competitors to secure market share.

Figure 9.3.3 Price match guarantee

Product line pricing is again a feature used to maximise profits. Companies offer a range of upgrades, enhancements or options to a primary product. Motor vehicles are excellent examples of product line pricing where management offers a range of add-ons to improve or vary the product eg. metallic paint, alloy wheels, upholstery stain protection, window tinting, navigation systems, on-road assistance, vehicle insurance, etc. The goal being to maximise profits, ie. the more options agreed to, the more the consumer pays. The most important factor in the success of product line pricing is the volume of sales of the primary unit. Some companies develop a strategy where they have slender profit margins on the initial primary product but have greater profits factored into the add-ons.

Psychological pricing is based on a price that looks better, for example, $9.99 per kilogram instead of $10.00 per kilogram. This is why many prices are listed with a .99, .98 or even a .49 ending. Psychological pricing is used to give the consumer the impression of paying less. Consumers process the price tags from left to right and on many occasions only focus on the dollar amounts. The theory here is that companies may charge the maximum amount up to the largest cent component, (99c), and still benefit form a lower psychological price perception. This belief is further enhanced when marketers reduce the size of the print for the cents portion of the price.

Figure 9.3.4   Psychological pricing example

Promotion: advertising; publicity; personal selling

Promotion is the means selected for communicating with the market. Multiple strategies are often employed to work in concert with each other to reach multiple markets and reinforce the product message in a variety of forms or media. Promotion in all its forms is about encouraging the consumer to make a positive buying choice in favour of the promoter. Promotional campaigns are mostly composed of a variety of media. The type of media employed is often determined by the product itself, specific campaign goals, advertising budgets and timescales. Methods can include print media, television spots, radio spots, online marketing and blogs, promotional events, product placement in films and customer or celebrity endorsements.

INTERNATIONAL MINDEDNESS

When developing marketing campaigns, companies take account of different cultures and sectors in the target market.

© IBO 2012

Marketing strategists have a comprehensive range of alternatives to consider when developing a marketing plan. Traditionally a market sector or segment would be examined and a strategy based on traits of this group examined. Today, mechanisms of delivery have broadened beyond print, television, the internet and e-commerce

into the still evolving field of social media. Add to the mix regional and cultural differences, globalisation of technology and multicultural markets. Language can be a barrier to access in foreign or multicultural markets. The power of company logos and graphic representations can assist with communication in these circumstances. Cultural interpretations, beliefs and differences can extend beyond specific words into the meaning behind symbols and even colours. These elements all need to be treated with knowledge and cultural sensitivity.

Placement in the marketplace can also be a function of culture, ie. is the product best placed at a local community market, strip mall, shopping plaza or chain store? Entire cultures and on occasion market sectors within these cultures shop in a variety of ways. With this in mind, product placement can be as a much a consideration of the product as it is a coming to terms with market environment.

THEORY OF KNOWLEDGE

Some advertisers emphasise the 'science' behind their products. Does this suggest that some people may see scientific knowledge as being more reliable than knowledge in other areas of knowledge?

© IBO 2012

Some products such as computers and cars lend themselves to definitive testing techniques. These benchmark tests allow consumers to compare like with like data and make informed decisions based on their interpretation of the 'science' or data behind the product. Many consumers take comfort in facts and figures. They are easily defined and supported. Many people find the use of quantitative data makes comparison of like products much easier based on performance specifications as determined by a series of standardised tests. Example of these types of comparative tests include, crash test ratings for vehicles, computer processor speeds measured in megaherz, or wattage for kitchen appliance motors.

Many products do not lend themselves to science or data based analysis. Depending on the product under review 'expert' opinion or user experience may, however, have influence over consumers. Even celebrity endorsement has the power to affect consumers and their buying choices, particularly in the field of lifestyle goods and services. This type of data is often in a qualitative form and examples include, accommodation recommendations and online product reviews.

AHL

9.4–MARKET RESEARCH

ESSENTIAL IDEA

Market research is any organized effort to gather information about markets or customers.

© IBO 2012

NATURE OF DESIGN

Market research often identifies how to improve the product, service or system and increase its chance of success within a particular sector or segment. The price a user is prepared to pay is usually determined through market research. This in turn sets an upper limit of cost to the design and production of a potential product, service or system. Market research has a crucial role in determining the constraints a designer has to work within.

© IBO 2012

AIM

Often designers will work on projects that have new and radically unfamiliar contexts. This will deepen their understanding of market research, equipping them with a range of tools and skills that they can employ in many areas of life and empowering them as lifelong learners.

© IBO 2012

Purpose of market research

Market research is designed to better match product development with the end user. A range of research strategies are required to evaluate potential markets, examine socio-economic trends within demographic groups, determine appropriate marketing strategies, and consider the latest technological fads and scientific breakthroughs.

The idea generation phase may be used when developing a new iteration of a product and involves the search for alternative solutions. This creative component of the design process uses the specification as a starting point. Designers here deal more with design concepts rather than complete and detailed solutions. Designers will

research a range of sources for inspiration and choose from a variety of approaches to support the generation of ideas. These approaches are sometimes grouped loosely under the heading of cognitive organizers. Examples of creativity tools include:

- TRIZ

- SCAMPER

- mindmapping

- brainstorming

- concept maps

- six thinking hats

- morphological analysis.

Sketching and note taking are keys to the successful documentation of ideas. During this stage all of the creative alternatives should be evaluated before the most promising solution is selected.

Consumers' reaction to technology and green design and the subsequent impact on design development and market segmentation.

Consumer groups may be categorised based on their reactions to technology. An individual's reaction may be based on a number of factors and may change over time or vary determined by the technology in question.

Technophiles are early adopters of technology. They are often just as fascinated with the technology of the device as they are with its features and functions. They are prepared to pay a price premium for early entry into the market just to acquire the latest product.

Technocautious individuals, however, tend to wait for technologies to prove themselves in the marketplace. They are often adopters at the second-generation level of product development. They may also wait for market leaders to appear, improved features and price reductions.

Technophobes are more than cautious in their adoption of new technologies. They may not feel comfortable with new ways of working and often subscribe to the theory that what they currently have is, and will always be sufficient for their needs.

Our beliefs about, and attitudes towards, the environment are deeply rooted in history. More recent responses to the environment and the so called 'green' movement has only been evident since the 1960s.

The following tracks our changing attitudes toward the environment over time. Many ancient cultures express a belief that they are part of nature, and live in harmony with it, taking only what they need to survive. The impact of these cultures is therefore generally taken as being sympathetic with the local ecosystem and the principles of environmental sustainability. If this is true, these cultures may represent only those civilizations that have faced environmental issues of their making, and found a solution. There is much evidence to suggest that many ancient civilisations collapsed from the ecological change brought about by their own actions and ignorance of its environmental consequences.

Until recently, most modern cultures have seen themselves as separate from nature and that, through technology, they have been liberated from such primitive concerns. With the onset of the Industrial Revolution this mastery over nature was becoming more evident. At that same time, a small number of people also began to express disquiet at both the rate of change of society and the local environment. Authors such as the Englishman Thomas Malthus, (1766–1834), warned that population growth, if unchecked would exceed the capacity of the earth to provide food, a position again proposed by Paul Ehrlich in his 1968 publication, *The Population Bomb*. Projections of the date at which such calamities would occur were averted, however, by technological changes that increased food production. The American author Henry David Thoreau, (1817–1862), promoted the benefits of a simple life and advocated the conservation of virgin forest as a standard by which change could be measured. Industrialisation as a rule, however, proceeded with little regard for its impact on the environment.

Widespread concern for the environment is a relatively recent consideration. The origins of popular awareness and understanding of environmental degradation probably lie with the publishing of *Silent Spring* by the biologist Rachel Carson in 1962. Carson noted the effects of the use of DDT to control mosquitoes, on the environment and the food chain. Expanding on the theme, *The Closing Circle: Nature, Man & Technology*, by Barry Commoner in 1971, detailed a number of instances of environmental degradation by industrial pollution. Commoner also proposed what he called the four laws of ecology:

- nature knows best

- everything must go somewhere

- there is no such thing as a free lunch

- everything is connected to everything else.

In 1971, Greenpeace was established, initially to oppose US atomic bomb tests, and subsequently became involved in the environmental movement more generally. Greenpeace rapidly became a focus group for protests against environmental pollution. Environmental concerns were further raised by a number of revelations regarding the disposal of toxic waste and the inadequacy of many safety control systems, among them: Minamata (1968), The Love Canal (1978), Three Mile Island (1979), Bhopal (1984), Chernobyl (1986), and the Exxon Valdez (1989).

In 1979, scientists James Lovelock and Lynn Margulis published *Gaia: A new look at life on Earth*, in which they proposed a controversial hypothesis that the Earth could be considered to be a superorganism that could respond to changes using a self-regulatory, or homeostatic, process. This hypothesis added support to the suggestion that human activity might not only change the local environment but might set in train changes on a worldwide basis that might be irreversible. About this time, concerns about a rise in atmospheric carbon dioxide and its possible influence in global warming began to appear in the popular press. Today, market segmentation based on people's attitudes to green issues is based on the following groups.

Eco-warriors are individuals who take a proactive role in championing causes for the environment by caring for the natural world in their daily lives and decision-making. The Eco-warrior movement in Australia even developed a flag symbolising their ethical stance. The flag has four colours. Red, yellow and black represent indigenous cultures worldwide, while green is indicative of nature and the environmental movement. In the centre of the flag is a tripod symbol representing unity. This flag first appeared in the late 1990s when environmental activists gathered to protect an area of high ecological value.

Eco-champions are individuals who promote awareness of environmental issues within organizations. As an example, Cardiff University Wales, encourages members of staff to embrace sustainable practices. The university's website outlines a program inviting staff to nominate an eco-champion whose responsibility is to, "To promote and encourage the reduction in unnecessary energy and water consumption, minimise waste production and ensure efficient recycling of unwanted resources."

Eco-fans are defined by their enthusiasm to adopt environmentally friendly practices as consumers. They seek to help others in applying these same principles. Eco-fan groups around the world aim to spread the practice of environmentally friendly consumption and lifestyle.

AHL

Eco-phobes objectify the environment and see it as a machine that produces resources and energy for the use and control of mankind. Eco-phobes champion technological solutions to problems and see environmentalists as resisting progress. In these terms, environmental protection is seen as an inefficiency that only increases company costs, causes delays and reduces profitability.

In the field of fashion environmentally friendly designers recognised the power of public feeling about green design when they developed lines of goods promoting an eco-friendly agenda while still encouraging consumption. Bags of all description soon appeared bearing the printed message: "I am not a plastic bag" and trend-conscious shoppers proudly displayed their green credentials through their purchase.

Products that embody an individual's values and attitudes promote positive ideological belief responses. 'Green' or sustainably designed products would promote ideopleasure responses in those with a strong commitment to the environment. Companies that support charitable organisations would also solicit positive ideo-pleasure responses from consumers.

Consumers are now also better informed about the environmental impact some products and their manufacturing practices have on the environment. This increased environmental awareness translates into consumers making purchases based on this additional criterion. Many companies now promote their 'green' credentials through advertising campaigns, product information sheets and web links explaining their policies. Companies must respond to legislation and market demands but an increasing number also have a social conscience and may even see financial benefit when developing product lines.

Market research strategies

Market research strategies may involve a variety of techniques including: expert appraisal, user trial, consumer surveys, patent investigations, literature searches perceptual mapping, environmental scanning and competition or SWOT analyses. Designers may be required to confer with; marketing people, manufacturers, clients and, in some instances, the public, (if conducting their own market research, or user trials).

Traditionally new product development involves manufacturers exploring the needs of the market and developing appropriate products in response. This process can be complex and expensive but helps to ensure market success. While incremental improvement of existing products is the most common form of product development, manufacturers still require information to assist them in determining the direction these modifications should take. Market research, data collection and analysis by manufacturers that may involve:

- competitor product analysis

- user trials to test product acceptance

- 'what-if' scenarios evaluating product profitability

- investigation of unfilled or alternative niche opportunities

- market dynamic analysis (growth/decline, recent trends, etc.)

- user surveys and interviews focusing is on customer buying habits and attitudes

- targeting existing customers to gather their views on an existing product to seek ways of improvement.

Manufacturers regularly observe market competition sales to test their level of comparative success. Innovation, modifications and adjustments of products by competitors may also provide clues to manufacturers of market trends.

Market research strategies, advantages and disadvantages

The starting point for any research project is the collection and evaluation of prior learning relevant to the topic. This is the aim of a literature search. The literature search therefore involves the systematic search for published material in order to establish the current levels of knowledge and criticism related to the topic of interest and to inform future research directions. This search is usually performed using sources of information recognised as being authoritative, such as peer reviewed academic journals, books and published theses, but may also include information published by consumer magazines, government agencies and industry.

Market research is less reliable for innovative products. Design teams and researchers have to rely on gathering as much feedback as possible from prototypes rather than generations of market-successful product developments. Early markets are also volatile and unpredictable places, characterised by high technological and customer uncertainty. Until customers form clear preferences about what constituents a successful, marketable product there is a great deal of variation in design and technologies on offer, not all of which can survive in a competitive marketplace.

Redevelopment of an existing product is more common due to the fact that market demand has already been established. Redevelopment may only involve incremental adjustments to form or features of an existing product.

A properly conducted literature search will uncover the state of knowledge about a topic, preventing unnecessary duplication of effort while highlighting areas of potentially fruitful study. A problem with literature searches, particularly in the current age of electronic information retrieval, is the shear amount of information that can be retrieved and must be sorted through for relevance to the specific project being undertaken.

The search for published resources was traditionally begun by consulting volumes containing a collection of abstracts from papers published, within the targeted field of study, such as Engineering Abstracts, Metallurgical Abstracts, etc. Every article published in any particular year was listed in the annual volume of abstracts. Entries were also arranged in alphabetical order by subject and author. These compendiums were, however, generally available only at major institutions such as Universities and Colleges so that access to such resources for research had some geographical limitations. While each article found would generally contain a list of references for further examination, a researcher would usually have been required to examine a significant number of annuals in order to ensure coverage of the field. As prospective papers were found, the researcher would commonly create an index card onto which the details of the abstract and reference would be entered for later consultation. In this way, a reference index of articles relevant to the specific research topic was created. The manual nature of the process was however relatively laborious and time consuming.

The introduction of ICT, (Information & Communications Technology), has revolutionised the whole process of searching abstracts and the development and management of resources. Today, abstracts are stored on searchable databases and are available to anyone with access to the internet. Searches on key words in tools such as Google Scholar for example can uncover numerous articles some of which can even be downloaded free of charge, while other articles are available for download from the publisher as pdf files for a small fee.

Similarly, the management of personal reference/bibliographic databases has immensely benefited from ICT, with numerous programs available to record, organise and search abstracts collected. Programs such as Bibus, EndNote®, RefWorks®, ProCite®, and Reference Manager® along with many others allow the searching of internet databases and the download and storage of abstracts, along with the interfacing with popular word processing programs, to assist in the formatting of references.

A user trial, (also known as task analysis), is a trial in which members of the community for which the product is ultimately intended are observed using the product. The investigator records the participants during the trial for later analysis. These trials are usually undertaken in a laboratory environment as initial observations, in which the participants are asked to perform a number of tasks simulating typical use. The recording of such trials may include the use of hidden cameras and/or data loggers that record participant interaction with the product. An advantage of a user trial is that because the participants are not specialists, usability issues can be highlighted, that is information about how users actually interact with the product is obtained. In addition, a relatively large number of participants can be included at low cost. A disadvantage of such a trial is that inexperience with the product may result in simple errors-of-use by the trial participants.

User research involves the questioning of users regarding their experiences and opinions of the product. Methods typically used include: questionnaires, participant diaries and focus groups. Collection of data is generally easy and relatively cheap, however, the data obtained is generally more qualitative than that obtained by user trials and it may be difficult to keep participants from deviating from issues related to the product. User research collects data from participants about their experiences with, and responses to, the product, typically using questionnaires or interview techniques. User trials observe the actual interaction that has taken place as recorded by an investigator or data logging equipment. User research is therefore generally more qualitative in nature compared with the more quantitative nature of user trials. A graphical representation of the mix of user evaluation techniques is presented in Figure 9.4.1 showing how psychological factors such as consumer attitude, (user research) and behaviour, (user trial), are incorporated into both qualitative and quantitative forms of investigation. This is a process in which an expert, chosen on the basis of his or her training and knowledge of the area concerned, is asked to give their opinion. An expert appraisal is generally qualitative in nature and has the advantage that a limited number of participants are required. Because of this, such appraisals are often completed quickly and typically include advice on potential directions for development.

AHL

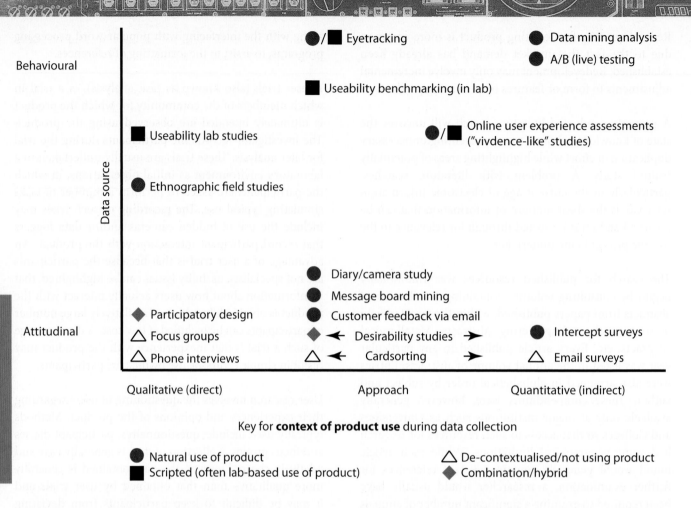

Behavioural

Data source

Attitudinal

● /■ Eyetracking

● Data mining analysis
● A/B (live) testing

■ Useability benchmarking (in lab)

■ Useability lab studies

● /■ Online user experience assessments ("vivdence-like" studies)

● Ethnographic field studies

● Diary/camera study
● Message board mining
● Customer feedback via email

◆ Participatory design
△ Focus groups
△ Phone interviews

◆ ← Desirability studies →
△ ← Cardsorting →

● Intercept surveys
△ Email surveys

Qualitative (direct)　　　　　Approach　　　　　Quantitative (indirect)

Key for **context of product use** during data collection

● Natural use of product
■ Scripted (often lab-based use of product)

△ De-contextualised/not using product
◆ Combination/hybrid

Figure 9.4.1　User evaluation techniques and research methods based on data source vs approach vs context of product use, image modified from Christian Rohrer (2008).

A disadvantage of expert appraisals can be the difficulty of locating someone with the appropriate depth and breadth of knowledge to provide a comprehensive and authoritative opinion free of bias.

Perceptual mapping is a graphic marketing tool used to determine and then convey market structure analysis by identifying the relationships between competing products, buying choices and future recommendations made by consumers.

Statistical procedures may be used to convert raw data collected in surveys into perceptual maps. Perceptual maps plot comparative responses from consumers against a predetermined set of product attributes. The simplicity of the final result makes perceptual maps popular with marketing teams for communication with management or clients.

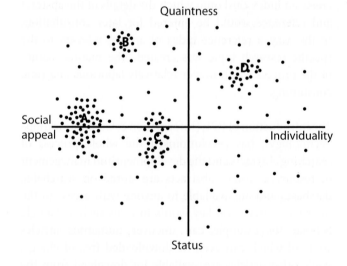

Figure 9.4.2　Perceptual map, image modified from Mydogategodshat via Creative Commons Attribution-Share Alike 3.0 Unported

The marketing environment is defined as that group of external influences that directly or indirectly impact on an organisation's ability to generate ideas, products and services. The process of examining the market for these influences is known as environmental scanning and is used as a mechanism to identify both market place opportunities and threats. Organisations constantly scan the market environment in order to better understand developing trends and assist with their future planning. The process involves both searching for information and reviewing information, but is essentially a three part plan involving the following.

- Scanning the marketplace through market observations, review of trade journals, evaluating government regulations and examining industry-wide sales figures.

- Analysing and interpreting data to identify potential market opportunities and threats.

- Planning a response in terms of marketing plans and future product development or creating strategies that attempt to influence the market environment itself.

INTERNATIONAL MINDEDNESS

Determining the purpose of market research allows designers to clearly identify who needs to be included and their differing requirements.

© IBO 2012

The success of any product, including new food products in the marketplace depends entirely on its ability to meet the tastes, trends and requirements of the target market. To maximise the chances of product success and ultimately financial viability, meeting consumers' demands is paramount. Initially, however, market surveys may be employed to determine:

- price placement

- current market solutions

- customer niche and demand

- brand recognition and product perception.

One of the hidden dangers of not clearly and accurately defining the needs and features of the target market is an ill-defined product specification that may lead to a poorly designed or targeted product destined to fail in the marketplace.

The purpose of market research is to gather information on current and future customers. This data better informs marketing staff and designers alike. Once a market is identified and fully defined, market research aims to reduce risk by assisting decision makers to precisely cater for the specific needs of the identified group.

The collected data aids business decision making by fully understanding the needs of the target market. The correct interpretation of data reduces the risks involved in making these decisions. When calculating a potential market, analysts start with a large group and gradually pare down and refine the specific characteristics of the potential consumer group. Market research is about formulating the right questions. Some examples follow.

- Should we develop a new product?

- Will the market support a new product?

- What barriers exist to entering the market: competition, legislation, technology, etc?

- What are the critical needs of the target group?

- What demographics are represented by the group and where do they live?

- What are the purchasing trends within the group?

- Is this market sector covered by existing competitors?

THEORY OF KNOWLEDGE

What are the assumptions which underlie methods used to gain knowledge in this area?

© IBO 2012

The field of market research has a plethora of techniques from which to choose. They are all based on the assumption that the market or consumers know what is best or at least what appeals to them. The approach or approaches employed are mostly determined by the product in question but the type of data varies considerably.

Students should examine scientific approaches such as benchmarking, the conditions under which these examinations are undertaken and the types of data generated. They should also review qualitative approaches to measuring through such mechanisms as desirability studies.

Exercise

What impact does product type, sector and segment target audience have on the selection of market research? Provide examples.

9.5–BRANDING

ESSENTIAL IDEA

> Branding creates an identity for a product or company which makes it distinct from another and can provide added value.
>
> © IBO 2012

NATURE OF DESIGN

> In order to diffuse products into the marketplace, the identity of a company is typically embodied in a brand. The brand is communicated to the consumer through a value proposition. Designers help to communicate this by: building a strong user experience around the brand identity; determining content design; establishing the tone of message through advertisements; promotion.
>
> © IBO 2012

AIM

> A brand encapsulates the identity of a company and its products. The brand designer needs to ensure that the message of a company is communicated clearly and creatively to allow them to stand out from the competition.
>
> © IBO 2012

Brand loyalty

Product branding conveys to the consumer the company identity that may relate concepts of quality, status, uniqueness, desirability etc. Branding is an essential part of a company's overall marketing strategy. Well-planned and executed brand strategies drive a company's reputation and are designed to craft how the market views a brand. Managing a brand, responding to the market and developing innovative products are key strategies to maintaining a competitive advantage.

Brand identity is regularly quoted as a company's most valuable asset. It is designed to create product differentiation in the mind of the consumer. It most often consists of a symbol, (logo/trademark), colour, word or image placed on a product. Successful branding is designed to manage how consumers feel about a product. It has the capacity to both promote the company and generate sales. Consumers buy well-known brands based on previous experience and reputations of quality or performance. Companies that consistently deliver on 'brand promise' develop a strong consumer following or customer loyalty.

Loyal consumers who commit to a brand continue to purchase products irrespective of price or convenience. They make positive recommendations to their friends to also purchase products within the brand family.

A variety of strategies are employed by companies to encourage brand loyalty including, rewards programs, discounts, special offers and exclusive trials.

How brands appeal to different market segments

Marketers pride themselves on being able to identify the traits of specific market segments and pitch their product precisely to meet the needs of the identified group. After conducting extensive research these groups are formed with members of similar characteristics.

Companies and brands in particular often choose to target more than one segment. This practice is called multi-segment marketing. Multi-segment marketing can take place using a variety of strategies. The following are two examples.

- Selling a single product over multiple market segments based on its universal or mass market appeal and designed to meet needs that exist within all members of the targeted group. e.g. Apple iPhone.

- A range of product lines may be developed within a brand to appeal to a range of market segments e.g. automobile models that cater for first car buyers, families, sports and prestige market customers all within the one brand. Food manufacturers may offer healthy, organic, special dietary requirement or frozen alternatives.

- Tweaking existing products to cater for multiple markets eg. cultural variations - Macdonalds.

Firms that market the same product globally or to multiple regions with different preferences target multiple segments. The product may be tweaked to ensure it is adopted or that it meets a need unique to a certain segment. For instance, some regions may prefer food flavours that won't sell in others. While the core product remains the same, select flavours may be distributed to certain regions based on local preferences. International marketers may need to modify products according to local government regulations and language interpretations.

While a company's global identity delivers it much strength in the marketplace, there are still market segments where consumers prefer brands that reflect the country of origin, particularly those countries whose national identities are associated with specific traits or products eg.:

- Turkey - rugs

- Thailand - silk

- Italy - fashion design

- Australia - woollen products

- America - cotton and denim.

The difference between a trademark and registered design

Trademarks are recognised as one a company's most valuable assets. Trademarks may be images, logos, patterns, symbols or words. They are used to identify and differentiate a product in the marketplace. Embodied within the trademark is the identity, integrity and reputation of the product/company. Trademarks appear on products, in advertising, as signage and on packaging.

Typically trademarks perform two very important functions:

- easily distinguish products and services from others in a crowded and competitive marketplace

- provide a memorable symbol that conveys a message about the quality of the product or service.

While trademarks are created under common law simply by their use, and their registration is not compulsory, by registering a trademark many advantages are gained. These benefits include:

- centralised recording of an individual's or company's right to use the trademark

- public, searchable

- establishes a legal right to exclusive use

- permits legal defence against others using the registered mark

To register a trademark, both a drawing and an in-use specimen must be provided. Appropriate trademark in-use specimens could include samples of products, tags, packaging and advertising. Companies applying to register

their own trademark must first check to see if their design impinges on the rights of others who may have already registered the same or similar trademark.

Successful registration allows you to use the registered trademark symbol as shown in Figure 9.5.1.

Figure 9.5.1   Trademark and registered design symbols

Anyone claiming rights to the use of a symbol or logo for use as trademark may do so regardless of filing for a registration. The use of the registered trademark symbol may only be used, however, after successfully completing the formal registration process.

Figure 9.5.2   Trademark and registered design examples

The implications for a company of positive and negative publicity on brand image

Research shows that, from a consumer's perspective, global brands: espouse quality, represent cultural or social ideals and come with expectations of ethical responsibility.

In this case, global brands may be selected by consumers in the belief that the products are of higher quality and the company possesses greater credibility. Ownership of globally branded products may convey prestige and social status in the eyes of many consumers.

Coca-Cola® is a global leader in the beverage industry. It offers hundreds of subsidiary brands involving itself in the soft drink, water, fruit juice and sports drink markets. It has a brand identity recognized the world over. It does this through carefully and consistently presented, standardised packaging and graphics.

AHL

273

It has not always been plain sailing for globally branded and marketed products. Anti-globalization campaigners have targeted the likes of Coca Cola®, Nestle® and Macdonalds®. Demonstrators have attacked transnational companies over their policies relating to exploitation of workers, pollution and the exporting of western corporate capitalism.

Nike and Apple have had accusations of forced overtime, child labour, and poor working in its of off shore factories. Demonstrators have often become the main focus of news reports generating unwanted publicity. In the United States alone 40 anti-sweatshop organisations were identified in 2001. These single issue focus groups form but a small part of even larger numbers of individuals and associations targeting issues such as environmental awareness, human rights and globalisation.

Effects of product branding

Branding is designed to create product differentiation in the mind of the consumer. It most often consists of a symbol, (logo/trademark), word or image placed on a product. Successful branding is designed to manage how consumers feel about a product. Consumers buy well-known brands based on previous experience and reputations of quality or performance. Branding has the capacity to both promote the company and generate sales. Some manufacturers are able to offer their products at a price premium based on the popularity of branding or benefits accrued to the consumer through functionality, ease of use, reliability, brand loyalty or perceived prestige gained from purchasing and owning a particular product.

At the pre-purchase stage this evaluation is largely, by necessity, based on reports from various sources such as friends, consumer groups, advertising, manufacturers specifications and reputation for quality and cost.

A powerful influence is also prior experience of the consumer with the brand. Following purchase, the consumer will assess value for money in terms of how well their expectations of the product have been met. At this stage, considerations of functionality, reliability, ease of use, running costs and performance become measurable factors.

Clever marketing strategies along with strong brand identification can sell not only products but an image. Purchasers are persuaded that by owning the product, the brand will convey on them status, success, prestige, freedom etc. This message is particular strong amongst adolescents who are still developing their own identity and may seek to transplant values from a coveted brand and project them by owning a prized item. Unfortunately,

many of the most prized brands come at a premium cost due to high demand (and in some cases exclusivity of the product).

Positive effects accrued from the ability to purchase items seen as highly desirable can be feelings of 'inclusion', an improved self image and greater confidence. Peer pressure may be one of the larger forces driving consumption of 'popular' brands. Those who cannot afford the cost of owning these prized consumer brands may also feel outcast or devalued.

Over the long term, the extent to which the product has maintained the characteristics for which it was purchased becomes increasingly important, however, fashion trends and desirability of a product may still be overriding factors in a consumer's choice.

Contribution of packaging to brand identity

Packaging fulfils an important role in the marketing and promotion of products in the marketplace, by attracting the attention of consumers over and above that of competitor products. This is often achieved by appealing to emotional cues that establish and reinforce brand recognition and loyalty. It is this aspect of packaging that has led to its description as the 'silent salesman' and resulted in packaging becoming an important part of the marketing process.

It has been estimated that a product needs to be recognised by the consumer from a distance of 3 to 5 metres in less than 10 seconds if it is to be selected over its competition.

Product packaging and prominent brand placement allows a manufacturer to expand their product range while maintaining consumer recognition and loyalty over lesser-known brands. Well-designed packaging also plays a role in facilitating impulse buying. While the shape of packaging is often generic in nature to provide functionality, some shapes have become synonymous with their brands.

Packaging design is another way of developing a new product. It can reformulate or reinforce the brand identity, separating the product from competition, while reinforcing messages judged to be important, such as traditional values, while reducing images of being old fashioned. The provision of a number of alternate package sizes can also provide a wider range of buying options to the market. Some special offer, or promotion logo can also be added to the original design.

Packaging and presentation must match the image and quality of the product. Poor package development may result in negative consumer experiences, which can quickly translate into negative brand equity and potentially, reduced sales.

Evaluating the global impact of branding

Global brands are seen as successful, having beaten off the competition. This success is seen by consumers as product validation and is also associated with quality. Global brands trade on an imagined cultural ideal or global identity. With ownership, they generate a feeling of belonging to a larger community.

Globalisation is leading towards one big market. The textiles industry in particular is characterised by great competition, however, maintaining low costs is simply not enough to be competitive, particularly when threats associated with unauthorised copying and misuse of trademarks make trading for legitimate brands difficult.

In this situation, more than ever, branding must clearly reinforce and promote product differentiation. This process encourages the consumer to make a purchase based on the assumption that buying the garment will give the consumer some satisfaction.

A major advantage associated with globalisation is the economy of scale-benefits associated with packaging, labels, brand recognition, market acceptance, marketing, promotions, and advertising. While branding and brand management is of paramount importance in the global textile industry, non price-factors such as variety, response times, quality, personalisation and differentiation all influence demand for one product over another.

Apart from yielding economies of scale, globalisation pragmatically encourages consumers around the world to develop similar preferences and speeds up a brand's time to market globally instead of focussing on local modifications.

Through the joint strategies of permeation and saturation, market leaders like Billabong and Nike have achieved global product recognition and market dominance. Their products abound in shopping malls across Europe and America, while at the same time peppering market stalls across Asia.

Market leaders dominating particular fields tend to build on their success, not only by improving sales but also by acquiring other companies with appropriate technology, expertise and market share. This has the effect of increasing distribution networks, sales outlets and market share. It also has the effect of reducing competition and giving companies stronger control over pricing and availability.

An example of this was the acquisition and integration of Reebok into the Adidas Group for US$3.8 billion. While this acquisition strengthened Adidas' market share, Nike was still the global leader in the sports industry, with enormous exposure and purchasing power across the globe.

Another example of a market leading, global brand, Billabong International Ltd. sell their branded merchandise at sporting shops throughout Australia, Europe, Japan, South America, and North America. A manufacturer and distributer of surfing, skating, and snowboarding apparel and accessories, Billabong has built its business through its Australian base and has spread from there. Billabong executive Paul Naude, is quoted in the August 2000 issue of WWD as saying, 'Up until two years ago, Billabong had numerous licensees around the world, but in the last couple of years, our focus has been on becoming a truly global brand. We are moving much more to wholly owned subsidiaries and taking control of key markets and secondary markets and setting ourselves up to maximise the brand's potential in those areas.

Marketing strategies and global expansion are not always successful. The Billabong company has undergone a significant collapse in earnings following the global crisis of 2007. In 2013 it was expected to sell for a value of around 3% of its 2007 worth.

INTERNATIONAL MINDEDNESS

Global brands can have the effect of stifling competition and reducing diversity in the marketplace. They may also replace local brand names. The shift towards global brands is also attributed to the consumer's preference for brands with a global image over local competitors, even when quality and value are not visibly superior.

> A globally recognised and appealing brand allows organisations and companies to engage with global markets. This raises ethical issues with some products.
>
> © IBO 2012

Globalisation is bringing cultures, business, manufacturing marketing and consumerism together. Examples include off-shore manufacturing and global call centres.

Just some of the big questions in this field would include the following:

- Are ethical values part of national identities and therefore vary from culture to culture?

- Is it possible to have global ethical standards?

- Is it appropriate for businesses and governments to make decisions solely on what is in their best interest?

- Is it ethical for companies to comply with local or national laws that may still have adverse global impacts eg. generation of greenhouse gases, denuding of forests and so on?

Controversial philosopher Peter Singer asks "should economic values to trump everything else–the environment, the rights of workers, social issues?" (2002)

References

"*One World: The Ethics of Globalization*", Peter Singer (New Haven: Yale University Press, 2002) and "*World Poverty and Human Rights*," Thomas Pogge (Cambridge: Polity, 2002)

Exercise

Identify a global brand that may generate ethical issues in another culture or country e.g. McDonalds in India

SAMPLE QUESTIONS

1. The marketing mix or 4Ps is composed of
    A   planning, preparation, policy, particulars
    B   product, price, place, promotion
    C   presentation, permanence, placement, price
    D   propaganda, percentiles, producing, price

2. Psychological pricing engenders

    A   use of all five senses.
    B   a physiological response
    C.   price perception on the consumers part
    D   price exaggeration on the consumers part.

3. Market research is conducted to

    A   reduce waste
    B   check the success of a product
    C   meet manufacturing requirements
    D   best match product development with consumer needs

4. Brand loyalty is best expressed when

    A   consumers purchase only brand name products
    B   consumers speak positively about a product to others
    C   consumers accrue points based on brand purchases
    D   customers continue to make purchasing decisions based on a brand name irrespective of price.

5. Discuss the advantages and disadvantages associated with corporate responsibility programs.

6. Explain the use and purpose of perceptual maps in marketing.

7. Explain the difference between product development and product diversification.

8. Explain why companies adopt an imitation strategy rather than developing new products of their own.

9. Explain how companies may brand similar products to meet different market segments.

10. Compare and contrast the activities of marketing and advertising.

COMMERCIAL PRODUCTION

10

CONTENTS

AHL

10.1–JIT AND JIC

ESSENTIAL IDEA

Just-in-time and Just-in-case are opposing production strategies utilised by the manufacturer.

© IBO 2012

NATURE OF DESIGN

Whilst inventory creates a safety net for companies, maintenance and potential waste of resources can have significant implications for companies and the environment. Manufacturers must evaluate and analyse each market and determine whether a JIT or JIC strategy is the best to follow.

© IBO 2012

AIM

(This unit shows) an in-depth knowledge and understanding of the potential success of a product can lead manufacturers to decide in favour of JIC or JIT. This can vary from one product to the next and requires experience and intuition.

© IBO 2012

Just in case (JIC)

Just-in-case can be considered to be the opposite of just-in-time. Large inventories are held ready to be used 'if or when' they may be required. Just-in-case is more of a traditional approach to manufacturing. This excess capacity to manufacture, not only includes materials and components but extends to the workforce and manufacturing capacity. The advantages of JIC manufacturing include its ability to respond better to unpredictable spikes in demand while higher storage costs are incurred as a consequence of this approach.

Just in time (JIT)

Just in time management systems aim to eliminate or at least reduce all forms of waste caused as a by-product of manufacturing, while simultaneously improving product quality and productivity. All stages of production, from the procuring of raw materials to product inventory and distribution, are managed on a needs or just-in-time basis. To be successful, JIT requires careful predictions of needs throughout the production chain. This can only be maintained through smooth, effective and efficient quality assurance at each stage of production. Also called lean manufacturing, JIT has been commonly adopted by carmakers and budget computer manufacturers. The advantages of JIT manufacturing include the prevention of waste and overproduction. Overheads are reduced as are warehousing space and inventory held. Improved production management and quality control systems, all lead to an improved return on investment. Carefully timed and linked transport networks also improve product distribution.

Linked directly to online systems receiving orders from individual customers, or larger distribution companies, manufacturers employing JIT processes are able to tune their manufacturing directly in response to specific requests. Linking of CAD/CAM and computer management systems can also play a significant role in monitoring inventories, raw materials, order processing and communication with suppliers and customers. JIT manufacturing falters if there is any disruption to the supply chain. Delays in supply caused by natural, political or technological disruptions can affect productivity. With little or no inventory to fall back on, even minor disruptions to supply can cause production to shut down.

In developing countries, the lack of infrastructure can result in problems in storage and distribution systems. In industries where product freshness or deterioration is an issue, such as the food industry, spoilage rates as high as 20 to 40 percent have been recorded.

INTERNATIONAL MINDEDNESS

Effective business processes and practices developed in some countries have been exported successfully.

© IBO 2012

A variety of successful manufacturing systems have been developed over time. Many of these systems have built upon the success of their predecessors before being adopted globally or at least internationally.

Henry Ford's mass production, moving assembly line of 1910—1913 revolutionised the early car industry. This method allowed workers to concentrate on one task only and raised production while at the same time reduced the cost of the product to the consumer. Efficiencies were gained through smooth, continuous production runs. The process quickly swept across the American automobile industry but also saw its benefits applied across a range of industries around the globe. Producers of domestic appliances such as refrigerators, washing machines and radios quickly reaped the benefits of mass production. The outbreak of WWII saw the assembly line system converted to the war effort where uniforms, armaments, ammunition and even aircraft were mass produced. Assembly line production unfortunately de-skilled and often demoralised workers and due to its highly specialised nature required no input from the individual regarding quality control.

W Edwards Deming was an American engineering and physics graduate with an interest in statistics and systems thinking. During World War II he helped American manufacturers focus on the precision required to produce items of quality. He is probably best known for his efforts in rebuilding the manufacturing base of post-war Japan. His management system encouraged manufacturers to consider quality over quantity and concentrate their efforts on continuous improvement by examining, evaluating and refining the systems critical to effective and efficient production. Deming's philosophy ranged over the entire production cycle and its associated systems incorporating concepts of leadership, communication, company culture and employee training to name just a few. By the 1980s Japan's devastated economy had captured many of the world's largest export markets and was dominant in the fields of electronics, car production and steel making.

JIT concepts have now been readily adapted by manufacturing enterprises around the world. The Dell Computer Corporation effectively uses JIT manufacturing to customise the assembly of computer systems based on individual client orders. In an industry where stock can be outdated in as little as three months, a reduced inventory but trustworthy supply lines and reliable distribution networks ensures customers receive their orders in a timely manner.

THEORY OF KNOWLEDGE

Manufacturers decide whether to pursue JIT or JIC as a production strategy depending on their perception of where the market is going. To what extent do different areas of knowledge incorporate doubt as a part of their methods?

© IBO 2012

Over time a series of socio-political events have eroded manufacturers' confidence in their ability to predict the range of variables required to maintain the efficiencies offered by JIT systems. How can manufacturers plan when seemingly unpredictable, random events may affect supply chains, distribution networks and the cost of commodities? Unpredictable events such as government changes, random acts of terror and natural disasters can all have an effect on local and global supply and/or manufacturing. In some industries, fickle and constantly changing fashion trends impact markets and consumer behaviour. These trends may be influenced by popular culture, celebrity endorsements, etc. This level of uncertainty must also be taken into account when formulating long-term business plans.

The question, however, is largely about how we can make predictions about the future with any certainty. How do different areas of knowledge make such decisions, what method do they use, and how do they deal with doubt?

Students should consider if religious systems simply comfort the believer that God knows best. Does this relieve the faithful of doubt about the outcome? [1]

Nobel Prize winning physicist Robert Feynman "Scientific knowledge is a body of statements of varying degrees of certainty -- some most unsure, some nearly sure, none absolutely certain." [2]

"True science teaches, above all, to doubt, and to be ignorant." [3]

"Most institutions demand unqualified faith; but the institution of science makes skepticism a virtue." Robert King Merton 1910, *Social Theory and Social Structure*, 1962. [4]

Students will be able to find many quotes that should be used to support their own arguments, that is, they should not rely on these quotes to build an argument only to illustrate it.

Remember the question asks to what extent is doubt incorporated in their method. It could easily be restated as; what method do different areas of knowledge use to make predictions about their future and how is doubt incorporated in that prediction?

[1] *Theistic belief and religious uncertainty* (2008) http://infidels.org/library/modern/jeffrey_jordan/belief.html

[2] Robert Feynman 1988, *What Do You Care What Other People Think?: Further adventures of a curious character*

[3] Miguel de Unamuno 1913, *The Tragic Sense of Life*.

[4]Robert King Merton 1910, *Social Theory and Social Structure*, 1962.

Exercise

Elaborate on the sentence below by Dr Stuart Firestein.

"Creation myths from the ancient Greeks to the Old Testament give complete descriptions of how the universe was created. No doubt there. Alternatively, do science, cosmology, geology, archaeology, biology–give incomplete descriptions filled with open questions?"

Stuart Firestein 2102 , *Doubt Is Good for Science, But Bad for PR*, Wired magazine, 2012

10.2–LEAN PRODUCTION

ESSENTIAL IDEA

Lean production aims to eliminate waste and maximise the value of a product based on the perspective of the consumer.

© IBO 2012

NATURE OF DESIGN

Lean production considers product and process design as an on-going activity and not a one-off task, and should be viewed as a long term strategy.

© IBO 2012

AIM

The role of the workforce in lean production is paramount, relying on their wisdom and experience to improve the process, reducing waste, cost and production time. Recognising this results in motivated workforces whose interests are in the success of the product.

© IBO 2012

Characteristics of lean production

The characteristics of lean production include extremely limited inventories, highly skilled workers, constant improvement in pursuit of perfection including no tolerance for defects, high levels of product diversity and customisation in an environment seeking cost reductions.

Principles of lean production

The principles of lean production are applied to the entire production process, that is, from supply chains through to manufacturing. It is achieved thorough well-designed quality control systems, with production volume and customisation based directly on market demand.

Cost reduction is achieved through the elimination of waste and costly errors. Strong links with suppliers guarantee the integrity of supply and maintain confidence to keep inventories as close to zero as possible. The workforce is empowered to associate with the company's quality goals and foster an environment of striving for constant improvement. Lean production may be summarised by the application of the following principles.

- Flexibility.

- Visual control aids.

- Market pull processing.

- Managing production flow.

- Waste reduction or minimisation.

- Constantly seeking improvement.

- Strong long-term relationships with suppliers.

- Error minimisation and perfect first-time quality.

Value stream mapping

Value stream mapping is also known as 'end-to end' system mapping. It is a simple but powerful tool that provides a visual aid to map the relationships between materials, processes, information and time.

Initially a paper and pen exercise, value mapping documents the information associated with production from the reception of raw materials through to product distribution. Today these 'maps' are computer generated and incorporate real-time production data. The supporting data accompanying production allows for detailed analysis which can be particularly useful when trying to reduce product cycle times. It is this insight into the chain of decision making/cause and effect that can prove most useful.

A variety of software packages exists for value stream mapping allowing photos and videos to be added to the map to replace the more traditional flow chart connectors. Simulations of current processes may also be critically examined over time or alternative value stream simulations may be prepared for direct comparison.

The purpose of values stream mapping is to identify processes that do not provide value. Processes that do not provide value are designated as waste. Value stream maps may be used to optimise individual processes, whole-of-factory production or even manage supply chains between multiple organisations. What if scenarios may be simulated to model future production alternatives.

In the end, value stream mapping is used to identify areas of production that may be able to be streamlined

or improved. This process is an integral part of lean manufacturing's philosophy of continuous improvement

Workflow analysis

Workflow analysis supports value streaming and classifies all tasks in a process. Tasks are categorised as value-adding, value-assisting, or non-value-adding.

A value-adding activity or operation transforms a component and is an indispensable part of the overall process. These operations are the processes for which a customer is willing to pay. Operations that are not categorised as value adding should be simplified, streamlined, reduced, integrated into other activities or removed.

A value-assisting activity or operation does not add value to the component, however, these operations are integral to the manufacturing process and cannot be omitted. Preventive maintenance, inspection, statistical process control, etc. and so on are value-assisting operations.

Non-value-adding operations are those activities that will not be missed if they are removed from the process. These activities are often categorised as waste. Delays, superfluous material movement, holding inventory or storage are all seen as non-value-adding operations.

Product family

A product family is a grouping of products and their variants that all pass through similar processing steps and common equipment just prior to shipment to the customer. This part of the production cycle is known as the downstream end. Product families often used as the unit for analysis through value-stream maps.

The easiest way to simplify and represent reality once the product families are established is to create a product family matrix. A product family matrix simply consists of a grid with the vertical axis listing products and the horizontal axis displaying manufacturing process steps working backwards from the customer towards the supply of raw materials, that is, from downstream to upstream. Operations are then plotted in the appropriate grid squares, allowing for ease of identification of common product/operation groupings or families.

Figure 10.2.1 shows a sample product family matrix. The circled products, A, B and C have the final three operations in common and therefore form a product family group. The essential idea behind product families is to create a production line with a synchronised and efficient flow that allows products to be produced at a predictable, market-driven rate

Assembly steps and equipment

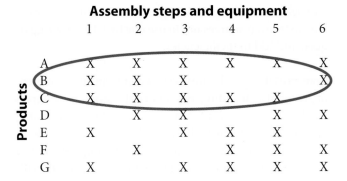

Figure 10.2.1   Product family groupings using a product family matrix

Role of the workforce

Lean manufacturing leverages the commitment of every employee to drive its agenda of constant improvement. Devolution of power in a fair, respectful and equitable environment empowers every employee to be an agent of change. A highly trained and skilled workforce is better equipped to identify small, systematic and incremental improvements that accumulate to provide benefits in business practice and greater efficiency in meeting company objectives and goals. Typical principles preparing a workforce for effective use of lean strategies would involve the following.

- Employees should communicate decency and respect in all of their interactions.

- Management implement an instruction program educating the workforce in the skills required to work together effectively.

- Work areas are maintained in a safe, clean and orderly fashion.

- Communication informs all employees of business goals, plans and achievements.

- Principles of fairness and equity to all are visible.

- The dual principles of honesty and integrity are applied to every aspect of the workplace.

Kaizen

Lean production is based on the principle of kaizen — or continual incremental improvement. Through kaizen, workers employ analytical techniques, such as value stream mapping and a technique called 'the 5 whys', to quickly identify opportunities to eliminate waste and improve productivity. Kaizen may result in new ways of performing operations, procedures, duties or involve resequencing of tasks. Kaizen is employed by all workers at every level of the organisation working together towards a common goal — constant improvement.

Lead time

Lead time is the average time it takes for one product unit to pass through the entire process, from start to finish, including any time waiting between sub-processes. Mathematically, lead time may be expressed as:

Lead time = sum of all process times + sum of all delay or queue times between processes

Reduction of lead time is an important part of lean manufacturing.

The 5Ss: sort; set in order (stabilise); shine; standardise; sustain the practice

5s is a lean tool used in conjunction with other lean manufacturing approaches to organise and then maximise the efficiency of the workplace. Originally developed in Japan, the 5s have been translated into an English equivalent as shown in Figure 10.2.2.

5S IN JAPANESE	IN JAPANESE
Seiri–tidiness	Sort
Seiton–orderliness	Set in order
Seiso–clean, shine	Shine
Seiketsu–standardisation	Standardise
Shitsuke–discipline	Sustain

Figure 10.2.2   5s Japanese translations

5s is regularly recommended as an introduction to lean processes due to its simple, visual approach. This approach helps to empower staff and improve morale, reduce lead time, improve workplace safety, reduce machine down time and improve product quality. The 5s are explained in detail below.

Sort. This phase concerns itself with the removal of unnecessary items from the workplace. This also involves use of space, and simplification of operations. Items and processes that are redundant to production or even office operations should be removed leaving only that which is determined as necessary.

Set in order. A simple mantra sums up this step; a place for everything and everything in its place. Strategic placement of these tools and holders improve efficiency and workflow. Visual cues through labelling also allow for easy identification of tools and their purpose.

Shine. This refers to the cleanliness of the workspace, tooling, equipment and materials. It is the responsibility of employees at all levels to maintain the cleanliness of the workplace.

Standardise. This approach identifies efficient or normal operations and provides best practice on how to deal with abnormal or inefficient conditions in the workplace. These instructions or standards must be clear, easy to understand and easily communicated to workers. Once again, visual cues may be used by employing colour coding as an effective and efficient means of communication.

Sustain. Sustaining concerns itself with the discipline of maintaining systems that address the root causes of inefficiencies through well trained staff and the use of visual aids. It refers to the commitment required to initiate and maintain the first four of the 5s.

The 7 wastes: overproduction; transporting; waiting; inappropriate processing; unnecessary inventory; unnecessary/excess motion; defects

The 7 wastes or 'muda', (the Japanese word for waste), specifically identify a series of wasteful activities found in manufacturing. The 7 wastes principles are deliberately designed to be generic to all manufacturing. The core of this philosophy is that waste occurs in a variety of forms and should be reduced and if possible removed from their manufacturing cycle. Within lean manufacturing there are strategies that exist to deal with each of the wastes, thereby improving overall efficiency, performance and quality. The 7 wastes are identified and detailed below.

Overproduction occurs when operations continue after demand has been met. It can be also occur when products are made earlier than necessary, resulting in excess inventory that requires storage.

Inventory is stock that is not currently required to meet immediate customer demand. Inventory may take the form of raw materials, partly processed product and finished product. Inventory is problematic because it requires additional movement and storage.

Waiting, queueing or delays consume the precious commodity of time. This wasteful practice refers to time lost where no value is being added to the product. Queueing or waiting adds to product cycle or lead times. Downstream resources not in use due to delays, waiting or queueing add to inefficiencies.

Transportation is the unnecessary motion or movement of materials, including raw materials, work in progress (undergoing transportation between processing operations) and finished goods. Transportation adds to production cycle times, is not a value adding process and increases the opportunity for damage associated with additional product handling.

Inappropriate operations includes extra processing, reprocessing to repair faults or handling related damage, and excess inventory generated by over-production. This can be one of the more challenging wastes to both detect and remove.

Unnecessary or excess motion refers to movement of employees and tooling due to inefficient workspace design. Motion is another process that adds no value to the product. Within the lean system 'work' is productive movement while motion is defined as moving without working.

Defects are defined as products or services that do not meet customer specifications. Defects detected within the manufacturing phase require reworking or scrapping and are thus wasteful. If these products or services should travel into the marketplace they generate customer dissatisfaction and create inefficiencies of their own.

Advantages and disadvantages of lean production

Lean manufacturing processes naturally bring about efficiency and cost reductions but they also provide a number of other benefits including:

- space saving due to lack of inventory or excess finished product

- quality of product is constantly under improvement

- better client satisfaction as product is delivered on time and to the specification required

- competitive advantage over other manufacturers.

Due to the nature and pressure for constant improvement, lean manufacturing may suffer from low staff morale and additional gains may also be won but at costs that are uneconomical and unsustainable. Other disadvantages may include:

- disruptions in supply chains can have significant effects on production and, ultimately, product supply concerns for customers

- lean manufacturing requires a whole new way of thinking for employees and managers

- physical plant and equipment setups often require reworking at significant initial investment cost

- lean techniques may be overused, greater returns are evident at the earlier stages of introducing the process and future gains are harder won.

INTERNATIONAL MINDEDNESS

The implementation of lean production has benefits for the global environment.

© IBO 2012

Lean manufacturing's emphasis on reducing or eliminating waste and delivering quality products clearly has benefits for the environment. Waste in the view of lean manufacturing extends well beyond the workshop floor and even encompasses administrative operations.

Environmental waste is categorised in the lean manufacturing process as any unnecessary or excess use of resources (including energy) and the generation of by-products released to the environment that could cause harm. Environmental wastes can occur during the manufacturing, use or end-of-life disposal phases of a product's life.

Mitch Kidwell (2007), in his article 'Lean Manufacturing, the Environment and the Bottom Line', states, "Even if environmental wastes do not get first priority, it is likely that eventually lean will get around to addressing them. In some cases, this will happen through lean activities not intentionally focusing on environmental wastes. However, companies may consciously choose to focus kaizen on particular environmental waste".

THEORY OF KNOWLEDGE

The importance of the individual is recognised in design processes. Is this the case in other areas of knowledge?

© IBO 2012

There is a wealth of material for students to explore in the range of philosophies that permeate socio-political, scientific and religious frameworks. In the design context, the design process recognizes the importance of the beneficiary (the consumer, that is, the individual).

As Novack (2002) writes, "Marxism is based on the individual, his or her nature, freedom and development and their links with society as a whole. It does, however, propose that 'no individual, however talented, strong-willed or strategically situated, can alter the main course of historical development, which is shaped by supra-individual circumstances and forces.'" [1]

In scientific fields people are recognised based on the quality of the models and theories they postulate. In some cases the importance or perceived importance of an individual can and has overshadowed their achievements, often with negative consequences. As theoretical nuclear physicist Jennings (2012) notes "British physics after Isaac Newton (1642 – 1727) fell behind the progress on the continent because the British physicists were too enamoured of Newton. But the most egregious example is Aristotle (384 BC – 322 BC). The adoration of Aristotle delayed the development of knowledge for close to two millennia". [2]

Contrast the approach science takes with religion, where many faiths are based around the teachings of one or more individuals. Examples include Judaism (Moses), Jesus (Christianity), Islam (Mohammed) Sikhism (Zoroaster) and Mormonism (Joseph Smith).

[1] Novack G, *Marxist writings on history and philosophy*, Resistance Books, 2002, pp. 48

[2] Jennings B, *The Role of the individual in science and religion*, 'Quantum diaries', 2014, from www.quantumdiaries.org/2012/01/27/the-role-of-the-individual-in-science-and-religion/

Exercise

How do the arts value the contribution of individuals?

AHL

10.3–COMPUTER INTEGRATED MANUFACTURING (CIM)

ESSENTIAL IDEA

Computer-integrated manufacturing uses computers to automatically monitor and control the entire production of a product.

© IBO 2012

NATURE OF DESIGN

When considering design for manufacture (DfM), designers should be able to integrate computers from the earliest stage of design. This requires knowledge and experience of the manufacturing processes available to ensure integration is efficient and effective. Through the integration of computers, the rate of production can be increased and errors in manufacturing can be reduced or eliminated, although the main advantage is the ability to create automated manufacturing processes.

© IBO 2012

AIM

The integration of computer control into manufacturing can streamline systems, negating the need for time-consuming activities, such as stocktaking, but also reducing the size of the workforce.

© IBO 2012

Elements of CIM: design; planning; purchasing; cost accounting; inventory control; distribution

CIM systems incorporate technologies or methodologies used to increase productivity through the integration of design, planning, engineering and processing operations in manufacturing plants using computer systems. CIM is a programmable computer-based manufacturing system linking design, engineering, manufacturing processes and industrial robots, using automated workstations.

CIM systems can monitor operations from raw materials intake to final product marketing. CIM allows for the storage, retrieval and analysis of complex data providing manufacturers with valuable information relating to equipment maintenance scheduling, process optimisation time and resource management. Major motivations for the implementation of a CIM systems approach is the need for manufacturing industries to quickly and efficiently respond to changes. CIM systems control and link the following components:

- personnel

- marketing

- materials handling

- product design (CAD)

- computer management

- machine tools and equipment (CAM).

A key consideration when implementing CIM is its compatibility with existing systems and infrastructure. Implementation of CIM may be best handled through a gradual or staged process instead of wholesale restructuring. Components of CIM may be added as deemed necessary as part of a plant overhaul.

Many automobile manufacturers have chosen CIM systems to manage and coordinate their already high level of automation. Integrating the ordering stage into the process involves taking into consideration customers with very specific requirements. Incorporating incoming orders with materials and third-party component inventories improves flexibility and reduces warehousing, allowing for JIT (just-in-time) manufacture. On the production floor, a variety of computer-controlled machines may be arranged to sequentially perform a range of operations. Components are often transferred automatically from station to station where machines, in teams, perform their programmed tasks eg.; holding, rotating, welding, painting, etc. These processes are performed along what are known as 'flow', or 'transfer', lines, the control of which is flexibly managed by a computer. Employing this networked system, components are transferred between stations using robot assistance. Movement of components through their various stages of assembly is managed by a computer 'hands off' system and assemblies are monitored for quality control at every stage, reducing wastage and improving consistency. Data from process control points is also logged and stored for reporting and review purposes.

CIM systems provide many benefits to manufacturers including lower inventories and reduced warehousing requirements. Computer managed machinery improves machine utilisation, offers greater scheduling flexibility and reduces manufacturing and lead-times. Labour and its associated on-costs should be reduced and have flow on effects to overall cost efficiencies. Improved access to production data allows managerial reviews for historical comparison and analysis. Manufacturers, however, may find initial setup costs high. The challenges of computerisation and staff restructuring, however, may have negative affects on staff morale. Customers should benefit from price reductions, improved quality. Mass customisation is easier within CIM production plants. Consumers may even be able to follow the production of their order through online interfaces with the plant.

CIM and scales of production

Given the high cost of implementing CIM systems, manufacturing scales of production have to be sufficiently large enough to justify the transition. Most often CIM is implemented in factories with large production throughput and a significant workforce. CIM is particularly advantageous to large production runs involving complex manufacturing operations (requiring coordination) and complex products.

Batch production environments are well suited to CIM systems where repetitive patterns of operation occur. The benefits lie in the flexibility of the system and the automated coordination of setup and changeovers.

Smaller plants employing non-repetitive, specialised manufacturing operations have found less use for CIM systems.

INTERNATIONAL MINDEDNESS

A CIM system allows for efficient global workflow and distribution.

© IBO 2012

Even as early as 2001, Gunasekaran et al. recognised that "companies undertake projects in automation and CIM for a variety of reasons not the least of which is to achieve a competitive advantage."

In a connected world, cooperation and collaboration twenty four hours a day seven days a week is an imperative. The use of CIM systems enables real-time data exchange between design and manufacturing teams at both planning and execution stages. CIM systems also monitor production quotas and quality control thus ensuring the meeting of deadlines while minimising waste. The interconnected nature of these systems means that this data is not only available to manufacturers but also to distributors and clients around the world.

CIM is not only for complex, capital-intensive manufacturing such as car making, but also for fast-response manufacturing requiring flexibility such as textiles and fashion. Lei and Goldhar, (1991), make the point "CIM combines the benefits of economies of scope with the scale economies traditionally garnered only with large, rigid and dedicated factories."

THEORY OF KNOWLEDGE

Technology has a profound influence in design. How have other areas of knowledge been influenced by technology?

© IBO 2012

AHL

Students should consider the relationship between technology and areas of knowledge as symbiotic where one continually influences the other and vice versa. The digital revolution would not be possible without the knowledge to drive the change yet the technological change itself has had huge influence on how we gather, store, organise, analyse and communicate information in every area of knowledge. With this in mind consider the question; which has the most profound effect, the knowledge or the technology?

"Designers do not develop new ideas with perfection in mind" (Petroski 2003) [1]. They think in terms of iterative improvement over time as advances in technology open up new possibilities and new problems to be solved. It is the same in the humanities as new knowledge, better knowledge transfer and communication through advances in technology offer new insights into the past, present and future. The transatlantic cable and wireless as two examples of technologies that greatly increased the speed of communications between nations.

Project 2061 is an example of a long-term science-based US research and development initiative. Benchmark statements such as the one below challenge students to investigate the areas of science, mathematics, and technology.

"The human ability to influence the course of history comes from its capacity for generating knowledge and developing new technologies—and for communicating ideas to others." [2]

AHL

Exercise

What role does artificial intelligence have in the acquisition and creation of new knowledge?

Students could consider developing technologies such as nanotechnology and artificial intelligence and how these may work in tandem to gather analyse and evaluate information.

Research evidence to support this proposition.

References

[1] Petroski H *The evolution of useful things*, Vintage books, New York, 1992, pp. 25

[2] American Association for the Advancement of Science 2009, from www.project2061.org/publications/bsl/online/index.php?intro=true

10.4–QUALITY MANAGEMENT

ESSENTIAL IDEA

Quality management focuses on producing products of consistent required quality.

© IBO 2012

NATURE OF DESIGN

Designers should ensure that the quality of products is consistent through development of detailed manufacturing requirements. They also need to focus on the means to achieve it. The importance of quality management through QC, SPC and QA reduces the potential waste of resources.

© IBO 2012

AIM

The implementation of quality management strategies requires a critical and complete understanding of the needs of a product. To ensure efficiency and efficacy, these measures need to be designed into the product and its production system.

© IBO 2012

Quality control (QC) and quality assurance (QA)

Quality control represents the creation of a system of process controls that lead to the production of products that meet defined specifications of quality. Quality control ensures that process inputs such as temperature, pressure, speed, time, etc. are monitored and adjusted appropriately throughout the production process. Using this approach, variation in the production process is minimized and quality is said to be built into the product rather than relying only on final inspection. Inspectors may be provided with checklists and descriptions of unacceptable product defects. Testing may be visual or require some form of technology such as X-ray or ultrasound. Central to the quality control process is the drive for continual improvement embodied in the Shewhart Cycle known as the PDCA cycle, representing the stages of Plan, Do, Check and Act, illustrated in Figure 10.4.1.

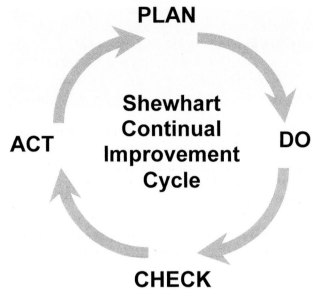

Figure 10.4.1   The Shewart PDCA cycle

The philosophy of quality control and quality assurance was promoted by a number of consultants after World War II as part of a general movement toward quality management. This process has been largely credited with the rapid reputation for quality gained by products from Japan in the 1950s and 1960s. Notable among those involved in the quality movement were W. Edwards Deming, Joseph M. Juran and Walter A. Shewhart. These men, among others, changed the focus of quality from the removal of non-complying product during final inspection, to one of 'building in' quality at every stage of the process, thus avoiding waste and costly re-work.

Quality assurance refers to the maintenance of a system that ensures that each stage of the process from design and purchasing through to final packaging and invoicing meets quality requirements. Companies operating under quality assurance systems employ a process that details the procedures by which they manage their business at each stage of their operations, in order to identify and eliminate issues that may affect quality. The quality assurances approach aims to eliminate the need for intensive final inspection by ensuring that quality has been assessed progressively throughout production.

The international standard for quality assurance is ISO9001 and companies operating under a quality assurance regime must regularly open their systems to external audit to confirm that they are maintaining their systems, in order to retain quality assurance registration.

Statistical process control (SPC)

Statistical process control refers to the use of statistical methods of monitoring processes in order to maintain the process within defined limits. Figure 10.4.2 illustrates two commonly used control charts used to monitor variation of mean and standard deviation. The X-axis may represent sample number or time. By monitoring operations based on a statistical control of the various parts of a process, trends away from target can be highlighted and adjusted, in order to maintain conformity and quality of output.

Control Chart

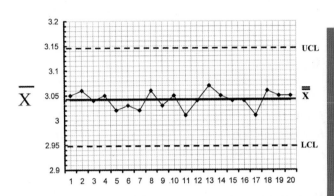

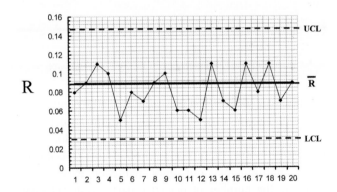

Figure 10.4.2   Process control charts monitoring variation of mean and standard deviation within upper and lower control limits.

Real-time SPC assists with:

- reducing costs

- improving productivity

- real-time decision making

- reducing product variability and scrap

- uncovering hidden process abnormalities

- improving reaction times to process changes.

When comparing systems, quality control focuses on the continuous testing of products to uncover faults and defects before reporting to management for final decision making.

Quality assurance, however, emphasises a process that details the procedures by which the entire business is managed, examining every stage of the operation in an attempt to identify and eliminate issues that may affect quality. On the other hand, statistical process control is a more scientific form of quality control that uses control charts to provide real-time feedback to management.

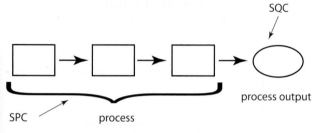

Figure 10.4.3   SPC and SQC modified from Jack B. ReVelle's Quality Essentials: A Reference Guide from A to Z, ASQ Quality Press, 2004, pages 185–186.

INTERNATIONAL MINDEDNESS

Effective quality management can have major benefits for the environment.

© IBO 2012

Quality management systems, such as quality control and quality management, deal routinely with the reduction of waste through the constant monitoring of products and processes. While these approaches do not specifically target environmental outcomes, reduction in waste by reducing the number of defective parts produced saves raw materials, energy and space for storage of products below specification.

Improvement in a company's environmental performance can still be enhanced if consideration is also given to non-product wastes, use of toxic materials and the production of toxic by-products. There are specific environmental management programs that may be employed to effectively deal with these issues.

Research conducted by Dunk (2007) found a relationship existed between product quality, competitive advantage and environmental accounting. It would be reasonable to infer from this that quality management systems could have major benefits for companies both in financial and environmental terms.

THEORY OF KNOWLEDGE

There are commonly accepted ways of assuring quality in design. How do other areas of knowledge ensure the quality of their outputs?

© IBO 2012

Students should consider a range of tools and techniques used across the various areas of knowledge. Some of these approaches are identified below. This list is by no means complete and should only act as a starting point for further investigations.

A mathematical tool that may be used to measure quality of output in a range of areas of knowledge is standard deviation.

In Science, measurements of quality are used to determine acceptable tolerances or limits of error. Statistical analysis of results can identify some erroneous data or results. Reproducibility is one of the main tenets of the scientific method. It requires reproducibility: an entire experiment or study to be reproduced by the researcher or completely independently by another. Students will find many examples of experiments that have been both successfully and unsuccessfully reproduced.

The quality of published historical research and research in the social sciences is determined by the appearance of work in peer reviewed journals. Peer review is a means of initially determining the quality of the research and findings. Subsequent publication allows a still wider audience to examine and comment on the work. Individual journal rankings in which research may appear and tracking of citation data also provides information about quality

Initially literary works must find a publisher who assesses the work as not only being of a certain literary standard but that will be commercially successful in terms of sales. Similarly works of art need to find an audience through gallery exhibition and sales.

Exercise

Review past winners of the Archibald prize, an Australian portraiture prize, the subject of which is preferably of a distinguished public figure from the arts, science or politics within Australasia. Compare and contrast the winning portrait as chosen by the trustees of the Art Gallery of NSW to the winner of the People's Choice Award as voted for by the public visiting the Archibald exhibition. Compare with the Turner Prize (UK).

10.5–ECONOMIC VIABILITY

ESSENTIAL IDEA

Designers must consider the economic viability of their designs for them to gain a place in the market.

© IBO 2012

NATURE OF DESIGN

Designers need to consider how the costs of materials, manufacturing processes, scale of production and labour contribute to the retail cost of a product. Strategies for minimising these costs at the design stage are most effective to ensure that a product is affordable and can gain a financial return.

© IBO 2012

AIM

The economic viability of a product is paramount for the designer if they are to get their product into production. Understanding how to design a product to specification, at lowest cost and to the appropriate quality while giving added value, can determine the relationship between what a product is worth and how much it costs.

© IBO 2012

Cost effectiveness

Costs that contribute to final product vary both in their type and relative value. The range of these costs includes but may not be limited to:
- marketing
- distribution
- transportation
- government taxes
- energy consumption
- overhead expenditures
- research and development
- capital costs (plant and machinery)
- warehousing and inventory storage
- profit margins value and price of raw materials
- time manufacturing (hourly rates for employees).

Value for money

When evaluating any product, questions of cost and value for money invariably arise. Consumers will decide what they are prepared to pay for the product on offer based on their individual circumstances and judgements. They will also make decisions about the various degrees to which the other defining characteristics meet their needs or desires.

Costing versus pricing: fixed costs; variable costs; cost analysis; break-even

Fixed costs do not vary with sales, ie. expenses that must be paid no matter how many goods or services are sold. Examples of the fixed costs include all start-up costs, rent, building maintenance, capital equipment (machinery/computers) etc. Fixed costs are often quoted in annual amounts.

Variable costs vary with output. They generally increase at a constant rate relative to production which, in turn, is designed to meet sales predictions or market orders. These costs include: wages, utilities (water, electricity), materials and components used in production, raw materials, inventory warehousing and transportation.

Cost analysis involves the examination and evaluation of the separate elements of cost including profit. Cost analysis is employed to determine if a product or service fits within a fair and reasonable price range. Price analysis, however, is the process of determining if the ticketed price for a product or service is fair and reasonable, without examining the specific elements of cost and profit.

'Break even' occurs where neither profit is made nor loss incurred. Graphically it can be represented as the intersection of the two lines – sales income and costs, (a combination of fixed and variable costs). Figure 10.5.1 indicates fixed costs, variable costs and the breakeven point. Mathematically, the breakeven point may be calculated as:

$$\text{Breakeven point} = \frac{\text{Fixed Costs}}{(\text{Unit Selling Price} - \text{Variable Costs})}$$

AHL

After the breakeven point, profit can be made.

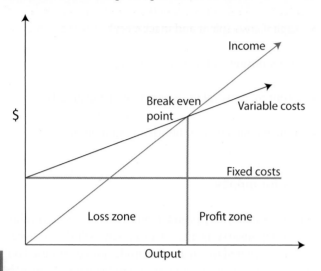

Figure 10.5.1 Profit/loss graph

Pricing strategies: price-minus strategy; retail price; wholesale price; typical manufacturing price; target costs; return on investment; unit cost; sales volume; financial return

Product pricing can be a complex issue involving research and development outlay, manufacturing costs, marketing and advertising expenditures and profit margins. There exist a variety of strategies that may be employed to determine product pricing. Their selection depends on individual markets, company style, distribution methods and even the position of the product in the product life cycle.

Price minus

Price minus (also known as market minus or retail minus) strategies allow the market to determine product pricing. The price minus price strategy determines pricing before the product is manufactured. The selling price is set based on market demand and establishes a price that the market will sustain. From this price, all of the commercial costs associated with bringing the product to market are determined. The constraint of contribution the company is prepared to make towards the manufacture of the product is then used to drive design, engineering, manufacturing and marketing costs.

Retail pricing

The manufacturer's suggested retail price (MSRP), list price or recommended retail price (RRP) of a product is the price which the manufacturer recommends that the retailer sell the product. The intention is to help to standardise prices across locations. Some stores make it a part of their identity and business plan to always sell at,

or even below, the suggested retail price, others do so only under sale or clearance conditions.

Wholesale price

The wholesale price is higher than the price paid to the manufacturer but lower than retail price. Wholesale prices are made available to retailers, and sometimes consumers, due to the purchase of large quantities.

Typical manufacturing price

This strategy incorporates cost of resources or raw materials together with unit cost contributions from both fixed and variable costs ie. labour, utilities, rent, etc. Once this total cost has been determined, a profit margin is added to generate the selling price.

Problems associated with this method include:

- Final selling price is based on cost which may produce a price that is not acceptable to the market. Expensive features that consumers are not prepared to pay for may be incorporated in the design. Target costing addresses both of these issues.

- Research and development costs are not included in this model. Life cycle costing addresses these issues.

Target costing

Target costing is essentially a marketing approach to pricing. Target costing determines an appropriate price for a product in advance of its manufacture. It is rated as one of the most important techniques used to monitor the product design, manufacturing and use phases to assist with maintaining projected profitability.

Target costing works in the reverse order to many other pricing systems. It starts with the final selling price and works backwards by removing profit to generate an initial cost.

An emphasis is placed on the early planning and design phases to force design teams to rationalise their decisions against costs. Needlessly expensive processes or product features may cause reconsideration of the design or, potentially, abandonment of the entire project.

Target costing is most appropriate with products that are constantly renewed, re-developed or upgraded on a regular basis. It is of less value in service oriented businesses where labour costs constitute the bulk of expenditure.

AHL

If the selling price of a product is marked up 50% from its cost, then the formula for calculating the various components for a predicted sale price of $30 is as follows:

Selling price = Cost + Mark up

150% = 100% + 50%

$30 = $20 + $10

A number of design decisions can influence the final cost of a product including:

- over-complicated designs

- standardisation components

- economy of scale of production

- number of components needed

- the number and variety of features

- product quality including materials and tolerances

- number and complexity of manufacturing operations

- point of manufacture ie. location and associated distribution.

Return on investment

Return on investment (ROI) is often quoted as a profitability ratio. The higher the ROI, the better the return. It is not necessarily the same as profit. ROI considers the money invested in the company and the return realised on that investment based on the net profit of the business. Most commonly ROI is calculated in the following fashion:

$$ROI = \frac{Revenue - Cost\ of\ goods\ sold}{Cost\ of\ goods\ sold}$$

or

$$ROI = \frac{Net\ profit}{Total\ assets} \quad \frac{\$200,000}{\$100,000} = 200\%$$

ROI may be applied to sections of the business such as advertising, product pricing, capital equipment etc.

Unit cost

Unit cost is the total of all costs involved in manufacturing storing and selling a product. Unit costs include a percentage of all fixed costs (ie. rent, plant and equipment) and all variable costs (labour, utilities, materials, etc.) involved in production. Generally due to economies of scale, the larger the manufacturer, the lower the unit cost.

Sales volume

Sales volume is the number of products or services sold over a given period of time. Sales volumes may be broken up into a variety of time periods eg. annually, quarterly, etc. They may also be examined by demographic groups, geographic regions or reviewed in terms of company or an individual salesperson's sales.

Financial return

Investment in plant and equipment, staffing, materials, marketing and associated costs surrounding the manufacture and sale of a product are done expressly to make a profit. This profit is the financial return.

INTERNATIONAL MINDEDNESS

The cost effectiveness of a product can determine whether it can enter economically diverse national and international markets.

© IBO 2012

Cost effectiveness is only one of the variables that will determine a product's ability to enter economically diverse national and international markets.

Organisations must accept that differences in values, customs and lifestyles may mean successful products in a local domestic market may have little appeal in national or global markets

The OECD recognises the pressures of costs when manufacturers wish to insert their products into national or global markets. The report *Globalisation and competitiveness: relevant indicators*, commissioned by the OECD in 1995 highlights the problems of product expansion into new markets when it states "Multinational firms try everywhere to introduce the same production techniques, the same products, the same consumer habits, the same work organisation, etc., as a result of which markets become increasingly alike".

The report then goes on to document barriers to expansion such as: market competition, differences in wages, inflationary pressures, exchange rates, trade barriers, effectiveness of marketing, varying levels of technological development, transportation and distribution.

AHL

Designers and manufacturers must carefully weigh the costs versus the benefits associated with standardisation of global products as opposed to customising a product line to meet local consumer needs and tastes.

THEORY OF KNOWLEDGE

The retail price of a product is partly based on evidence of its potential position in the market. What counts as evidence in various areas of knowledge?

© IBO 2012

The concept of evidence is critical to the study of knowledge. Students should investigate evidentialism (a theory that knowledge is only true or verified if it is supported by evidence). Evidentialism also supports skepticism, disbelief and suspension of belief.

In the article *Science relies on evidence*, evidence is stated to be "test results and/or observations that may either help support or help refute a scientific idea. In general, raw data are considered evidence only once they have been interpreted in a way that reflects on the accuracy of a scientific idea." [1]

In the humanities and social sciences, digital research using large-scale data analysis is proving increasingly popular, however as Gibbs and Owen point out "large amounts of data for research should not be considered opposed to more traditional use of historical sources..... data certainly can be employed as evidence for a historical argument, (but) data are not necessarily evidence in themselves".[2]

Gibbs and Owen proceed to argue that it is the interpretation of data that generates real evidence in the humanities.

Students should investigate the many forms evidence takes in pure mathematical research. A few examples of mathematical forms of evidence are axioms self-evident and well-defined.

Another interesting form of mathematical evidence is known as 'evidence coming as a new clue, midstream.' Students should research the 'Monty Hall probability puzzle' to see this type of evidence applied to problem solving.

Exercise

Students should consider the following statements by eminent thinkers and consider if they are applicable to all areas of knowledge.

"A wise man proportions his belief to the evidence." David Hume [3]

"It is wrong always, everywhere, and for anyone to believe anything upon insufficient evidence." William Clifford [4]

"There are no facts, only interpretations." Friedrich Nietzsche [5]

References

[1] *Science relies on evidence, Understanding Science,* University of California Museum of Paleontology. 13 June 2014 from http://www.understandingscience.org/article/alvarez_01

[2] Gigbbs FW and Owens TJ, *The Hermeneutics of Data and Historical Writing* (Spring 2012 version) from Writing history in the digital age, http://writinghistory.trincoll.edu/data/gibbs-owens-2012-spring/

[3]*Philosophical essays concerning human understanding,* 1748

[4] *The ethics of belief and other essays,* Prometheus Books, 1999

[5] Nietzsche F, *Notebooks* (Summer 1886 – Fall 1887)

AHL

CASE STUDY

Sample quality assurance report

The following report has been reproduced with the kind permission of the Henkel Corporation, Rocky Hill, CT, www.henkelna.com. This article was previously published by Scott D Anderson in *Medical Design*, April 2010.

Examining the effect of sterilisation on bulk adhesive properties

Sterilisation can greatly influence the integrity of a medical device, especially those bonded with adhesives. Therefore, it is critical that device manufacturers select the adhesive best suited for the substrate materials, end-use environment and sterilisation technique.

The data shown in Charts 1 and 2 reflect the post-sterilisation performance of three light cure acrylic adhesives used to bond 22-gauge (ga) stainless steel cannulas to either polycarbonate or plasma-treated polypropylene hubs.

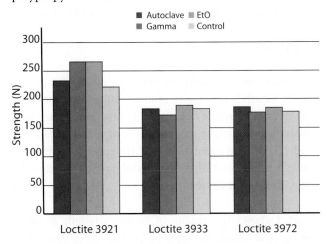

Chart 1 22 ga needle pull strength on polycarbonate

The pull strength data from this study on actual devices shows post-sterilisation performance similar to that of the untreated control group.

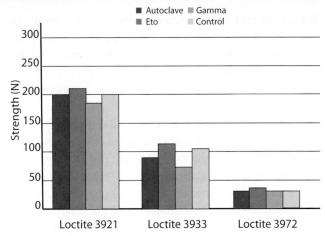

Chart 2 22 ga needle pull strength on treated polypropylene

Often there is actually an improvement in strength. This improvement may be the result of elevated temperatures enhancing the adhesive's cross-linking reaction, or of annealing that actually relaxes stress on the component.

But what happens when we eliminate both substrates and joint design from the test and look only at the properties of the adhesive itself and how it is affected by sterilisation? To answer this question, let's focus on the performance of typical light cure acrylic and light cure silicone adhesives when exposed to autoclave, ethylene oxide and gamma irradiation sterilisation.

Adhesives studied

This study tested the Loctite® light cure acrylic adhesives referenced in Charts 1 and 2:

3921™, a highly fluorescent, 150 cP (centipoise) adhesive that provides bond strength on dissimilar materials. This material is commonly used in needle bonding applications.

3933™, a 3250 cP adhesive that provides bond strength to polycarbonate and other thermoplastics with minimal stress cracking. This material is typically used for bonding thermoplastic substrates in fluid devices such as housings for filters and fittings.

3972™, a 4500 cP adhesive that provides tack-free curing capabilities at wavelengths greater than 254 (nm), including the visible wavelengths in excess of 405 nm. This material is used in devices where there is significant adhesive exposed in the bond line, for example, in tube fittings where the bond line is not encapsulated between two substrates and a tack-free surface is required to prevent contamination.

AHL

These light cure acrylic adhesives were selected primarily due to their glass transition temperature (T_g) and their ability to be cured under ultraviolet (UV) and/or visible (Vis) wavelengths. T_g is the temperature at which a substance changes from a glassy solid to a rubbery soft material. Loctite® 3921™ has a T_g of 82°C, while 3933™ and 3972™ have T_gs of 54°C and 49°C respectively. Glass transition temperature is critical to the performance of a medical device exposed to sterilisation. An adhesive is far less likely to support a load once its T_g has been exceeded as the material becomes soft and pliable, losing its rigidity and strength. While the adhesive's ability to support a load returns after cooling down, any assembly that is under stress during the sterilisation cycle may fail at sterilisation temperatures. The study also included testing two silicone adhesives formulations. For this, the cure method was the most important performance criterion in the selection process:

5056™, a 2 200 cP light cure silicone, offers superior heat and moisture resistance and bonds well to silicone tubing and polycarbonate or thermoplastic fittings. This traditional light cure adhesive will not cure in areas that are not exposed to light of the appropriate wavelength and intensity during the curing process.

5240™, a 25 000 cP dual cure silicone, cures on exposure to light and moisture and offers high tear strength. The secondary moisture cure mechanism allows the adhesive to cure in shadowed areas where light cannot reach. Both of these adhesives would typically be used for bonding respiratory devices such as masks or breathing circuits, or for assembling components made from silicone substrates.

Test method

Glass transition temperature was not a critical factor in the selection of silicone adhesives as the T_g of silicones is typically in the -40°C range and all of the tested sterilisation methods operated above the T_g of silicones.

For this study, Henkel's lab manufactured bubble-free films from all the test adhesives. These films were made in moulds that allowed light transmission and generated films with consistent thicknesses of 0.8 mm for the light cure acrylics and 2 mm for the silicones.

Post-cure, the adhesive films returned to ambient conditions and were prepared into test samples. The cured light cure acrylic films were machined into tensile bars with dimensions of 150 mm by 6 mm. The elastomeric silicones were punched into dog bone shapes with dimensions of 25 mm wide at the jaws of a mechanical properties tester and 6 mm wide at the neck and an overall length of 115 mm.

This shape allowed the force to be concentrated in the neck area, forcing failure away from the jaws.

Once the specimens were prepared, gamma irradiation, ethylene oxide and autoclave sterilisation processes began. The gamma irradiation took place for 108 minutes between 27.3 kiloGray (kGy) to 30.5 kGy. The ethylene oxide specimens were exposed to sterilant for six hours at 15.2 in Hg absolute at 54.4°C. The autoclave samples were exposed for six minutes to 120°C temperatures at 0.103 megapascal (MPa).

Once the sterilisation processes were completed, the samples were tested in a mechanical properties tester for elastic modulus, tensile strength at break, and elongation at break. Samples were placed in the mechanical properties tester and pulled until they broke. Different measurements were taken for each attribute tested.

- Elastic modulus, for this study, is defined as the ratio of stress over strain. This attribute is more relevant for rigid materials such as light cure acrylics than for flexible materials such as silicones. For this reason, silicones were not included in the modulus testing.

- Tensile strength at break measured the strength of the adhesive in terms of force per unit area. For this study, tensile strength was the point on the stress-strain curve where the adhesive sample failed rather than where the sample yielded.

- Elongation, reported as a percentage, measures how far the adhesive can be stretched prior to breaking.

Study results

The results of this study are represented in Charts 3, 4 and 5. Chart 3 reports modulus results and illustrates that gamma, ethylene oxide, and control results are very consistent. Autoclave exposure, however, reduced the rigidity of 3972 by more than 50%. The end-use application truly determines whether this loss of rigidity is critical for the success of the device.

Chart 4 shows the results of tensile strength at break testing. The tensile strength of Loctite® 3921™ increased after autoclave while its modulus decreased. The tensile strength of Loctite® 3933™, Loctite® 5240™ and Loctite® 5056™ was very consistent across all sterilisation methods.

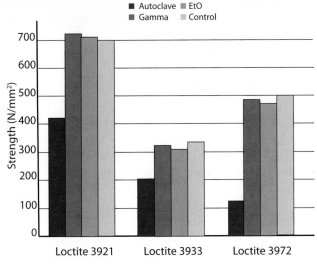

Chart 3 Modulus results

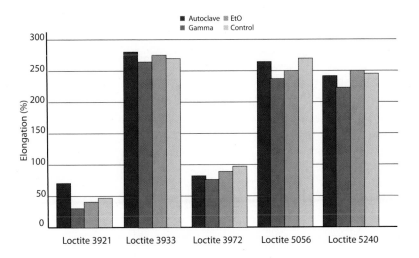

Chart 4 Tensile stength at break

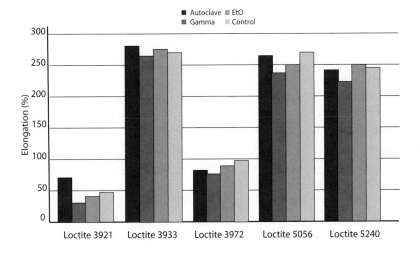

Chart 5 Elongation results

Chart 5 shows the results of elongation testing. After autoclave, the 3921™ exhibited an improved ability to stretch under stress. The remaining adhesives retained their ability to stretch or elongate even after sterilisation, regardless of the sterilisation method employed. Depending on the adhesive chemistry and sterilisation method selected, the study data shows similar performance in all three areas—modulus, elongation and tensile strength—to performance recorded before sterilisation. Put simply, the adhesives tested did not change dramatically as a result of sterilisation.

Conclusion

As a result of this study, engineers designing disposable medical devices should feel confident that the bulk properties of the adhesives will not change significantly when sterilised via ethylene oxide or gamma irradiation. Any changes to the structural integrity of a medical device after sterilisation is related to the interaction of the adhesive and the substrate materials, not to changes to the bulk properties of the adhesive.

Engineers designing non-disposable medical devices should be aware of the difficulties that autoclave presents to adhesives. While the silicones tested in this study performed well under autoclave, designers must understand that this study exposed the adhesives to only one cycle of autoclave sterilisation. A typical non-disposable medical device is exposed to hundreds of autoclave cycles over its usable life, a factor that will undeniably affect the long-term performance of the adhesive.

Regardless of the type of medical device being designed and manufactured, the relationship between the end use of the device, the substrates specified, the adhesive chemistry, and the actual design of the bond joint can all impact the strength of the final assembly, yielding different results for each device. To ensure a robust device design, engineers must thoroughly test the assembly under both manufacturing and sterilisation conditions.

AHL

SAMPLE QUESTIONS

1. Value stream mapping is
   A   a process used by cartographers
   B   used to determine product pricing
   C   used to assess environmentally friendly designs
   D   a visual aid to map the relationships between materials, processes, information and time.

2. If a firm is producing no product all, its totals costs will be

   A   no costs at all
   B   fixed costs only
   C   break even costs
   D   variable costs only.

3. Sales volume provides information about

   A   market competition
   B   the size of a product
   C   product features
   D   the number products or services sold over a given period of time.

4. Just-in-time management involves:

   A   large inventories ready for emergencies
   B.   rapid response to spikes in unpredictable demand
   C   involves rigorous quality control testing at the end of production
   D   involves rigorous quality control testing at every stage of production.

5. If manufacturing volume of a product increases, then total fixed costs will

   A   rise
   B   decline
   C   remain constant and cost per unit decreases
   D   remain constant and cost per unit increases

6. Explain how CIM systems incorporate technologies or methodologies to increase productivity.

7. Explain the difference between quality control and quality assurance.

8. Explain how target costing can be a powerful tool when designing a product.

INDEX

Symbols

2-D CAD 66
3-D modelling 66

A

Abrading 147
Abrasive water-jet cutting 145
Act of insight 183
Adaptation 184
Additive techniques 143
Adhering 157
Aesthetic characteristics 89
Aesthetic model 64
Affinity diagramming 228
Agricola, Georgius 97
Airbus Industries 134
Alloying 101
Anaface 216
Analogy 184
Anthropometric data 1
Appert, Nicolas François 172
Archimedes 183
Architectural innovation 180
Aristotle 107, 168, 187, 215
Asimov, Isaac 168
Assembly drawing 62
Austenitic structure 93

B

Babbage, Charles 161
Baekeland, Leo 118
Bass forecasting model 197
Batch production 142
Bauhaus school 211
Bazalgette, Joseph 45
Bedfellow, Darren 210
Bell, Alexander Graham 172
Bellamy, David 241
Benedictus, Edouard 184
Bierbaum test 83
Biocompatibility 115
Biocontrol 19
Biodiesel 50

Biomechanical aids 13
Biomechanical analysis 13
Biomechanics 12
Biomimicry 184
BioSteel® 121
Blow moulding 149
Bonaparte, Napoleon 172
Bottom-up and top-down modelling 70
Brainstorming 186
Brand loyalty 272
Braungart, Michael 251
Bronowski, Jacob 176
Brundtland report 235
Bulk Modulus 85
Burkus, David 172

C

CAD software 66
Calhoun, John 10
Carbon-reinforced plastic 139
Carson, Rachel 24, 240, 267
Casey, Steven 229
Casting 151
Cellini, Benvenuto 156
Ceramic composite sandwich 132
Cermet 134
Chance 184
Change of circumstances 201
Charlesworth, Hilary 199
Charpy impact test 86, 88
Christensen, Clayton 179
Circular design 194
Circular economy 23
Civil Disobedience 249
Clearance, reach and adjustability 5
Closure 213
Cochlea 89
Colour theory 214
Comfort 12
Commoner, Barry 24, 240, 267
Competition 202
Computer animation 71
Computer numeric control (CNC) 162
Computer simulation 203
Concept 218
Conceptual modelling 55